The CADCAM Process

The CADCAM Process

Barry Hawkes
AMIED
Lecturer-in-Charge CAD
Canterbury College of Technology

Pitman

PITMAN PUBLISHING
128 Long Acre London WC2E 9AN

First published in Great Britain 1988

ISBN 0 273 02572 4

Printed and bound in Great Britain

Contents

Preface

CADCAM is perhaps the most important development in the new technologies to engineers, designers and technicians of all specialisms. Elements of the composite term CADCAM are significant to every branch of modern engineering from heavy mechanical and plant to microelectronics, whilst CAD is being increasingly applied to such diverse fields as architecture, civil engineering, cartography, medical research, geophysics, clothes design, publishing, advertising and even entertainment.

In line with the preceding publications (*The Engineering Design Process* and *Engineering Design for Technicians*), basic principles have been emphasised by concentrating mainly on mechanical design and manufacture—the core area which lends itself to the full spectrum of CADCAM. This new book thus gives a total view of the CADCAM process for aspiring product engineers and technologists undertaking courses at higher technician or first-year degree level. It provides full coverage of the B/TEC units "Computer-Aided Engineering, Level IV" and "Computer-Aided Design, Level V", but also includes many additional topics relevant to college, polytechnic and university engineering/computing courses. It is hoped that this book will also provide a useful reference to mature engineers wishing to update to CADCAM and to those studying engineering management.

The underlying theme throughout the book is that of CADCAM linking data directly between specialisms which were previously isolated. This theme is enlarged to encompass the philosophy of a fully-integrated process of product creation known as CIM (Computer Integrated Manufacture), existing within computer-linked organisations.

CADCAM and its associated disciplines involve a wealth of terminology for activities, hardware items, software languages, and codes, standards, and organisations. These are defined in the appropriate chapters, with an emphasis on software flexibility via the inclusion of in-house CAD program examples.

The essential ingredient of computer graphics is given high priority in descriptions of 2D draughting and 3D modelling techniques. This is extended to the coverage of computer-aided analytical methods using finite element analysis and ergonomic software.

Important aspects of CAM are discussed in descriptions of CNC equipment and programming, robotics, and flexible manufacturing systems.

The theme of integration is particularly evident in a chapter relating to organisation and planning. This lays emphasis on linking all computerised activities through a common database. Activities covered include systematic design, project planning, process planning, classification and coding techniques, and production management.

Despite its many advantages, the installation of a CADCAM system can be a daunting prospect for any company. The financial and social implications may be tremendous, and an incorrect specification or unwise choice of system could have disastrous consequences. The final chapter highlights possible hazards involved, and lists the techniques, facilities, and organisations available for overcoming these.

The most important feature of this book is its practical content, emphasised by the considerable number of program examples and real case studies included throughout. These have been made available by the kind permission and help given by individuals in colleges, polytechnics and industry. I would like to express particular thanks to Hobourn-Eaton Ltd and to the Ford Motor Company, for their extensive case studies, both of which uphold the dominant theme of linked data and integrated activities. The Hobourn case study continues throughout most chapters of the book and describes the successive linked stages of the CADCAM process applied to one of their products (an oil pump). This case study is supplemented in the final chapter with a description of Hobourn's experiences during their own conversion to CADCAM.

The Ford case study interrelates much of the material in its preceding chapters with the description of the complete CADCAM process, from design conception of finished product, applied to the automobile industry.

B. R. Hawkes
Maidstone

To Gill, Georgia, and Robert.
Thanks again.

Introduction to CADCAM

1.1 What is CAD?

The origin of the acronym CAD (Computer-Aided Design) is generally acknowledged to lie in a series of lectures given by a distinguished pioneer in this field, named Ivan Sutherland, at the Massachusetts Institute of Technology during the early 1960s.

In fact, engineers have been using computers as an aid in complex design calculations since the early post-war development of the mainframe computer, and primitive versions of today's CAD equipment were in existence by the mid 1950s. However, CAD has really come into its own since the development of the microprocessor made it possible to quickly create, modify, and manipulate complex graphics displays on the screen of a VDU (visual display unit).

In the modern sense, CAD means a design process using sophisticated computer graphics techniques, backed up with computer software packages to aid in the analytical, development, costing, and ergonomic problems associated with design work.

The term CADD (Computer-Aided Drawing and Design) is also sometimes used, but in this publication we will take CAD to include basic computer draughting techniques as part of the complete design process.

Advantages of CAD

1 Faster rate of producing drawings
On average, a draughtsman using a CAD system can produce drawings about three times as fast as could be done on a drawing board. This speeds up the whole design process and gets the product onto the market more quickly. It can also mean a faster response to requests for quotations.

2 Greater accuracy of drawings
A conventional drawing is accurate only to the eye of the draughtsman and the thickness of a pencil lead. By contrast, any point on a CAD drawing has an exact position, and a technique known as *zooming* (discussed later in more detail) allows any part of the CAD drawing to be "blown-up" to show

components in more detail. Therefore, all detail and assembly drawings produced by CAD are completely accurate. A separate "accurate layout" drawing is never required with CAD.

3 Neater drawings
The presentation of a conventional drawing is entirely dependent upon the line work and printing skills of the individual draughtsman, whereas the plotter of a CAD system produces superior line work and text whoever operates the system. Also, many conventional drawings are spoilt because of the mess and indentations caused when lines are erased. CAD allows any number of lines to be quickly erased without leaving any trace on the final drawing.

4 No repetition of drawings
Once a drawing or part-drawing is completed, it may be stored in the computer memory for future use. This is particularly useful when drawing a range of components with a similar shape. A stored drawing can also be recalled to design jigs and fixtures, analyse tool paths, and design press tools. By conventional means, a separate drawing is required for each of these tasks.

The computer memory is also ideal for compiling libraries of symbols, standard components, and geometric shapes.

5 Special draughting techniques
Apart from zooming, CAD systems have many more special draughting techniques which were not available by conventional means. These will be discussed in later chapters.

6 Quicker design calculations and analysis
There is now a vast range of computer software for carrying out design calculations in a fraction of the previous time.

7 Superior design form
Powerful computer modelling techniques, such as finite element analysis, have freed the designer from the shackles of restrictive conventional formulae and allowed more inventive shapes to be developed. These shapes may be quickly modified and optimised for cost savings to an extent which would have previously been too time-consuming.

8 Less development required
CAD simulation and analysis techniques can drastically cut the time and money spent on prototype testing and development—often the costliest stage in the design process.

9 Integration of design with other disciplines
The vastly superior communications available under an integrated computer network enables CAD to work far more closely with other engineering departments than was possible under the old type of design organization.

1.2 What is CAM?

CAM (Computer-Aided Manufacture) concerns any automatic manufacturing process which is controlled by computers. Its origins lie in the development of numerically-controlled (NC) machining in the late 1940s and the 1950s. When these techniques began to be controlled by computers in the late 1950s and the 1960s, the term CNC (Computer Numerical Control) was adopted. CNC now encompasses many different automatic manufacturing processes, including milling, turning, flame-cutting, laser-cutting, punching, and spot-welding.

Parallel developments in computer-controlled robots and automated factories led to the evolution of complete manufacturing units, controlled by central computer systems and organised under a philosophy known as FMS (Flexible Manufacturing Systems).

The term CAM has thus come into use as a general heading for all of these disciplines, and any other emerging computer-controlled manufacturing technology.

The most important elements of CAM are thus:
a) CNC manufacturing and programming techniques.
b) Computer-controlled robotics manufacture and assembly.
c) Flexible Manufacturing Systems (FMS).
d) Computer-Aided Inspection (CAI) techniques.
e) Computer-Aided Testing (CAT) techniques.

Advantages of CAM

Specific advantages are relevant to the individual CAM disciplines, which will be discussed in subsequent chapters.

In general terms, advantages of CAM are concerned with its accomplishment of the following objectives:

a) Higher production rates with lower workforces.
b) Less likelihood of human error and the consequences of human unreliability.
c) Greater versatility of manufactured form.
d) Cost savings due to increased manufacturing efficiency (e.g. less material wastage) and increased efficiency of storage and assembly.
e) Repeatability of production processes via storage of data.
f) Superior product.

1.3 What is CADCAM?

CADCAM is an integration of CAD and CAM techniques into one complete process. This means, for example, that a component can be drawn on a VDU screen and the graphics data then transferred via coded electrical

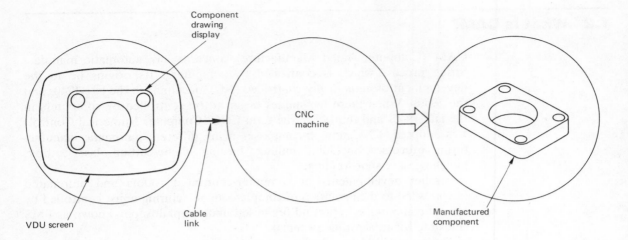

Component
drawing
display

CNC
machine

VDU screen

Cable
link

Manufactured
component

Fig. 1.1 Simplified principle of the linked CADCAM process

signals along a cable link to a manufacturing system, where the component would be automatically produced on a CNC machine. This is a vast over-simplification, which will require a great deal of enlargement in subsequent chapters, but it does help to illustrate an additional, and perhaps the most important, advantage of both CAD and CAM, i.e. their ability to communicate directly with each other. The basic principle is depicted in Fig 1.1.

Once it became apparent that data could be exchanged between CAD and CAM systems, the development of the CADCAM philosophy, and of the acronym itself, was perhaps inevitable. Progress in this direction has been enhanced by the development of computer-aided CNC programming techniques and languages, some of which use screen graphics methods very similar to those of CAD.

Fig 1.2 shows a good example of an integrated CADCAM organisation.

1.4 Associated Disciplines

An obvious extension of the integrated CADCAM process is that of both CAD and CAM communicating with other computer systems.

Many associated disciplines have now been developed, with new terminology, and the inevitable acronyms, appearing almost weekly. All computer-controlled engineering activities are covered under the general heading of CAE (Computer-Aided Engineering). In addition to CADCAM, CAE also includes the following:

a) Computer-Aided Production Management (CAPM) procedures.
b) Computer-Aided Process Planning (CAPP) procedures.
c) Project planning using computer software.
d) Computer-aided tool and process design.
e) Computer-aided development.
f) Computer-aided factory layout design (including graphical robotics simulation).

Fig. 1.2 The Integrated CADCAM organisation [*Konsberg Ltd*]

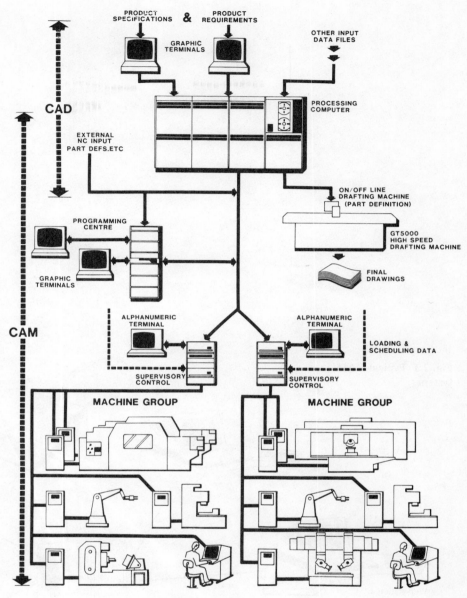

The complete integration of CAE disciplines, along with those of business and accounting systems, is termed CIM (Computer-Integrated Manufacture). CIM is still in its infancy and often run from a *host computer* system with a *common database*. These topics are discussed in Chapter 7.

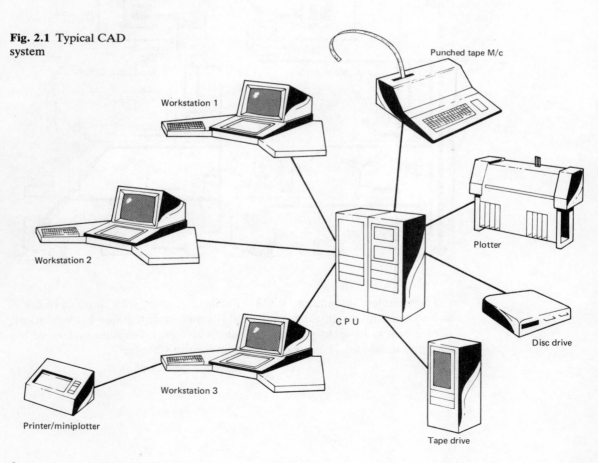

Fig. 2.1 Typical CAD system

Workstation 1

Punched tape M/c

Workstation 2

Plotter

Workstation 3

C P U

Disc drive

Printer/miniplotter

Tape drive

CAD Hardware 2

A complete CAD system consists of hardware and software components. It is ultimately controlled by the *central processing unit* (CPU), which is the central element of the computer system, and is part of the *hardware* of the CAD system.

Instructions to perform operations are supplied in the form of programs which are called the *software* of the CAD system.

Fig 2.1 shows a typical CAD system.

The total hardware components of a CAD system are

a) The CPU.
b) A number of *workstations*.
c) *Shared peripherals* between the workstations.

2.1   The Central Processing Unit (CPU)

Fig 2.1 shows the CPU enclosed in a central host computer which is usually assisted by a smaller processer at each workstation. The CPU contains three main elements:

1   The CONTROL UNIT which retrieves each computer instruction in correct sequence, interprets the instructions, and conveys the appropriate actioning signals to other parts of the computer.

2   The ARITHMETIC LOGIC UNIT (ALU) which performs the elementary additions and subtractions, the basis of all computer mathematical operations.

3   The CORE MEMORY STORE where programs and data are held while in use. Memory storage capacity is measured in *bytes*. Each byte represents a single character of instruction code and is made up of eight *bits* (binary digits). Larger measures of memory include the Kilobyte (Kbyte) which equals one thousand bytes, and the Megabyte (Mbyte) which equals one million bytes. Core memory gives speedy response during the execution of programs, with capacities up to about 2 Mbyte in the majority of CADCAM systems. For permanent storage and higher capacity, peripheral storage devices such as discs and tapes are used.

CPUs may be categorised by the maximum wordlength of code which may be processed per instruction cycle. The number of bits in each word is an indication of the processing power of the computer. The common wordlengths are 8 bits, 16 bits, and 32 bits.

Broad classifications of CPU may be listed as:

1 8-bit MICROCOMPUTER, capable of only basic 2D geometry or simple analytical calculations.

2 16-bit MICROCOMPUTER, capable of handling medium complexity 2D and 3D geometry and some finite element analysis work, but not currently suitable for sophisticated applications such as advanced solid modelling. However, at the time of publication, the capacity of 16-bit microcomputers is increasing to an extent that they seem likely to assume many of the CADCAM activities which have been restricted to the larger systems.

3 32-bit MINICOMPUTER, capable of handling complex geometric software and large quantities of data. This grade of CPU is also suitable for multi-user systems running several workstations and separate activities.

4 MAINFRAME COMPUTER, used in large organisations for handling massive amounts of data and a multitude of concurrent activities and separate software applications. Mainframes often host hundreds of remote workstations operating and communicating over a vast network (sometimes covering thousands of kilometres and crossing international boundaries).

2.2 The CAD Workstation

Fig 2.2 shows one example of a CAD workstation. A typical CAD workstation is made up of

a) A graphics screen called the VISUAL DISPLAY UNIT (VDU).
b) An ALPHA-NUMERICS DISPLAY (word and number screen).
c) A WORKSTATION PROCESSOR.
d) An electronic COMMAND TABLET.
e) A MENU facility.
f) A CURSOR CONTROL device (or DIGITISER).
g) A KEYBOARD.
h) A PRINTER/MINI-PLOTTER device.

Fig 2.3 shows some common arrangements of a CAD workstation.

The Visual Display Unit (VDU)

All computer drawings are displayed on the VDU. Sometimes written statements (alpha-numerics) are also displayed on this screen, or there may be a separate alpha-numerics screen. Typical alpha-numerics displays include computer drawing commands, tutorial messages, and drawing function menu displays.

Fig. 2.2 A CAD workstation [*Computer Vision*]

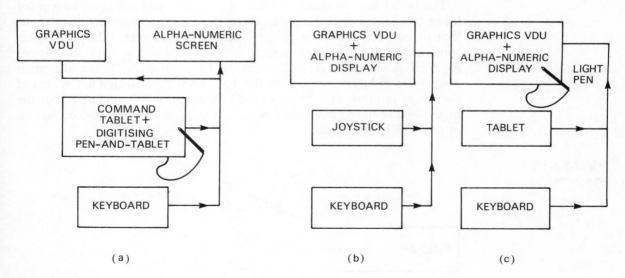

<table>
<tr><td>GRAPHICS VDU</td><td>ALPHA-NUMERIC SCREEN</td></tr>
<tr><td colspan="2">COMMAND TABLET + DIGITISING PEN-AND-TABLET</td></tr>
<tr><td colspan="2">KEYBOARD</td></tr>
</table>

(a)

<table>
<tr><td>GRAPHICS VDU + ALPHA-NUMERIC DISPLAY</td></tr>
<tr><td>JOYSTICK</td></tr>
<tr><td>KEYBOARD</td></tr>
</table>

(b)

<table>
<tr><td>GRAPHICS VDU + ALPHA-NUMERIC DISPLAY</td><td>LIGHT PEN</td></tr>
<tr><td>TABLET</td></tr>
<tr><td>KEYBOARD</td></tr>
</table>

(c)

Fig. 2.3 Common arrangements of CAD workstations

Most CAD VDUs operate via a device called the *cathode ray tube* (CRT). The CRT is basically an evacuated glass tube in which a beam of electrons is fired from an electron gun onto a phosphur-coated screen, resulting in an illuminated trace being displayed on the screen.

Over the past twenty years, a number of CRT types have been developed, the most prominent coming under the headings of

a) Direct view storage tube (DVST)
b) Vector refresh
c) Raster refresh

Both the DVST and vector refresh displays operate on the principle of creating images on the screen by displaying straight-line vectors between two desired points. Curves are thus formed as a series of short, straight vectors, as shown in Fig 2.4.

Raster displays operate on a completely different principle which will be explained later.

Fig. 2.4

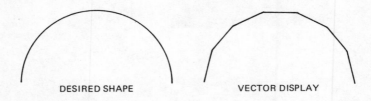

DESIRED SHAPE   VECTOR DISPLAY

Storage Display (DVST)   Most of the older CAD systems had VDUs which incorporated a DVST. The principal concept of the DVST is that drawing information is sent to the screen once only, and is permanently displayed without any control from the CPU.

The DVST has the standard CRT electron gun and deflection system for location of the beam onto the screen, but also incorporates flood guns located between the main electron gun and the screen. The flood guns continuously bombard the screen with electrons, but with insufficient localised intensity to create any image by themselves. When the main electron beam hits the screen, the flood electrons are attracted to the area of the image resulting in a "switched-on" display, which is retained after the main beam is moved to another location. Fig 2.5 shows a simplified diagram of the DVST operation.

Fig. 2.5 DVST operation

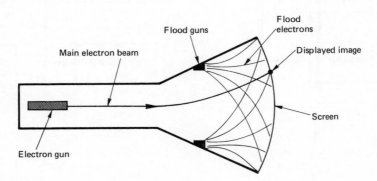

Graphics displays from a DVST are notable for their excellent quality of line. However, the erasing of any element on the drawing can be undertaken only via an operation in the flood guns which automatically erases the entire drawing. The inability to erase and edit individual areas of the drawing is thus a major drawback of the DVST system.

Another disadvantage is that the display is insufficiently bright for efficient viewing in normal lighting conditions. The VDU thus has to be stationed in a dimly-lit location, or alternatively, may be incorporated with a hood or shroud.

Coloured images are not usually available with a DVST. This can be a distinct disadvantage—particularly for 3D layout drawings, such as in piping design. Animation is also difficult to achieve, a factor which effectively disallows such vital facilities as tool-path simulation and dynamic analysis of mechanisms. Finally, being a vector display CRT, the DVST cannot efficiently create filled-in areas on a drawing.

This list of serious limitations has led to the steady decline in the use of DVSTs for modern CAD systems.

Vector Refresh Display This type of CRT was developed to overcome the many shortcomings of the DVST whilst retaining the concept of straight-line vector display between two points. Unlike the DVST, vector refresh CRTs repeatedly update the screen display every fraction-of-a-second under control of the CPU. Thus vector refresh systems employ a simpler CRT, with no flood guns, and a beam of electrons which is continuously being projected onto the screen. Fig 2.6 shows a basic CRT which could be used as either vector refresh or raster systems.

Fig. 2.6 Basic CRT (raster or vector refresh)

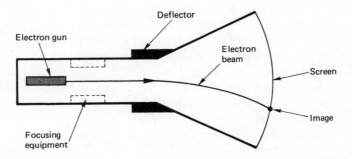

The refresh characteristic overcomes the main objection to the DVST by allowing individual elements of the drawing to be readily erased, with the modified drawing quickly displayed on the next screen refresh.

Vector refresh displays are particularly noted for their bright, clear image; excellent quality of line; and high drawing speed. The refresh operation is also well-suited to fast-moving animation of the screen display in either 2D or 3D. They are particularly advantageous if a light-pen is required as the cursor-control device. (Light-pens are discussed later.)

The chief disadvantages of vector refresh CRTs are their comparatively high cost, and their tendency to "flicker" on complex drawings if the refresh rate becomes less than the flicker threshhold of the eye. Being vector displays, they share the inability of the DVST to efficiently create filled-in

11

areas of drawing and also allow no way of providing a cheap hard-copy "mini-plot" of the screen display.

Colour displays are possible using vector refresh, but again are only available at high cost.

Raster Refresh Display As with vector refresh displays, raster CRTs refresh the screen display, continuously but the raster method differs considerably from vector displays in the way it builds up graphics onto the screen.

To a certain extent, the cathode ray tube in a raster VDU is a highly sophisticated version of that found in a domestic television set. Unlike the vector methods, which draw complete elements between points, a raster display is made up of thousands of picture element dots or *pixels* as they are known. These are controlled by the intensity of the electron beam as it sweeps across the screen from one side to the other. The beam always starts its sweep from the top left-hand corner of the screen, regardless of what has been drawn, finishes on a horizontal line to the right, moves down one row of pixels, returns, and starts again from the left. The display is completed when the beam has reached to bottom-right of the screen. It then "refreshes" by commencing the whole procedure again at the top-left. Each refresh operation takes about 0.02 seconds.

The quality of line is dependent on the *resolution* (i.e. the number of pixels to the screen). This varies from 320×240 pixels (low-resolution screen) to in excess of 1024×1024 pixels (high-resolution screen). The sequence of raster display bears no relationship whatever to the order in which the drawing was constructed.

Fig. 2.7

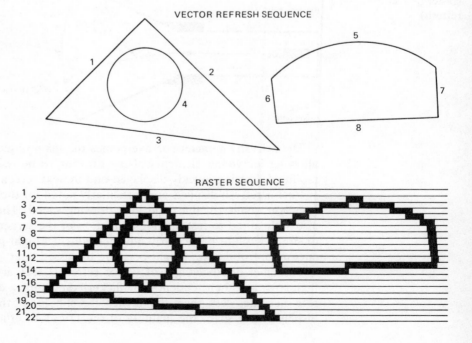

VECTOR REFRESH SEQUENCE

RASTER SEQUENCE

In general, the nature of the raster operation results in an inferior line quality to that of vector displays, since the pixel range is not continuous and results in a "stair-casing" effect, both in straight lines and in curves. Fig 2.7 compares the sequence of operations, and resulting effect, of a drawing done with vector refresh and alternatively with raster.

The sequence of the pixel display pattern must be calculated for each refresh stroke, and the raster system is thus very demanding in its memory requirements. For this reason, raster displays are invariably accompanied with sizeable local workstation intelligence. The crudity of raster graphics creates particular problems with 3D modelling and dynamic animation, which increases the necessity for extensive local graphics processing.

However, the raster display has rapidly become the most popular of the VDU options, due to its low cost and versatility. As with vector refresh, there is no problem in erasing individual elements of a raster drawing. Unlike vector refresh, there is no flicker of the display, and the creation of filled-in areas of the drawing is easily achieved. Raster refresh produces a bright, clear image in either colour or monochrome.

The raster VDU system is particularly suited to the operation of most low-cost hard-copy mini-plotters, since these usually work on a similar raster principle.

Colour Display

Individual colours are primarily described by the term *hue*. This refers to a value of wavelength in the electro-magnetic spectrum and provides a unique identification to the resulting colour perceived. The primary colours (red, blue, and green) are each produced from a single hue. Any other colours are produced by combining primary hues (e.g. the secondary colour cyan is produced by combining blue and green hues). The term *chroma* refers to the purity of the colour visualised and may be measured by the relative position, on a chromaticity chart, of its dominant wavelength to white. (White is an equal-energy mixture of all colours.)

The Colour CRT   The distinctive feature of the colour raster display is that the colour CRT has three electron guns, compared with one only for a monochrome raster CRT. Each of the three guns corresponds to a primary hue (red, blue, or green). The screen of the colour CRT is made up of thousands of phosphur spots arranged in groups of three (one for each primary hue). Each spot will be illuminated in its appropriate primary hue when hit by the beam of the respective gun, thus creating a colour pixel. The three beams are kept apart by tiny holes in a metal sheet called a shadow mask, situated close behind the screen.

By combining any two of the three primary illuminations, three secondary hues may be created, or white may be displayed by combining all three illuminations simultaneously. Further combinations may be obtained by varying the intensity of the beams. CADCAM systems may thus provide thousands of different hues by intensity control, via program commands.

A popular modern colour display system employs a PIL (precision-in-line) tube, in which the guns are arranged along a horizontal line and the beams strike horizontal configurations of phosphur spots.

Colour systems may be costly in comparison with monochrome and are very demanding on memory resources. However, they are an invaluable asset in certain applications, particularly where clear distinction of elements at varying depths is required. Typical examples include piping layouts, multi-layered PCB work, and 3D solid geometry applications.

The colour raster CRT is another facility whose advance will undoubtedly correspond with the increase of local workstation intelligence.

The Workstation Processor

During the earlier development of CAD, the emphasis was on the central host computer to supply the vast majority of storage and graphics command facility. Workstations were, in effect, merely "dumb" terminals with little, if any, separate processing hardware. With the advent of the raster CRT and the continuous advancement of graphics techniques, there has been a corresponding trend towards the use of "intelligent" workstations with their own local processor.

The workstation processor (sometimes called a *graphics manager*) is a computer (commonly 16-bit, 256–768K) within each workstation, which assists the host computer in speeding up graphics displays on the VDU, whilst relying on the host computer for memory storage capacity.

Highly sophisticated facilities, such as 3D modelling, are particularly demanding on host computer capacity. As such techniques become more popular, the advancing intelligence of workstations seems set to continue.

The Menu Facility

A CAD menu is a list of available drawing commands, e.g. LIST, CIRCLE, ARC, ZOOM, etc. Fig 2.8 shows one type of menu facility which is given on a screen display. When using this type of screen menu, drawing elements are usually selected by typing in an appropriate abbreviation at an alpha-numeric keyboard (or sometimes a *function box* consisting of special function keys). After selecting the required command, the screen display often responds by asking for more information, such as required size, position on the graphics screen, etc. *Pull-down screen menus* are discussed as part of the WIMP philosophy in Chapter 3.

Other common types of menu facility are provided via electronic command tablets or function keyboards.

The Electronic Command Tablet

Most types of electronic command tablet (sometimes called a *bit-pad*) are dual-purpose facilities which incorporate a menu and a *digitising area*.

Fig 2.9 shows a typical electronic command tablet. Fig 2.10 shows a typical command tablet menu written on a card which may be attached to the command tablet.

Fig. 2.8 Screen menu

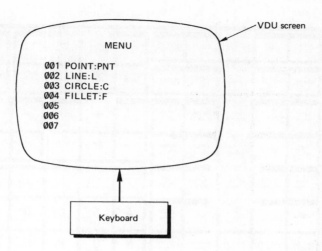

Fig. 2.9 Command tablet [*Computer Vision*]

The more powerful CAD systems provide several such cards with varying sets of commands, which may be overlayed on the menu area of the tablet to give an extensive choice. Most of the larger systems also allow further menu cards to be made up by the draughtsman for more specialised commands. Drawing commands are selected by touching the appropriate place on the card with either an *electronic pen* (Fig 2.11) or a *puck* (Fig 2.12).

If the pen or puck is moved over the digitising area of the tablet, it becomes a *cursor control device*. The cursor effectively locates drawing

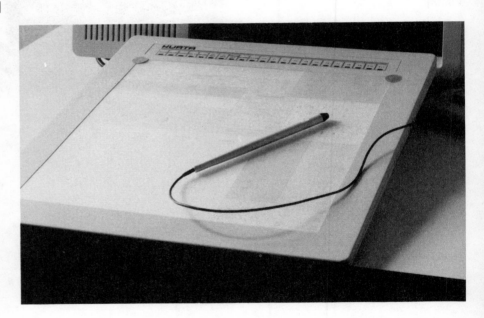

Fig. 2.10 Command tablet menu [*Tektronix*]

2-D DRAFTING TABLET MENU 1

WINDOW

REDRAW	BOX	SAVE
CENTER SCALE	MIN MAX	RESTORE

GRID

ON	ON W/O DISPLAY	OFF

PARAMETERS

DASH	LEVEL	PEN
ARC SMOOTH	NUMERIC FORMAT	TEXT FORMAT
ALPHA DEVICE	CURSOR DEVICE	TABLET WINDOW
DISPLAY SAVE ENVIR	CURSOR ANGLE	DEFINE CONST

CHECK

ITEM DATA	COORD	DISTANCE	ANGLE	INTER SECTION

COPY

MIRROR	RESCALE	ROTATE	TRANS LATE	MATRIX

POINT

FREE INPUT	MIDPOINT	ARC CENTER	ON ARC AT ANGLE	INTER SECTION

LINE

FREE INPUT	OFFSET	TANTO CURVES	PERP TO CURVE	DOUBLE TRIPLE

ARC/CIRCLE

THRU 3 POINTS	CENTER RADIUS	CENTER EDGE	2 POINTS ANGLE	FILLET ROUND

ANNOTATION

ARROW	CROSS HATCH	C LINE ARC	NOTE	ANGLE DIMEN
HORIZ DIMEN	VERTICAL DIMEN	PARALLEL DIMEN	RADIUS DIMEN	DIAMETER DIMEN

FREE INPUT

POINT	LINE ENDPOINT	ARC ENDPOINT	SYMBOL POINT
ABSOLUTE COORD	DELTA COORD	RADIAL COORD	IGNORE GRID

MODIFY

LEVEL	PEN	ITEM
DASH	CLIP	STRETCH

BLANK

LEVEL	PEN	ITEM
TYPE	ALL	ALL BUT WORKSET

UNBLANK

LEVEL	PEN
TYPE	ALL

ITEM SELECTION

POINT	LINE	ARC	SYMBOL
ARROW	CROSS HATCH	NOTE/ DIMEN	WORKSET

+	−	±	1	2	3	4	5
A	B	C	D	E	F	G	H
N (NO)	O	P	Q	R	S	T	U

Fig. 2.11 Electronic tablet pen

elements at their required position on the screen and usually takes the form of a pair of cross-hairs which appear on the screen after the drawing command has been selected. The drawing element (e.g. point, line, circle, etc.) required by the command will be displayed on the screen at the final position of the cursor with its origin at the intersection of the cross-hairs. The cursor control is also used to locate existing elements on the screen which are required to be modified.

The movement of the cursor around the screen corresponds to the controlling movement of the electronic pen or puck on the tablet, as shown in Fig 2.13.

16

WORKSET										
ADD ITEM	ADD REGION	ADD CHAIN	1	2	3	4	5	6	7	8	9	10
REMOVE ITEM	HI-LIGHT	INIT	11	12	13	14	15	16	17	18	19	20

Figure — Tektronix command keyboard layout showing WORKSET, DELETE, SYMBOL, DRAWING, FILES sections and alphanumeric keys.

Fig. 2.12 Puck
[*Calcomp*]

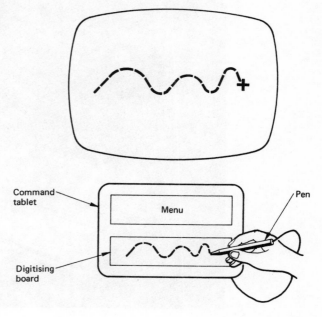

Fig. 2.13 Cursor
control via electronic
pen on command tablet

Command tablet

Menu

Pen

Digitising board

The Light-Pen This device allows direct contact between the user and the VDU screen. The light-pen is an electronic device which detects light signals when it is moved across the screen.

A drawing element may be created, or modified, by touching the screen with the tip of the pen at the required screen location, whilst pressing a button near the tip (Fig 2.14). In most cases, cursor cross-hairs are located on the screen and move in conjunction with the light-pen. As with the command tablet, the origin of the created drawing element lies at the intersection of the cross-hairs (Fig 2.15).

The operation of the light-pen is particularly suited to vector refresh displays, and although raster display systems may be designed to accommodate them, the extra computing required at the workstation processor usually makes this an impractical proposition. Given the increasing popularity of raster displays, this factor must be considered as a major limitation of the light-pen. Also, the advantage of direct screen contact is often outweighed by the discomfort of holding the pen up to the screen for prolonged periods.

Fig. 2.14 Operating a light pen [*Ford Motor Company*]

The Joystick Vertical and horizontal displacements of a joystick produce corresponding movements of the cursor on the VDU screen (Fig 2.16). Joysticks are suitable for raster display systems and have become very

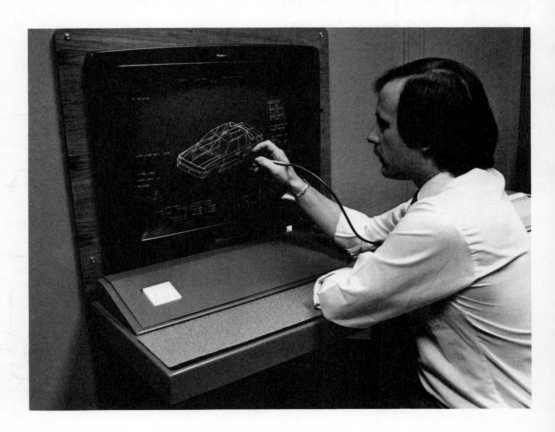

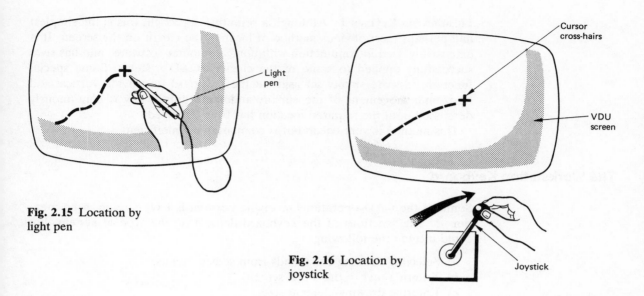

Fig. 2.15 Location by light pen

Fig. 2.16 Location by joystick

Fig. 2.17 Mouse [*Research Machines Ltd.*]

popular in the home computer market. In CAD systems, they are most effectively used in conjunction with screen-display type menu facilities.

The Mouse The operation of this device initially appears to be similar to that of the command-tablet/electronic-pen/puck arrangement. Indeed, the mouse looks very similar to a puck, and the two terms are, consequently, often confused.

The main difference is that a mouse is mounted on a roller-ball or wheels and does not require an electronic tablet surface. It may be moved on any flat surface to achieve the desired cursor location (Fig 2.17).

As with the joystick, the mouse is most suited to those CAD systems which employ screen menu displays, and is particularly suited to the WIMP philosophy, which is discussed in Chapter 3.

Location via Keyboard   Although a primitive approach, this is the simplest and perhaps most obvious method of locating the cursor on the screen. It is extensively used in conjunction with home computer software, and has seen successfully applied to some of the cheaper CAD systems. Some special function keys are simply set aside at the keyboard to provide vertical and horizontal movement of the cursor, and the required key is continuously depressed until the required location has been achieved.

This method is very cheap but is comparatively inefficient.

The Workstation Keyboard

Some of the CAD operations involving keyboards have already been mentioned. The functions of the keyboard depend on the type of system, but could include the following:

a) Selecting drawing commands from screen menus.
b) Entering text to the VDU screen.
c) Entering drawing element sizes.
d) Entering components or symbols from macro standards libraries.
e) Selecting CAD software.
f) Programming new software.
g) Cursor control on cheaper systems.

Fig. 2.18 Function box and alphanumeric keyboard [*IBM (UK) Ltd*]

Most CAD keyboards have the familiar alpha-numeric QWERTY layout of common typewriters, although many also have additional special function keys and communication command keys.

The *communication keys* are commonly used for direct access to the CPU outside the CAD software and conform to a standard graphics and text control code such as ASCII (discussed later in this chapter and during descriptions of numerical control principles in Chapter 9).

The *special function keys* (such as those previously described for primitive cursor control) may be housed in the same unit as the alpha-numeric keys, or there may be a separate *function box* comprised entirely of special function keys. These keys perform the equivalent of a series of graphic commands with a single touch (e.g. "Draw a tangent line between two circles"). Such complex commands are referred to as *macros*, and many types of function box are programmable to allow individual companies to develop their own appropriate selection of important macro functions. (The term "macro" is also applied to CAD software subroutines which are discussed in Chapter 3, to standard CAD component drawings and symbols which are discussed in Chapter 4, and to certain CNC part-programming procedures which are discussed in Chapter 9.) Function boxes are commonly used in conjunction with screen menus. Typical examples of CAD keyboards are shown in Fig 2.18.

The Printer

Most workstations are equipped with a printer, which gives a *hard copy* permanent record of alpha-numeric commands on paper. Some printers also give a *screen dump*—a small hard copy of the drawing on the VDU screen. Such copies are of primitive resolution and are intended only as a quick reference during the development of a drawing. A printer with graphics screen dump is sometimes referred to as a *mini-plotter*.

Several types of printer have been developed for CAD systems but by far the most popular is the *dot-matrix* printer (Fig 2.19). This is an electro-mechanical device which creates images on paper from thousands of tiny dots when thin wires act on an ink ribbon. Text characters and graphics elements are not displayed as separate items. The complete display is built up from reciprocating horizontal sweeps of the printing head as the paper winds round a rotating drum. Thus the hard copy is constructed from dots in a similar manner to a raster screen display, with a resulting appearance much the same. Dot-matrix printers are therefore highly suitable for use with raster VDUs and may be operated from the same workstation processor hardware.

Fig. 2.19 Working principle of the dot matrix printer

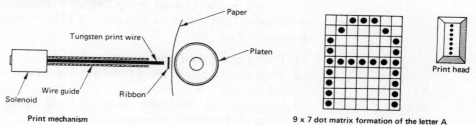

Print mechanism

9 x 7 dot matrix formation of the letter A

2.3 Transmission of Data

All data is transmitted from computer to workstation components via patterns of electronic pulses which make up signals of binary code. Each binary digit (or bit) is interpreted as having a value of either "one" (pulse emitted) or "zero" (no pulse emitted).

The most common type of binary code used in both CAD and CAM systems is the ASCII code (American Standard Code for Information Interchange) which represents each of its characters by binary numbers consisting of a sequence of seven bits. For example, if the ASCII code for a letter J is to be communicated from the computer, an equivalent sequence of pulses could be transmitted as shown in Fig 2.20, by switching on-and-off a 20 mA current at regular time intervals. This technique is known as a 20 mA current loop.

Fig. 2.20 ASCII signal for communicating the letter J (20 mA current loop)

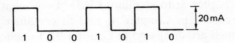

In fact, each signal consists of eight bits (a byte), but only seven of these are used to describe the character, the eighth being used to maintain either even or odd parity of the number of "ones" in each signal. The ASCII code is also extensively used to communicate signals in numerically-controlled machine operations and will be discussed again in this context as part of Chapter 9.

A list of common standard ASCII codes is provided on page 24.

Hardware is designed to transmit and receive signals at a specified rate of bits per second. In an asynchronous communication system (see page 23), this is commonly referred to as the *baud rate* of the equipment. The baud rate describes the total number of bits transmitted per second, including timing pulses, so the actual number of data bits transmitted per second is proportionally less than the baud rate. The common baud rates are: 75, 150, 300, 600, 1200, 2400, 4800, 9600, and 19200, with 9600 being the most popular in CADCAM equipment.

2.4 Networking of CAD Stations

Networking is the process of setting-up a communications link between workstations and the host computer CPU. Network types may be categorised in terms of:

1 Their type of data transmission.
2 Their *topology* (i.e. the way in which workstations and peripherals are distributed).
3 *Protocols* (i.e. the rules and standards under which information is exchanged between processors).

The two common types of data transmission are

Parallel transmission and
Serial transmission.

1 PARALLEL TRANSMISSION requires a separate wire for each bit in the binary code signal transmitted between the host computer and the workstation. For example, if each binary code signal consisted of eight bits, then eight wires are required. This system provides high-speed data exchange but can be very expensive and impractical, especially where remote workstations are involved.

Parallel transmission was a popular arrangement before the advent of the raster CRT and the workstation processor because it helped to speed up the response time at the dumb workstations. As these workstations were totally dependent on the host computer for any processing, each item of the workstation (e.g. VDU, keyboard, command tablet, etc.) had to be connected individually to the host with a separate cable (Fig 2.21).

Fig. 2.21 Dependent workstation network using parallel transmission

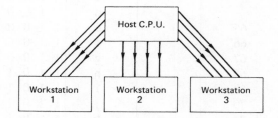

2 SERIAL TRANSMISSION uses a single wire along which each bit of the binary code is transmitted in turn. Since each bit has to wait its turn in the queue, serial transmission is much slower than parallel. However, as local workstation intelligence increases, this becomes less of a problem, and the cheapness and other practical advantages of having a single wire makes serial transmission the more popular alternative for networking a modern CAD system with intelligent workstations.

Serial transmission may be undertaken using either:

Asynchronous mode communication or
Synchronous mode communication.

In *asynchronous mode*, each character is transmitted separately as a single stream of bits. To define the start and end of each character, the streams are separated by timing pulses. Effectively, a character will be transmitted as a complete message as soon as a key is depressed at the keyboard.

In *synchronous mode*, complete blocks of characters are transmitted together. A stream of timing pulses is sent at the start of each block. These have the effect of synchronising the message at the receiving end, so that no time pulses are required between the characters. A synchronous mode system will not transmit any characters until the Return key (or equivalent) is depressed at the keyboard. A block of characters will then be transmitted in accordance with the keys previously depressed.

Standard ASCII codes

Character	Binary code $2^6\ 2^5\ 2^4\ 2^3\ 2^2\ 2^1\ 2^0$	Decimal Equivalent
0	0 1 1 0 0 0 0	48
1	0 1 1 0 0 0 1	49
2	0 1 1 0 0 1 0	50
3	0 1 1 0 0 1 1	51
4	0 1 1 0 1 0 0	52
5	0 1 1 0 1 0 1	53
6	0 1 1 0 1 1 0	54
7	0 1 1 0 1 1 1	55
8	0 1 1 1 0 0 0	56
9	0 1 1 1 0 0 1	57
A	1 0 0 0 0 0 1	65
B	1 0 0 0 0 1 0	66
C	1 0 0 0 0 1 1	67
D	1 0 0 0 1 0 0	68
E	1 0 0 0 1 0 1	69
F	1 0 0 0 1 1 0	70
G	1 0 0 0 1 1 1	71
H	1 0 0 1 0 0 0	72
I	1 0 0 1 0 0 1	73
J	1 0 0 1 0 1 0	74
K	1 0 0 1 0 1 1	75
L	1 0 0 1 1 0 0	76
M	1 0 0 1 1 0 1	77
N	1 0 0 1 1 1 0	78
O	1 0 0 1 1 1 1	79
P	1 0 1 0 0 0 0	80
Q	1 0 1 0 0 0 1	81
R	1 0 1 0 0 1 0	82
S	1 0 1 0 0 1 1	83
T	1 0 1 0 1 0 0	84
U	1 0 1 0 1 0 1	85
V	1 0 1 0 1 1 0	86
W	1 0 1 0 1 1 1	87
X	1 0 1 1 0 0 0	88
Y	1 0 1 1 0 0 1	89
Z	1 0 1 1 0 1 0	90
Space	0 1 0 0 0 0 0	32
&	0 1 0 0 1 1 0	38
?	0 1 1 1 1 1 1	63
!	0 1 0 0 0 0 1	33

Character	Binary code $2^6\ 2^5\ 2^4\ 2^3\ 2^2\ 2^1\ 2^0$	Decimal Equivalent
(	0 1 0 1 0 0 0	40
)	0 1 0 1 0 0 1	41
,	0 1 0 0 1 1 1	39
.	0 1 0 1 1 1 0	46
:	0 1 1 1 0 1 0	58
;	0 1 1 1 0 1 1	59
a	1 1 0 0 0 0 1	97
b	1 1 0 0 0 1 0	98
c	1 1 0 0 0 1 1	99
d	1 1 0 0 1 0 0	100
e	1 1 0 0 1 0 1	101
f	1 1 0 0 1 1 0	102
g	1 1 0 0 1 1 1	103
h	1 1 0 1 0 0 0	104
i	1 1 0 1 0 0 1	105
j	1 1 0 1 0 1 0	106
k	1 1 0 1 0 1 1	107
l	1 1 0 1 1 0 0	108
m	1 1 0 1 1 0 1	109
n	1 1 0 1 1 1 0	110
o	1 1 0 1 1 1 1	111
p	1 1 1 0 0 0 0	112
q	1 1 1 0 0 0 1	113
r	1 1 1 0 0 1 0	114
s	1 1 1 0 0 1 1	115
t	1 1 1 0 1 0 0	116
u	1 1 1 0 1 0 1	117
v	1 1 1 0 1 1 0	118
w	1 1 1 0 1 1 1	119
x	1 1 1 1 0 0 0	120
y	1 1 1 1 0 0 1	121
z	1 1 1 1 0 1 0	122
+	0 1 0 1 0 1 1	43
−	0 1 0 1 1 0 1	45
*	0 1 0 1 0 1 0	42
/	0 1 0 1 1 1 1	47
<	0 1 1 1 1 0 0	60
=	0 1 1 1 1 0 1	61
>	0 1 1 1 1 1 0	62

Asynchronous mode provides easy interfacing between CAD equipment supplied by different manufacturers. This may be achieved through a system of standard connections known as RS-232. Synchronous mode, which can transmit data at higher rates of bits per second, is more efficient and reliable but is currently less used in practice.

Three popular network topologies employing serial transmission are

Star network
Daisychain network
Cambridge ring

1 STAR NETWORKS are arranged so that each workstation is connected individually to the host by a single cable (Fig 2.22). Communications between the separate workstation components and the host computer are undertaken using a device called a *multiplexor*, which allows several devices to share one line simultaneously. Most star networks employ asynchronous communication.

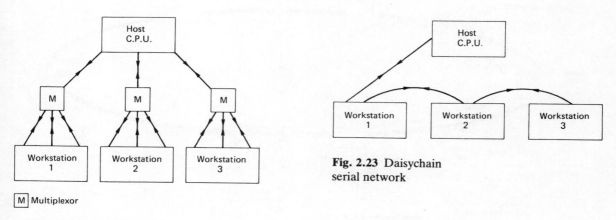

M Multiplexor

Fig. 2.22 Star serial network

Fig. 2.23 Daisychain serial network

2 The DAISYCHAIN NETWORK uses a single-cable connection between workstations, rather than individual host connection (Fig 2.23). Daisychain networks often employ a LAN (Local Area Network) which allows independent communication between intelligent workstations on a single high-speed data link, whilst using the host only for storage back-up. LANs are particularly useful for incorporating workstations with specific functions (e.g. database management, analytical capacity, etc.) which may be used elsewhere in the system when required.

Daisychain networks are becoming increasingly popular, having distinct practical advantages in cable connection, particularly where a progressive string of remote workstations is required. When a LAN is incorporated, this configuration becomes a powerful communications tool in a modern CADCAM system.

3 The CAMBRIDGE RING network (developed at Cambridge University) uses a continuous stream of data bits which circulate a ring configuration of workstations and peripherals. The system usually incorporates a LAN and is supported by a host computer. Information exchange in a ring network may be likened to a circular railway track arrangement which contains "carriages" of information. Individual workstations will take the information from a carriage if it contains the appropriate address. The inefficiency of this system is that all carriages pass through every station at a fixed rate, irrespective of individual requirements, and thus each workstation has to ignore a majority of unwanted carriages before receiving its own information.

Fig 2.24 shows a variation of the Cambridge ring which uses "variable train lengths". This enables shorter messages to result in shorter train lengths and thus speed up the information exchange.

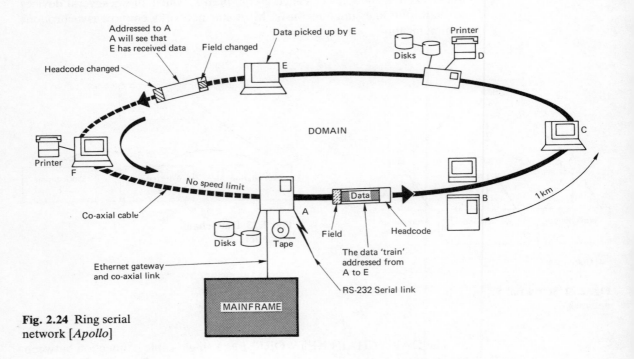

Fig. 2.24 Ring serial network [*Apollo*]

2.5 The Autonomous Workstation

As already pointed out, there is a current trend towards increased local intelligence at each workstation and less dependence on the host computer. An obvious further development is that of completely independent (i.e. autonomous) workstations where a host computer may not be required. Such a workstation is usually equipped with a 32-bit computer which can handle all the CAD software and storage facility for its own requirements. An autonomous workstation may exist as a single unit (often referred to as a *stand-alone system*). Alternatively, several may be effectively linked in a daisy-chain network (ideally incorporating a LAN). This concept is known as a *distributed system* which may be assisted by a host computer, but it is not essential (Fig 2.25).

Fig. 2.25 Distributed system of autonomous workstations.

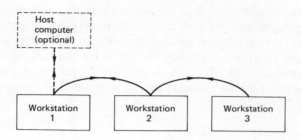

It should be emphasised that the basic principle of a distributed system (even if a host is incorporated) is that of complete independence of each workstation whilst allowing shared storage facility and communication through a LAN when required. A distributed system of autonomous work-stations has the following clear advantages:

a) Workstations do not become unusable in the event of failure elsewhere in the system.
b) They hold a particular attraction for smaller companies who may want to develop CAD by a modular approach, e.g. starting with a stand-alone workstation and adding more stations when required.
c) There is no noticeable decrease in interactive response speed when more workstations are added to the system.

2.6 Shared Peripherals

These hardware items are shared between the workstations of the CAD system. Typical shared peripherals include the plotter, magnetic tape drive, disc drive, and photoplotter.

Plotters

A plotter automatically produces an accurate hard-copy of the final computer drawing onto a paper sheet. Common types of plotter used in CAD systems include:

a) Vertical drum type
b) Flat bed type
c) Electrostatic
d) Ink jet.

Types *a* and *b* are *vector* devices which construct drawings from separate geometric shapes either in wet ink or with pressurised ball-point pens. These types usually have a number of pens for different colours or thicknesses of line. The pens are automatically selected in accordance with a "layering" technique applied during the creation of the CAD drawing. (Layering is discussed in Chapter 4.)

The *vertical drum-type plotter* has a roll of paper which is continuously wound and unwound on a rotating drum, in sequence with the moving pen. The paper may be continuous, or it may be a single sheet attached to a moving belt passing around the drums. The vertical plotter is generally faster, cheaper, and takes up less space than the flat-bed type. Also, if a continuous roll of paper is employed, this may be utilised for lengthy production runs. Vertical plotters are commonly designed for A0 size paper (Fig 2.26).

Fig. 2.26 Vertical drum-type plotter [*Benson*]

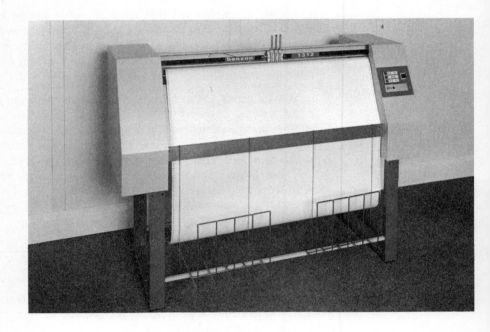

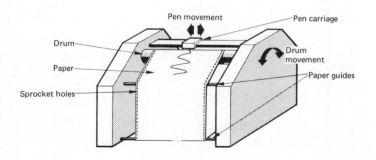

The *flat-bed plotter* uses a single sheet of paper held still on a flat horizontal surface while the pen automatically moves across it (Fig 2.27). Size range is commonly A3 to A0. The flat-bed type is more accurate than the vertical type and is thus useful for applications such as template drawings. Also, flat-bed plotters can accommodate sheets of inflexible material such as plastic or steel.

The *electrostatic plotter* is a more recent device which creates drawings from horizontal sweeps on a principle very similar to that of the raster CRT and the dot-matrix printer. It has a continuous roll of special paper which passes across a writing head containing thousands of tiny electrodes arranged in the form of a thin strip. When passed through a bath of toner, a drawing is formed from a vast pattern of tiny dots created by the electrodes (Figs 2.28, 2.29).

Fig. 2.27 Flatbed plotter [*Benson*]

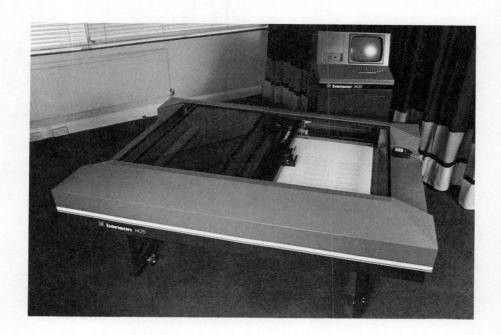

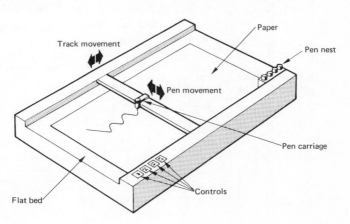

Fig. 2.28 Electrostatic plotter [*Versatec Electronics Ltd.*]

Fig. 2.29 Principle of operation of a colour electrostatic plotter [*Versatec Electronics Ltd.*]

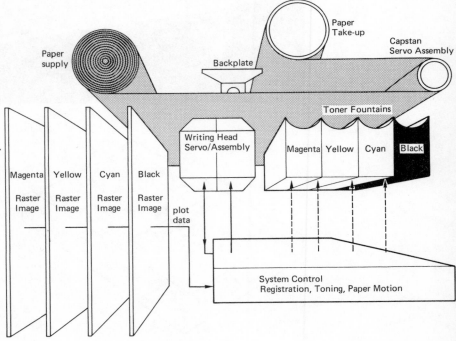

Fig. 2.30 Example of solid modelling plot from an electrostatic plotter [*Versatec Electronics Ltd.*]

A particular advantage of the electrostatic plotter is its ability to produce drawings unattended. This is not possible with the vector plotters as their pens could dry up at any time. Electrostatic plotters are also advantageous where "artistic" effects of extensive colour, filled-in areas and variation of tone are required on hard-copy (Fig 2.30). Hence they are being adopted particularly in CAD systems with sophisticated 3D modelling techniques.

They have the current disadvantages of high cost and slight inaccuracy of line resolution, but advances in technology are rectifying both of these factors.

The *ink jet plotter* operates on a similar raster principle to that of the electrostatic plotter and also creates hard copy images from thousands of tiny dots. In the ink jet plotter, however, the writing head consists of a carriage containing three jets which squirt a controlled volume of ink at regular time intervals. The carriage slowly travels across a continuously rotating drum to which the paper is attached. Each jet conforms to a primary colour hue and can create a vast range of coloured images by combination of primaries and variation of intensity as achieved on the raster colour CRT.

The ink jet plotter can perform all the "artistic" effects described for the electrostatic plotter and the two devices are often in direct competition in these applications.

Magnetic Tape Drives and Disc Drives

Magnetic tape drives are useful for storing large amounts of data (up to 100 Mbyte per tape) such as for extensive drawing libraries.

Disc drives are used for speedy storage and recall of data and software. They fall into two categories: floppy and hard

The smaller *floppy disc* will usually contain either an application software package or current data being used by the individual draughtsman. The simplest type of floppy disc contains typically 250 K of memory. However, a *double-density* disc allows twice the information to be stored by packing the data closer together. The memory may be doubled again by using *double-sided* discs. Thus a double-sided, double-density floppy disc commonly contains 1 Mbyte of memory, which can be increased to as much as 1.5 Mbyte.

The larger *hard disc* is often a permanent fixture in the computer (commonly referred to as a winchester disc). This is usually used to store large amounts of current data such as unfinished drawings or frequently used standards. This data can later be transferred to long-term storage on magnetic tape or floppy disc when no longer urgently required. Winchester discs commonly store between 20 Mbyte and 500 Mbyte of memory.

Other systems use hard discs which may be extracted from the computer when full up with data.

Large Digitiser

Commonly of A0 size, this item looks much like a conventional drawing machine on a pedestal stand (Fig 2.31). In fact, it is really a large version of the digitising area of the electronic command tablet. It is particularly useful where a company has a large stock of existing paper drawings which they wish to store into a CAD system.

A drawing may be placed on the board of the digitiser, and a puck or electronic pen scanned over the existing lines. The shape being "traced" will be simultaneously diplayed on the VDU screen just as shapes would be created using a command tablet.

Fig. 2.31 A0-size digitiser [*Benson*]

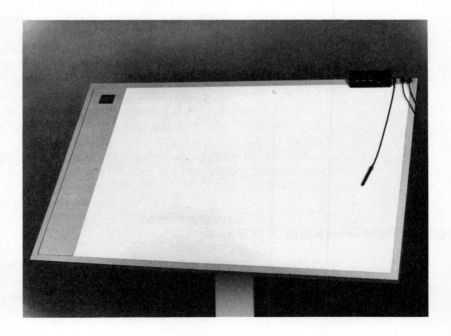

Punched-tape Machine

This may be used as an intermediate stage between CAD and CAM. Coded messages concerning the drawing on the VDU screen are sent from the workstation to the tape machine via the CPU. The tape machine then outputs each coded message in the form of a pattern of punched holes on a continuous reel of paper. The completed reel may then be fed into a numerically controlled machine tool which automatically produces the component. This facility may now be superseded by a direct interface between the CAD system and a CNC machine tool, as discussed in Chapter 9. It is the latter approach which may accurately be described as a CADCAM process.

Photoplotter

This is a peripheral used in the design and production of printed circuit boards (PCBs). The drawing on the VDU screen is transferred to a hard-copy on a sheet of photographic film placed on a flat-bed. The hard-copy is "drawn" by a head containing a light-emitting fibre-optic cable which creates a photographic impression of the VDU display. The completed film is then used in a copper-etching process which produces the finished PCB.

CAD Software 3

The purpose of all software is to provide the programmed instructions for the operation of hardware devices.

3.1 Levels of Computer Software

Software communicates in a pattern of code called a *language*. The most primitive language is called *machine code*, which speaks directly to the hardware equipment in either binary (two digit) or hex (hexadecimal or sixteen digit) signals. *Assembly language* is a shorthand technique for writing machine code. This enables the programmer to write in mnemonic code, i.e. a code in letters which are similar to the descriptive command, such as LDA (Load register A). The assembly language command is then converted into machine code by another program called an assembler.

The direct communication of a machine code program provides speedy computer response, but the arduous nature of writing such programs, even with an assembler, makes machine code far too impractical for applications of any complexity.

The writing of software is made much less involved with the aid of *high-level languages*, which are used in most areas of CAD and CAM.

Translators convert high-level languages into binary messages which may be understood by the hardware. Translators may be of either interpreter type or compiler type. *Interpreters* translate high-level languages in single statements, which is time-consuming. One of the most popular and "user-friendly" of interpretive high-level languages is Basic, which is widely used in home microcomputers. Basic is inexpensive and versatile, but slow computer response restricts it to the simpler types of program. *Compilers* are more expensive, but give a much faster computer response, since they quickly translate the entire program into binary language before running it continuously in machine code. Typical high-level compiler languages used in CAD software include Fortran, Pascal, and C.

CAD software may generally be categorised as

1 SYSTEM SOFTWARE or
2 APPLICATION SOFTWARE

Fig. 3.1 Software
hierarchical structure

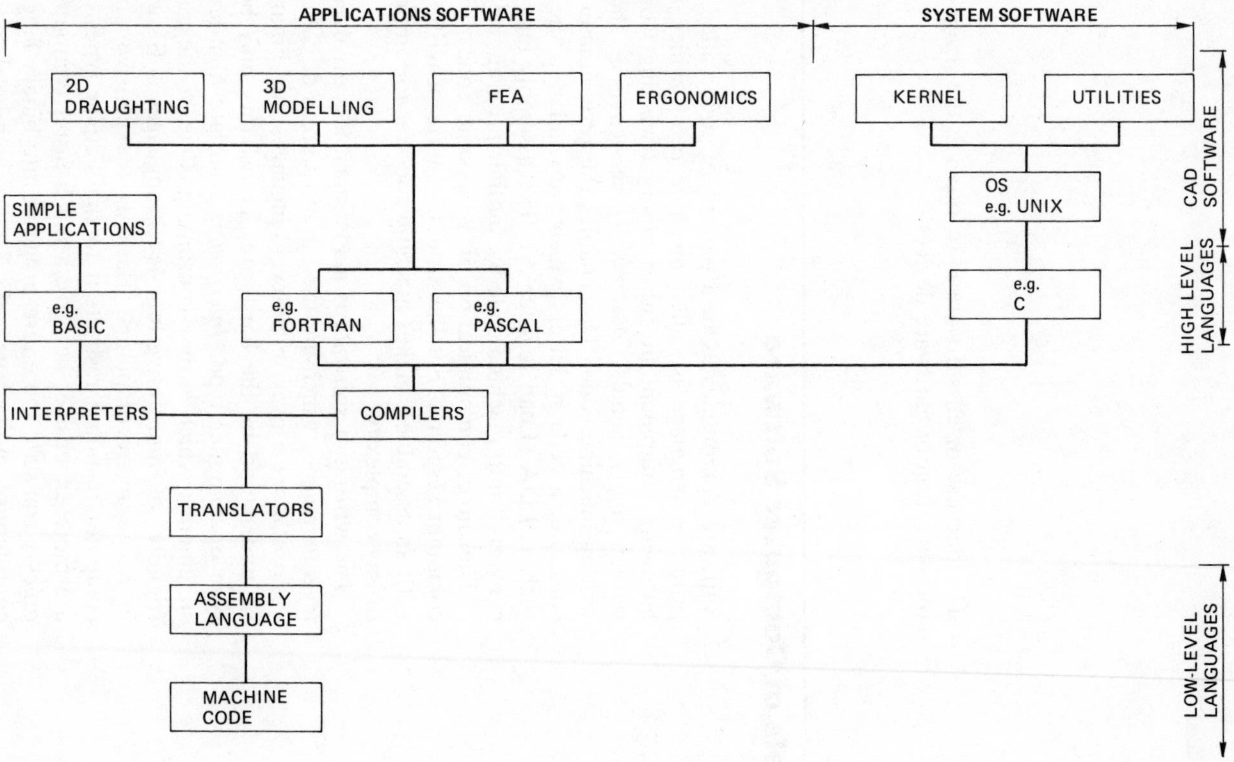

Fig 3.1 shows how CAD software fits into the hierarchical structure of software systems.

3.2 System Software—the Operating System

The *operating system* (OS) is the most important facility in CAD system software. The task of an OS is to manage and organise the computer operations undertaken in the CAD system.

Most operating systems are divided into two parts:

1 A principal single program called the *kernel*.
2 A collection of peripheral programs called *utilities*.

The OS Kernel Typical functions of the OS kernel include:

a) Organising storage space on hardware devices, such as hard discs, floppy discs, and magnetic tapes, into units where information can be stored and retrieved. These storage units are known as *files*. When using discs, this part of the software is known as a *disc operating system* (DOS).

b) Supplying directories, and conducting searches, for existing files and utilities. Several types of search operation may be specified, one of the most useful being the *wildcard search*. This allows the user to obtain a list of files which conform to a specified classification group. Wildcard searching is also a common feature of database management systems (which are discussed in Chapter 7).

c) Managing the simultaneous execution of different programs (called *time sharing*) and the communications between those programs.

d) Managing interface operations between programs and external hardware.

OS Utilities These are optional programs which complement the kernel by performing specific tasks for the CAD system, such as screen menu operations and specialist drawing file operations.

Common OS Types Perhaps the most well-known operating systems are CP/M and the IBM-developed MS-DOS. These have both been widely used in disc-operated microcomputers.

In the larger systems, the most important OS is Unix, which is now also gaining popularity for microcomputers. Unix was developed in 1969 by Bell Laboratories. It is written in a high-level compiler language called C, which was developed at the same time. C and Unix are thus inherently linked, with C being the most widely-used language run on Unix, and most Unix facilities written in C.

Unix has the following features:

a) It is a *portable* system which may be run on many different types of computer and hardware configuration.

b) It is time-sharing and may be operated on either a multi-user or a single-user basis.

c) It is multi-lingual. Although written in C, it may incorporate compilers for other high-level languages.

d) There is a wide and versatile range of utility programs available with Unix. This is a particularly significant factor with regard to CAD and CADCAM systems.

Screen Menu Utilities A set of utilities commonly associated with the Unix operating system encompasses a philosophy known as WIMP (Windows/Icons/Mice/Pointers).

WIMP utilities provide a *pull-down screen menu* facility which seems likely to supersede both tablet menus and other types of screen menu (see Chapter 2) in the near future. Fig 3.2 shows a typical pull-down menu display.

Pull-down screen menus incorporate a border of rectangular cell displays along the top, or around the perimeter, of the screen. In each cell is displayed a pictorial menu option, called an *icon*. An icon may be selected by using any of the electronic pointing devices described in Chapter 2 (e.g. mouse, puck, light-pen, joystick, keyboard, etc.). However, the mouse is currently the most popular. As the mouse is moved over a surface, corresponding movements of a displayed pointer (usually a small arrow) take place on the screen. When the arrow locates the required icon, a button on the mouse is pressed, and a more detailed secondary menu is then pulled down and displayed inside a window on the screen. Options from the pulled-down menu may then be selected, again with the mouse and arrow. Fig 3.3 illustrates the principle of WIMP.

Fig. 3.2 Pull-down menu display (icons along right and bottom of screen)

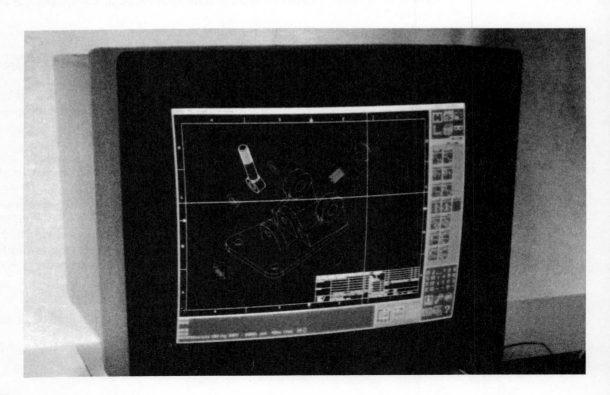

Fig. 3.3 Operation of pull-down screen menu (WIMP principle)

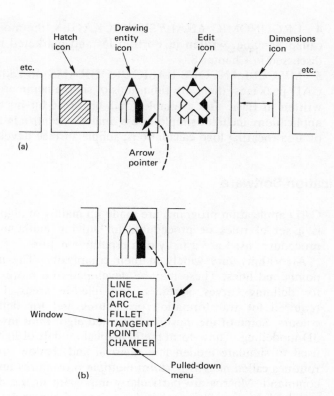

3.3 Application Software

Application software is usually supplied in disc packages and written in high-level languages by specialist companies. These packages may be specifically designed for one type of computer, but ideally will be compatible for a range of different hardware suppliers. Application software packages deal with specific computer-aided tasks. Most CAD application software is written in compiled languages such as Fortran and Pascal, although some simpler microcomputer packages are written in Basic.

Typical CAD applications include:

1 2D DRAUGHTING PACKAGES, available in varying degrees of sophistication, and run on 16-bit microcomputers, minicomputers, and mainframes. Draughting packages contain a range of drawing facilities, the most common of which are discussed in Chapter 4.

2 3D MODELLING PACKAGES, most efficiently tackled on 32-bit mini-computers upwards. 3D modelling facilities are discussed in Chapter 5. However, some simpler packages are now available for microcomputer.

3 FINITE ELEMENT ANALYSIS (FEA) PACKAGES, usually written in Fortran. As with 3D modelling these packages have traditionally been confined to minicomputers and mainframes, but in many cases FEA may now be tackled quite successfully on 16-bit microcomputers. Advanced packages may incorporate their own 3D modelling systems. FEA is discussed in Chapter 6.

4 ERGONOMIC ANALYSIS PACKAGES, the most famous of which is called Sammie, written in Fortran IV and marketed by Prime. Sammie is discussed in Chapter 8.

5 MISCELLANEOUS BASIC PROGRAMS. In addition to the advanced CAD packages, there are thousands of simple commercial packages, usually written in Basic and available for 8-bit or 16-bit microcomputers. Typical applications include: simple stress analysis; centroids and second moments of area; bearing load calculations; simple surface developments.

Generation of Application Software

CAD application programs are made up mainly of algorithms. An *algorithm* is a set of rules or procedures for solving mathematical problems. The procedures used are usually of a repetitive nature.

Algorithms vary widely in their complexity. The most primitive define points and lines. These may be developed into more advanced procedures for defining curves, surfaces, and filled-in areas. Other algorithms are required for transformation procedures and for defining line styles and colours. Some of the most sophisticated algorithms involve optical effects in 3D modelling. These form mathematical models of light rays, which may be used to simulate hidden line removal and shadow effects. Advanced subroutines called *macros* perform multiple procedures under the action of one command. Macros are particularly important in the development of CAD standard drawing libraries, as discussed in Chapter 4.

The efficiency of the algorithm lies in its simplicity of format compared with the complexity of the problem it can solve. A complex algorithm takes longer for the computer to process, and thus requires higher computing power for satisfactory operation. Advances in CADCAM technology are therefore as dependent on the ability of programmers to devise more ingenious algorithms as on developments in microprocessor technology and hardware enhancement.

3.4 The CAD Database

A database is a collection of files which contain data. Principles of database management systems are discussed in Chapter 7. It is the categorisation of drawing data which is the main concern in this section.

Graphical data held in CAD database files may be grouped into the following categories:

a) GEOMETRICAL DATA (e.g. points, lines, circles, planes, solids).
b) LINE-TYPE DATA (e.g. solid, dashed, etc).
c) TEXT DATA.
d) DATA defining HATCH PATTERNS and FILLED-IN AREAS.
e) LAYER DATA. (The principles of layering are discussed in Chapter 4.)

f) ASSOCIATIVITY DATA. This governs the relationship between geometric elements and their surrounding geometry. Geometric associativity is thus required to describe standard shapes, components, and symbols.

g) CONNECTIVITY DATA. This defines the manner in which components are attached in an assembly.

h) ATTRIBUTE DATA. This is drawing-related data which may not appear on the graphics display. Typical drawing attributes include material specifications on manufactured items, or sizes, ratings, and suppliers of bought-out items on assembly drawings. Attributes play an important role as *field data* in the files of the Database Management System (DBMS). DBMS fields are discussed in Chapter 7.

3.5 Graphics Standards

Software may be obtained as part of a complete CAD system (including all hardware items) from one supplier. This is called a *turnkey system*, which may prove very satisfactory for some companies. Suppliers of turnkey systems rarely manufacture all the items of the system. For example, in many cases they produce the software and buy in the hardware from varied sources.

Alternatively, users may wish to choose specialist application software packages from a range of different suppliers, and so obtain the best combination of programs to suit their own needs. This, of course, is only possible if all these packages may be run on the same host computer and associated hardware.

In either of the above cases, it is necessary that software and hardware be able to communicate with each other via standard codes of graphics data. The main aims of graphics standardization are thus:

a) To provide versatility in the combination of software and hardware items of turnkey systems.

b) To allow the creation of portable application software packages, which will easily run on a wide range of hardware makes and configurations.

c) To allow the transfer of graphical data between two or more different companies which may have completely different CAD systems.

Levels of Graphics Standards Communications

The major problem in introducing graphics standards and specifications has been one of gaining international acceptance. However, some have now achieved a dominant position and have been given various degrees of adoption by the two most important standards-making bodies, namely ANSI (American Standards Institute) and ISO (International Standards Organisation).

The levels of graphics standards communication are illustrated in Fig 3.4 and may be broadly grouped as follows:

Fig. 3.4 Levels of graphics standards communications

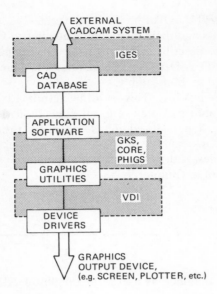

a) *Communication between graphics utility software and graphics output devices* (e.g. screens, plotters, etc.).

The most important standard in this category is VDI (Virtual Device Interface). Although it has now been renamed CGI (Computer Graphics Interface), the term VDI remains in wider use at the time of publication. VDI specifies a standard format for transferring graphical data between the graphics utilities and the device drivers. A *device driver* is a customised program which converts the standard graphics codes into data relevant to a specific type and make of graphical output device.

b) *Communication between application software and graphics utilities*.

The most universally accepted of these standards is GKS (Graphics Kernel System) developed in West Germany in 1979. GKS is a set of graphics standards for providing an interface between application software packages and the graphics utility programs of any CAD system. GKS is similar in concept to an earier American standard called CORE, which is still used by some CAD manufacturers. More recently, a set of standards called PHIGS (Programmers Hierarchical Interface for Graphics) has been proposed, for the purpose of eliminating some of the current restrictions of GKS. Enhanced facilities in the PHIGS specification include a more sophisticated, hierarchical structure of graphics data and the inclusion of 3D geometry data.

c) *Communication between different CAD systems*.

The specification of importance here is IGES (Initial Graphics Exchange Specification), which was developed between 1979 and 1982 and has been partially adopted by ANSI.

IGES is a standard format of codes for CADCAM data which may be completely independent of any system supplier. It thus enables graphical and manufacturing data to be transferred between dissimilar systems. IGES classifies different types of data in terms of *entities*, which may be in one of three categories:

1 GEOMETRY (e.g. points, lines, arcs, planes, finite element nodes, etc.).
2 ANNOTATION (e.g. dimension types, centre lines, arrow leaders, etc.).
3 STRUCTURE (e.g. geometric groups, macro definitions, circular arrays, etc.).

Fig 3.5 shows the philosophy of data exchange via IGES.

To use IGES, each CADCAM system is supplemented with two translator programs: a *pre-processor* and a *post-processor*. Outgoing data is collected from the CAD database of the transmitting CADCAM system and converted into IGES entities by the pre-processor. This independent IGES data is then transmitted to the post-processor of the receiving CADCAM system. The post-processor then converts the IGES entities into specific data understood by the receiving system.

Fig. 3.5
Communications via
IGES

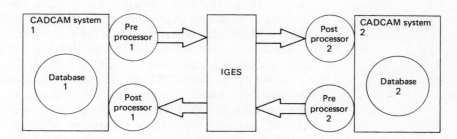

3.6 User-generated (In-house) Software

In most instances, it will not be the duty of designers and engineers to write their own CAD software. However, there are situations when a knowledge of simple programming techniques is useful, particularly when application software packages allow interface with in-house programs.

Typical applications could include:

a) Programs for generating parametric shapes which may be transferred to CAD systems not incorporating parameterisation as a standard facility.
b) Programs for calculating component sizes from given loadings, again transferring the generated shape to a CAD system.
c) Programs for writing schedules or calculating costs from drawing attribute data transferred from a CAD system.

In-house Program Examples

The following examples concern simple programs written in a version of Basic called Microsoft (courtesy Act Ltd) which interface with a versatile CAD software package called Autocad (courtesy Autodesk Inc). Autocad may be run on 16-bit microcomputer systems upwards.

Each example involves placing coordinate data from the in-house program, onto an ASCII text file (see Chapter 2) which may be understood by the CAD system. In the Autocad system, these text files are called Data Interchange Files (DXF).

PROGRAM EXAMPLE 1: **Parametric shaft**

Autocad does not include parametric macros (see Chapter 4) as part of its standard facilities, but parametric shapes may be programmed in-house. The system allows the user to write a program in Basic which will specify geometric parameters. These parameters may be transferred to a DXF file, whose data may then be transferred to an Autocad drawing file.

DXF files contain drawing information organised into *sections*, of which one, called *entities*, will be the main concern here. (In Autocad, the entities section contains geometry data only, and should not be confused with the definition of an entity in the IGES specification.)

Fig 3.6 shows the Basic program for drawing the half view of a shaft containing any number of portions with variable diameters and lengths. (To avoid confusion, the reader may assume that "Line" refers to a program line, whereas "LINE" refers to a straight drawing line.)

Line 1Ø3Ø allows the user to input a drawing filename (say SHAFT). Line 1Ø4Ø opens up a DXF file called by the filename chosen, with an extension .DXF added to it (i.e. our DXF file becomes known as SHAFT. DXF). In Line 1Ø5Ø, PRINT#1 tells the computer to print data to the DXF file, while Ø indicates a separation point in the file. Line 1Ø6Ø indicates that data for a file section is about to commence. In Line 1Ø7Ø, the 2 indicates that a section name will follow, whilst Line 1Ø8Ø states that the section name is ENTITIES.

Lines 1Ø87 to 117Ø allow the user to input geometric parameters for one portion of the shaft. There is provision for a chamfer or a fillet at each end of the portion. If a parameter is not required, a zero is entered. Fig 3.7 shows the nonsense shape which would be drawn if values were entered for all parameters. Names for the variable parameters (e.g. CL for leftmost chamfer) have been invented by the programmer.

Lines 123Ø, 1264, 127Ø, 141Ø, 157Ø, 159Ø, and 161Ø specify cartesian coordinates for start points of straight LINES (variables XS, YS) and finish points of straight LINES (variables XF, YF), in terms of input parameters. Following each of these Lines is a GOSUB instruction, which takes the program to subroutine 8ØØØ (i.e. Lines 8ØØØ to 812Ø), if parameter values are not zero. Each line of this subroutine is an instruction to print graphics data for drawing a straight LINE on an Autocad drawing file (via PRINT#1). In Line 8ØØØ, the Ø specifies that the next Line will contain entity data, which is then confirmed in Line 8Ø1Ø, as a LINE entity. The 8 in Line 8Ø2Ø specifies a forthcoming drawing layer description, which is confirmed in Line 8Ø3Ø, as layer number Ø. (Autocad allows an infinite number of layers to be specified. Refer to Chapter 4 for relevant information.) Lines 8Ø4Ø, 8Ø6Ø, 8Ø8Ø, and 81ØØ specify forthcoming cartesian coordinate data for the start and finish of the LINE (codes 1Ø, 2Ø specifying start, and codes 11, 21 specifying finish). Lines 8Ø5Ø, 8Ø7Ø, 8Ø9Ø, and 811Ø state that the required data is variables XS, YS (start) and XF, YF (finish). Line 812Ø returns the routine to its previous point in the program.

Fig. 3.6 Basic program for parametric shaft

PROGRAM	INTERPRETATION
1000 REM 1010 REM PARAMETRIC SHAFT 1020 REM	Title remarks
1030 LINE INPUT "DRAWING (DXF) FILENAME: ";A$ 1040 OPEN "o",1,A$+".DXF"	Input Filename and open DXF file.
1050 PRINT #1,0 1060 PRINT #1,"SECTION" 1070 PRINT #1,2 1080 PRINT #1,"ENTITIES"	Print data to autocad specifying an Entities file section.
1087 INPUT "POSITION OF LEFTMOST EDGE AT AXIS (X,Y): ";XX,YY 1090 INPUT "DIAMETER: ";D 1100 INPUT "SECTION LENGTH: ";L 1140 INPUT "LEFT CHAMFER: ";CL 1150 INPUT "RIGHT CHAMFER: ";CR 1160 INPUT "LEFT FILLET: ";FL 1170 INPUT "RIGHT FILLET: ";FR	Input Shaft parameters
1230 XS=XX:YS=YY:XF=XX:YF=YY+(D/2-CL+FL) 1240 GOSUB 8000 1264 XS=XX:YS=YF:XF=XX+CL:YF=YY+D/2 1267 IF CL<>0 THEN GOSUB 8000 ELSE 1270 1270 XS=XX+CL:YS=YY+(D/2):XF=XX+CL:YF=YY 1280 IF CL<>0 THEN GOSUB 8000 ELSE 1390 1390 XS=XX+FL:YS=YY+(D/2+FL):ARCR=FL:ARCAS=180:ARCAF=270 1400 IF FL<>0 THEN GOSUB 9000 ELSE 1410 1410 XS=XX+CL+FL:YS=YY+D/2:XF=XX+(L-FR-CR):YF=YY+D/2 1420 GOSUB 8000 1430 XS=XF:YS=YY+(D/2+FR):ARCR=FR:ARCAS=270:ARCAF=0 1440 IF FR<>0 THEN GOSUB 9000 ELSE 1570 1570 XS=XX+L-CR:YS=YY:XF=XS:YF=YY+(D/2) 1580 IF CR<>0 THEN GOSUB 8000 ELSE 1590 1590 XS=XF:YS=YF:XF=XS+CR:YF=YS-CR 1600 IF CR<>0 THEN GOSUB 8000 ELSE 1610 1610 XS=XX+L:YS=YY:XF=XS:YF=YY+D/2-CR+FR 1620 GOSUB 8000	Specify Cartesian coordinates for start of lines (XS, YS), end of lines (XF, YF), fillet centre (XS, YS). Also specify fillet radii (ARCR), fillet arc start angle (ARCAS), and fillet arc finish angle (ARCAF). GOTO subroutines 8000 and 9000.
1705 XX=XX+L	Shift horiz. start point
1710 INPUT "ANOTHER DIAMETER? (1,0): ";AD 1720 IF AD=1 THEN GOTO 1090 ELSE 2000	Option for another shaft portion
2000 PRINT #1,0 2010 PRINT #1,"ENDSEC" 2020 PRINT #1,0 2030 PRINT #1,"EOF" 2040 CLOSE 1 2050 END	End section End drawing file. Close DXF file. End program.
8000 PRINT #1,0 8010 PRINT #1,"LINE" 8020 PRINT #1,8 8030 PRINT #1,"0" 8040 PRINT #1,10 8050 PRINT #1,XS 8060 PRINT #1,20 8070 PRINT #1,YS 8080 PRINT #1,11 8090 PRINT #1,XF 8100 PRINT #1,21 8110 PRINT #1,YF 8120 RETURN	Subroutine 8000. Print data to autocad. Command to draw a straight line on layer 0. Specify start and finish coordinates.

9000 PRINT #1,0
9010 PRINT #1,"ARC"
9020 PRINT #1,8
9030 PRINT #1,"0"
9040 PRINT #1,10
9050 PRINT #1,XS
9060 PRINT #1,20
9070 PRINT #1,YS
9080 PRINT #1,40
9090 PRINT #1,ARCR
9100 PRINT #1,50
9110 PRINT #1,ARCAS
9120 PRINT #1,51
9130 PRINT #1,ARCAF
9140 RETURN
	Subroutine 9000.
	Print data to autocad.
	Command to draw an
	arc on layer 0.
	Specify:
	  arc centre
	  arc radius
	  arc start angle
	  arc finish angle

Lines 139Ø and 143Ø specify cartesian coordinates for fillet centres (variables XS, YS) and fillet radii (variable ARCR) in terms of input parameters, and start/finish arc angles of fillet (variables ARCAS and ARCAF). These Lines are followed by 14ØØ and 144Ø respectively, which take the program to subroutine 9ØØØ if the parameters are not zero. This subroutine prints data for drawing an arc to the Autocad drawing file. It is very similar in format to subroutine 8ØØØ. The stated entity this time is ARC, which determines that codes 1Ø and 2Ø now refer to forthcoming cartesian coordinates for an arc centre (consequently specified as variables XS, YS). In Lines 9Ø8Ø, 91ØØ, and 912Ø, codes 4Ø, 5Ø, and 51 state forthcoming data on arc radius (consequently specified as variable ARCR), arc angle start point (consequently specified as variable ARCAS), and arc angle finish point (consequently specified as variable ARCAF).

Line 17Ø5 shifts the horizontal starting point XX to the end of the shaft portion length, in the event of another diameter (i.e. shaft portion) being required.

Lines 171Ø and 172Ø give the choice of another diameter. If an input of 1 is entered, the whole routine is repeated for another portion of shaft. If zero is entered, the routine finishes.

Lines 2ØØØ to 2Ø3Ø print data to Autocad for ending the section (ENDSEC), and ending the drawing file (EOF). Lines 2Ø4Ø and 2Ø5Ø close the DXF file and end the program.

Fig 3.8 shows some shape variations which may be obtained on Autocad with the program. The complete shaft may be obtained, either by adapting

Fig. 3.7 Shaft parameters

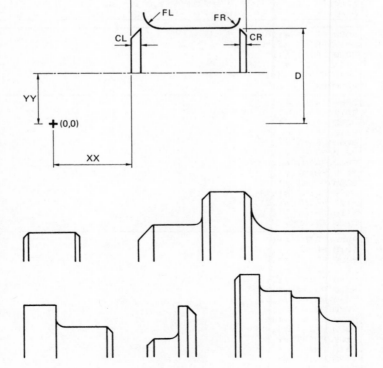

Fig. 3.8 Some shape variations available from parametric shaft program

the program to include a repeat loop (after every shaft portion) which converts Y coordinate values to negatives, or by using Autocad's very straightforward mirror image facility once the created drawing has been displayed.

Of course, the program is very primitive, and could be greatly enhanced with more subroutines for additional options, such as keyways, threaded ends, splines, undercuts, and dimensions. Another set of commands could print a screen menu of parameter options.

PROGRAM EXAMPLE 2: **Rigid coupling half**

A more ambitious project than the previous example is shown in Fig 3.9. A complete drawing of this coupling half (including dimensions, tolerances, symbols and text) could be created on Autocad with the aid of a Basic program of similar format to that of the parametric shaft.

This exercise emphasises that drawing parameters do not have to be dimensional. Although all the dimensions shown would need to appear as variables in the program, they could all be calculated via nine load/strength parameters. These would be input at the start of the program (similar to Lines 1Ø87–117Ø of the previous program), and substituted into formulae for calculating sizes, radii, and coordinates (similar to Lines 123Ø–162Ø of

Fig. 3.9 Coupling half from Basic program

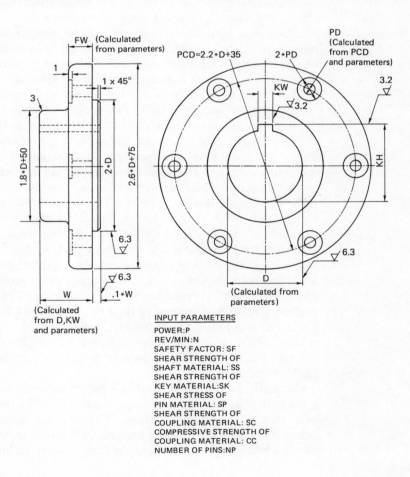

INPUT PARAMETERS

POWER:P
REV/MIN:N
SAFETY FACTOR: SF
SHEAR STRENGTH OF
SHAFT MATERIAL: SS
SHEAR STRENGTH OF
KEY MATERIAL:SK
SHEAR STRESS OF
PIN MATERIAL: SP
SHEAR STRENGTH OF
COUPLING MATERIAL: SC
COMPRESSIVE STRENGTH OF
COUPLING MATERIAL: CC
NUMBER OF PINS:NP

the previous program). Critically-stressed sizes would be calculated directly from the formulae. These sizes could then be used to determine secondary sizes from standard ratios. The keyway dimensions (including tolerances) could be automatically obtained from a subroutine which specifies these as standards for ranges of shaft diameters. To avoid impractical results, critical dimensions, such as the shaft nominal bore, could be rounded to the closest safe value of a stated range. Other tolerances, and surface finishes, could be pre-determined standards conforming to the application and calculated nominal sizes. The machining symbols could be created from a subroutine with variable surface finish value.

All straight LINES and arcs would be created by printing graphics data to Autocad via a DXF file. This would require identical subroutines to those of 8ØØØ and 9ØØØ of the previous program. Similar subroutines would be required for dimensions, text, and the different line-type of the centre-lines. Circles have the same subroutine as for arcs but excluding the start and finish angles.

PROGRAM EXAMPLE 3: **Surface development**
Fig 3.10 shows a BASIC program that will automatically calculate the cartesian coordinates for half the surface development of a rectangle-to-circle ducting transition piece, given overall dimensional input parameters (Fig 3.11). The coordinate data is transferred, via a DXF file, to the Autocad package, which draws the shape. Only half the development is initially generated for the purpose of easing production and saving material. In this example, the circle and rectangle have a common centre, and thus the second half of the development will be identical to the first half.

This program has a very similar format to Program Example 1. Lines 1Ø3Ø to 1Ø8Ø are identical to that program. Lines 1Ø9Ø to 113Ø specify the input parameters. Lines 114Ø to 122Ø automatically calculate the circle chordal lengths, true lengths of fold-lines, and true angles between the fold-lines. The calculations are merely a combination of Pythagoras' Theorem, the cosine rule, and arctangent calculations (an arccosine function not being available). Lines 123Ø to 142Ø calculate cartesian coordinates for the start (XS, YS) and finish (XF, YF) of each outside LINE and fold-line, with the values sent to subroutine 8ØØØ. This is identical to subroutine 8ØØØ of Program 1, printing graphics data for drawing each straight LINE to the DXF file, for subsequent transmission to Autocad.

The program initially generates the first quarter-portion of the development and then carries out one more repeat loop (controlled by Lines 1135 and 146Ø), which generates the next portion. The start of the second portion is shifted to the end of the first, via Line 143Ø. It is then rotated to touch the matching edge of the first, via a rotation angle (ANGROT). This is altered from zero on the second loop via Line 1225 (Fig 3.12). Parameters are adjusted for the second loop by swapping rectangle sides W and B in Line 145Ø.

Once the generated shape has been transferred to Autocad, it may be quickly repeated to simulate the second half of the development. Each half may then be individually "dragged" across the screen (both linearly and rotationally) using Autocad's impressive dynamic translation facility. This is extremely useful for optimizing the least amount of material required to cut

48

```
1000 REM
1010 REM SQUARE-TO-ROUND SURFACE DEVELOPMENT
1020 REM
1030 LINE INPUT "DRAWING (DXF) FILENAME: ";DRG$
1040 OPEN "o",1,DRG$+".DXF"
1050 PRINT #1,0
1060 PRINT #1,"SECTION"
1070 PRINT #1,2
1080 PRINT #1,"ENTITIES"
1090 INPUT "POSITION OF LEFT CORNER (X,Y): ";XX,YY
1100 INPUT "RECTANGLE WIDTH: ";W
1110 INPUT "RECTANGLE BREADTH: ";B
1120 INPUT "CIRCLE DIAMETER: ";D
1130 INPUT "HEIGHT: ";H
1135 N=2
1140 CH=3.14159*D/12
1145 ANGROT=0
1150 LA=SQR((.5*W)^2+H^2+(.5*B-.5*D)^2)
1160 LB=SQR((.5*W-.25*D)^2+H^2+(.5*B-.433*D)^2)
1170 LC=SQR((.5*W-.433*D)^2+H^2+(.5*B-.25*D)^2)
1180 LD=SQR((.5*W-.5*D)^2+H^2+(.5*B)^2)
1190 ANGA=ATN((SQR(LA^2-(.5*W)^2))/(.5*W))
1200 ANGB=ATN(SQR((2*LA*LB)^2-(LA^2+LB^2-CH^2)^2)/(LA^2+LB^2-CH^2))
1210 ANGC=ATN(SQR((2*LB*LC)^2-(LB^2+LC^2-CH^2)^2)/(LB^2+LC^2-CH^2))
1220 ANGD=ATN(SQR((2*LC*LD)^2-(LC^2+LD^2-CH^2)^2)/(LC^2+LD^2-CH^2))
1225 IF N=1 THEN ANGROT=3.14159-ANGA-ANGB-ANGC-ANGD-ANGE
1230 XS=XX:YS=YY:XF=XX+W*COS(ANGROT):YF=YY+W*SIN(ANGROT)
1240 GOSUB 8000
1250 XS=XX:YS=YY:XF=XX+LA*COS(ANGROT+ANGA):YF=YY+LA*SIN(ANGROT+ANGA)
1260 GOSUB 8000
1270 XS=XX+LA*COS(ANGROT+ANGA):YS=YY+LA*SIN(ANGROT+ANGA):XF=XX+W*COS(ANGROT):YF=
YY+W*SIN(ANGROT)
1280 GOSUB 8000
1290 XS=XX:YS=YY:XF=XX+LB*COS(ANGROT+ANGA+ANGB):YF=YY+LB*SIN(ANGROT+ANGA+ANGB)
1300 GOSUB 8000
1310 XS=XX:YS=YY:XF=XX+LC*COS(ANGROT+ANGA+ANGB+ANGC):YF=YY+LC*SIN(ANGROT+ANGA+
ANGB+ANGC)
1320 GOSUB 8000
1330 XS=XX:YS=YY:XF=XX+LD*COS(ANGROT+ANGA+ANGB+ANGC+ANGD):YF=YY+LD*SIN(ANGROT+
ANGA+ANGB+ANGC+ANGD)
1340 GOSUB 8000
1350 XS=XF:YS=YF:XF=XX+LC*COS(ANGROT+ANGA+ANGB+ANGC):YF=YY+LC*SIN(ANGROT+ANGA+
ANGB+ANGC)
1360 GOSUB 8000
1370 XS=XF:YS=YF:XF=XX+LB*COS(ANGROT+ANGA+ANGB):YF=YY+LB*SIN(ANGROT+ANGA+ANGB)
1380 GOSUB 8000
1390 XS=XF:YS=YF:XF=XX+LA*COS(ANGROT+ANGA):YF=YY+LA*SIN(ANGROT+ANGA)
1400 GOSUB 8000
1410 XS=XF:YS=YF:XF=XX+W*COS(ANGROT):YF=YY+W*SIN(ANGROT)
1420 GOSUB 8000
1430 XX=XX+W
1440 ANGE=ANGA
1450 SWAP W,B
1460 N=N-1:IF N=1 THEN GOTO 1150 ELSE 1470.
1470 PRINT #1,0
1480 PRINT #1,"ENDSEC"
1490 PRINT #1,0
1500 PRINT #1,"EOF"
1510 CLOSE 1
1520 END
8000 PRINT #1,0
8010 PRINT #1,"LINE"
8020 PRINT #1,8
8030 PRINT #1,"0"
8040 PRINT #1,10
8050 PRINT #1,XS
8060 PRINT #1,20
8070 PRINT #1,YS
8080 PRINT #1,11
8090 PRINT #1,XF
8100 PRINT #1,21
8110 PRINT #1,YF
8120 RETURN
Ok
```

Fig. 3.10 Basic program for surface development

49

Fig. 3.11 Overall dimensions (input parameters) of transition piece

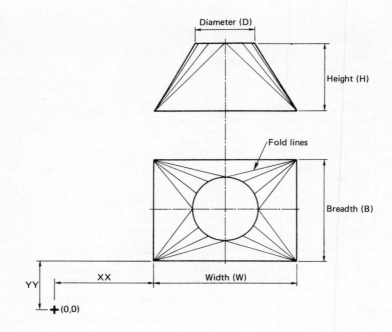

Fig. 3.12

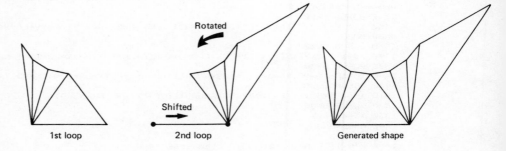

1st loop   2nd loop   Generated shape

out the complete shape. The chosen cutting arrangement is shown in Fig 3.13. This complete display may then be repeated for any number of developments required, the system again allowing dynamic adjustment for material savings. This technique is called *nesting* and is also discussed from the manufacturing context in Chapter 9. Fig 3.14 shows a nested arrangement display of four complete developments. Autocad also has the capability of transferring the data of such a display to a numerically-controlled flame-cutter or laser-cutter for automatic production, via interface with computer-aided part-programming (CAPP) software packages. The principles of CAPP are also discussed in Chapter 9.

Fig. 3.13

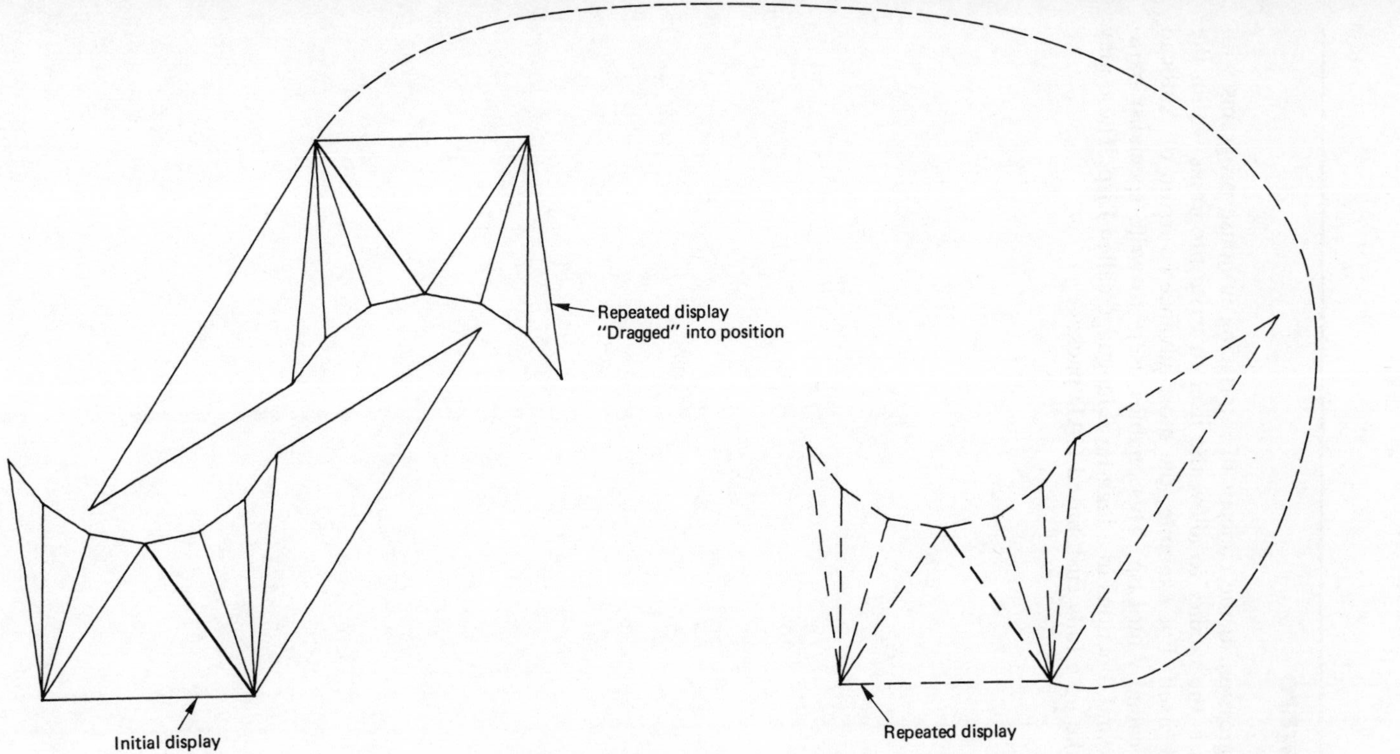

Repeated display

Repeated display
"Dragged" into position

Initial display

Fig. 3.14 Nested
arrangement of four
development

51

3.7 Customised CAD Software

A logical progression to the concept of interfacing in-house programs with CAD systems is the facility to allow the user to write programs within the CAD software itself. For example, the most advanced version of Autocad has a facility called AutoLisp. This enables users to write specialist parametric macros and functions in a high-level language called Lisp. These may eventually make up a fully customised CAD package.

Two-dimensional Draughting 4
Techniques

Chapter 5 draws detailed distinctions between 2D and 3D systems. For the purposes of discussions in Chapter 4, it will suffice to summarise the relative limitations of 2D CAD systems as

a) 2D systems recognise only "flat" shapes defined by points, lines, or curves contained within a two-dimensional plane.

b) Having no understanding of 3D shapes, 2D systems cannot automatically generate additional views to those already created on the VDU screen. Each view of a component (be it in orthographic, isometric, or any other type of projection) has to be drawn as an individual shape which is considered by the system to have no relationship with any other view displayed.

2D systems are primitive by comparison with 3D, but 2D is sufficient for a wide variety of applications and, at its lower cost, is an attractive choice for many companies. The majority of CAD orthographic engineering drawings and electrical circuit drawings are created on 2D systems.

Sometimes the term CADD (Computer-Aided Drawing and Design) is used to encompass both draughting and analytical design procedures. In this publication, however, basic draughting techniques are assumed to be an integral part of the overall design process and will thus be included under the heading of CAD.

4.1 Drawing Elements

Drawings of any complexity are built up from basic geometric elements, namely: points, lines, circular curves, and non-circular curves, which may be displayed on the screen in a number of ways.

Methods of Construction

In most systems, distances are assumed to be measured from the origin of two axes similar to the X and Y axes of a graph. These are displayed on the VDU screen but would not appear on any hardcopy produced from a plotter (Fig 4.1). The axes could be fixed during the creation of elements (called *absolute mode*), or there may be an option for the automatic shifting of axes, so that distances are measured from the end of each successive element (called *incremental mode*).

The method of construction adopted for a particular drawing will depend largely on the accuracy required. For example, a straight line could be displayed on the screen by

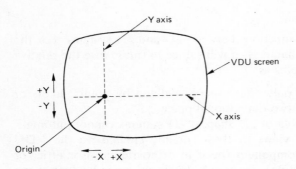

Fig. 4.1

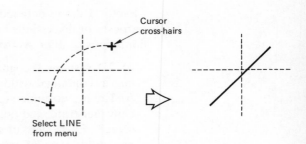

Fig. 4.2 Sketching a line

1 SKETCHING, which can be an effective method of quickly creating simple shapes where no great accuracy is required. The LINE command is selected from the menu and the cursor cross-hairs simply moved to the two extreme points of the line, each required point position being confirmed by pressing a button on the cursor-control device (e.g. digitising pen, puck, light pen, joystick, etc.) (Fig 4.2).

2 NUMERIC INPUT, which will provide a high degree of accuracy if required. Here, either cartesian or polar coordinate values are entered at the keyboard after selecting LINE from the menu, as indicated in Figs 4.3 and 4.4.

3 SNAPPING, which can provide both speed and accuracy at certain stages in the drawing construction. Here, the line will automatically "snap-on" to the closest point, or element-end to the cursor after pressing the control button (Fig 4.5).

The other basic elements, i.e. points, circles, arcs, and other curves, are displayed using similar procedures. For example, an accurate circle could be displayed by selecting NUMERIC and CIRCLE at the menu and then inputting the cartesian coordinates of its centre and its radius value at the keyboard. Alternatively, Fig 4.6 shows a circle being snapped-on to the end of a line.

Fig. 4.3 Accurate line using Cartesian coordinates

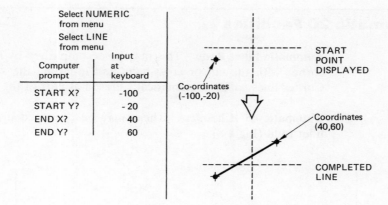

Select NUMERIC from menu

Select LINE from menu

Computer prompt	Input at keyboard
START X?	-100
START Y?	- 20
END X?	40
END Y?	60

Co-ordinates (-100,-20)

START POINT DISPLAYED

Coordinates (40,60)

COMPLETED LINE

Fig. 4.4 Accurate line using Cartesian/polar coordinates

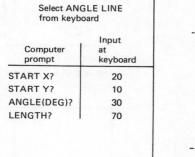

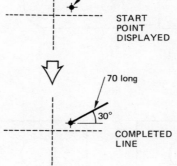

Select ANGLE LINE from keyboard

Computer prompt	Input at keyboard
START X?	20
START Y?	10
ANGLE(DEG)?	30
LENGTH?	70

Coordinates (20,10)

START POINT DISPLAYED

70 long

30°

COMPLETED LINE

Fig. 4.5 Snapping a line between two elements

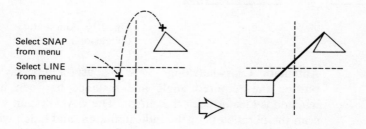

Select SNAP from menu

Select LINE from menu

Fig. 4.6 Snapping a circle to the end of a line

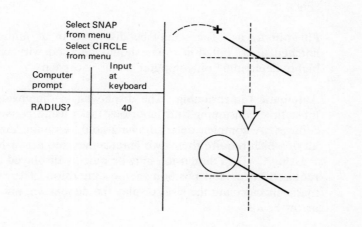

Select SNAP from menu

Select CIRCLE from menu

Computer prompt	Input at keyboard
RADIUS?	40

4.2 Automatic 2D Facilities

Automatic Fillet Radii   This may be accomplished by locating the required corner with the cursor cross-hairs and inputting the radius size (Fig 4.7). Corner lines will be automatically erased as part of the operation.

Automatic 45° Chamfers   These may be displayed in a similar fashion to fillet radii (Fig 4.8).

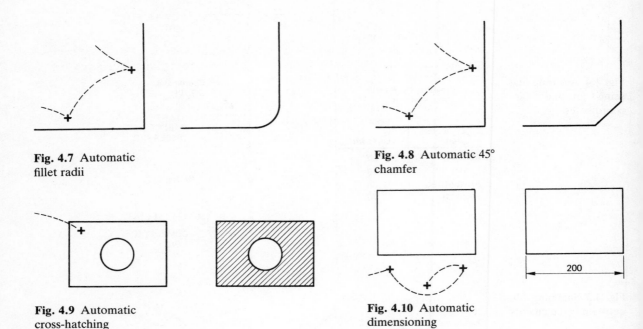

Fig. 4.7 Automatic
fillet radii

Fig. 4.8 Automatic 45°
chamfer

Fig. 4.9 Automatic
cross-hatching

Fig. 4.10 Automatic
dimensioning

Automatic Cross-hatching   This is a useful time-saving facility. After inputting the required angle and distance between lines, the area to be hatched is located with the cursor. The CAD system will then automatically scan the perimeters of the indicated area, and hatch within those perimeters (Fig 4.9).

Filled-in Areas   These may be displayed in a similar fashion to a cross-hatched area. Filled-in areas should be used with caution since they are highly demanding on computer memory capacity.

Automatic Dimensioning   The displaying of dimensions can be one of the most time-consuming and laborious tasks using conventional drawing procedures. A complex detail drawing could contain hundreds of dimensions, all of which require their own leader-lines and arrow-heads.

Using CAD, a dimension may be quickly displayed by simply locating the required edges and position of the dimension. The system will then automatically calculate the size, display the dimension, and draw the leaders and arrow-heads.

Automatic dimensioning is also particularly useful for determining the accurate value of an unknown dimension. If this were required for a complex assembly drawing, many hours of work may have been required producing accurate layout drawings by traditional means. Even then, the result would be subject to a certain amount of inaccuracy. By contrast, CAD produces a speedy and accurate result (Fig 4.10).

Editing Lines, or portions of the drawing, may be erased at any stage in its development, so that modifications can be made. Dimensions and cross-hatched areas are also easily erased and modified.

Trimming This is the CAD procedure for clearing the drawing of un-wanted construction lines. By locating two intersecting lines with the cursor, one will be automatically trimmed back to the profile of the other (Fig 4.11). The same procedure may be adopted for curves, or combinations of lines and curves.

Fig. 4.11 Trimming

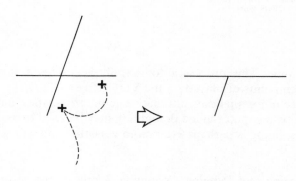

Fig. 4.12 Rubber-banding

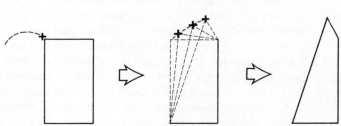

Rubber-banding Some CAD systems provide this facility, which allows the user to stretch or contort the shape created on the screen. This is a useful tool in the early stages of design analysis (Fig 4.12).

Grids These may be used as a time-saving facility in some applications using basic regular profiles, such as PCB design, hydraulic circuitry or simple shafts. A square or rectangular grid pattern may be displayed on the screen by inputting the required command and dimensions of grid spacing. Any lines drawn on this grid will automatically snap-on to the nearest corner (Fig 4.13). In some systems; it is also possible to start the grid from any desired point and rotate the grid to any desired angle. Construction grids do not appear on plotted hard copies.

Fig. 4.13 Use of construction grid

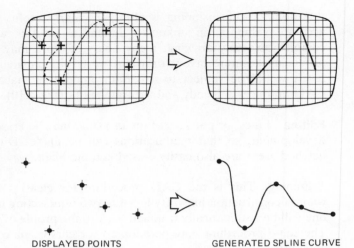

Fig. 4.14 Splining

DISPLAYED POINTS
(either sketched with
cursor, or accurately
defined with numeric
input).

GENERATED SPLINE CURVE

Splining This process automatically generates a smooth spline curve between points displayed on the VDU screen (Fig 4.14). Splining is particularly useful for analysing alternative geometric shapes, and is a perfect example of how computer-aided draughting may be used to assist the design process. 3D splining is perhaps even more versatile, and will be discussed in Chapter 5.

Zooming and Panning Zooming is one of the most valuable aids to the modern designer. Its origins, along with CAD in general, stem from early developments in integrated circuit design, when it became necessary to greatly magnify (or *zoom*) tiny areas of a circuit up to a practical display size for working on. It is interesting to note that later developments in CAD have been possible due to advancements in microelectronics and therefore these two specialisms have evolved with an interdependence on each other.

Zooming is now applied to all areas of computer-aided drawing and design. Individual localities of the drawing may be enlarged to any required scale for the purposes of observing, adding or editing intricate details. A zoomed area may then be panned in a required direction to observe or edit other features, as shown in Fig 4.15. Hard copy plots of zoomed areas are easily obtained since the hardware reproduces only that which is displayed on the screen at the time of the plot command.

There are virtually no limits to which displays may be zoomed. For example, if the complete layout of a power station were displayed on the screen, it would be quite feasible to zoom into, say, a small bracket supporting a digital display and perhaps obtain the dimension between two fixing bolts a few millimetres apart. Continuing with this example, it would then be possible to further zoom into the digital display and investigate the electronic circuitry. This illustrates the particular advantages of zooming for large assembly drawings. Using conventional means, any number of smaller

Fig. 4.15 Zooming and panning

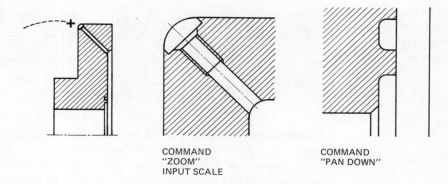

COMMAND
"ZOOM"
INPUT SCALE

COMMAND
"PAN DOWN"

Fig. 4.16 Rotation and translation

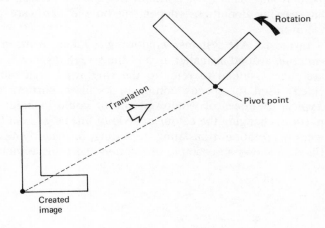

Rotation

Translation

Pivot point

Created image

sub-assembly drawings would be required. With the aid of zooming, only *one* assembly drawing is required for any size or complexity of arrangement.

Rotation and Translation Shapes created on the screen may be manipulated to any other position or orientation.

2D rotation is accomplished by selecting the appropriate command at the menu and inputting the required angular movement and pivot point.

Translation involves moving the created image to another coordinate position on the screen, and requires similar operations to that of rotation (Fig 4.16).

In some systems it is possible to observe the display actually moving on the screen. Animated dynamic displays are an essential feature of mechanism analysis, but are commonly confined to the more sophisticated systems with 3D facility. The majority of 2D systems would simply give a fresh display of the new position and orientation.

Rotations and translations are particularly useful when recalling components from standards libraries (shortly to be discussed in this chapter). They are also essential features of nesting procedures, which are widely employed in multi-component profile cutting operations such as milling and flame-cutting. (See Chapters 3 and 9.)

Fig. 4.17 Creation of tooth-rack profile using transformation procedures

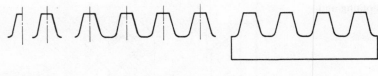

START MIRROR   REPETITIONS   COMPLETE
IMAGE

Transformations   Apart from rotation and translation, many systems incorporate other facilities such as mirror image and stepped repetition. Fig 4.17 shows how a drawing may be given a mirror image and then the operation quickly repeated to complete most of a tooth-rack profile.

Windowing   This term is frequently encountered in computer studies and has varying definitions, depending on the hardware and software manufacturer.

In most CAD systems, windowing is taken to mean enclosing a box, or *window*, around a smaller area of the screen display. Subsequent commands are then assumed to refer to the windowed area only. The technique is chiefly used for speedy editing of localised portions of a screen display. Typical examples of windowed editing could include: erasing a windowed portion; changing the colour or style of line (e.g. solid to dashed) within the window; rotating, translating, repeating, or magnifying a windowed portion. Fig 4.18 shows an example of rotation and translation of a windowed area.

Fig. 4.18 Windowing

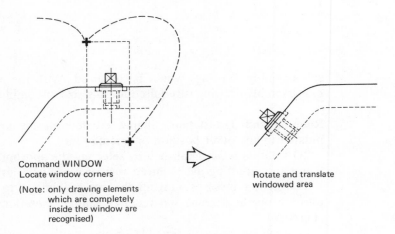

Command WINDOW
Locate window corners

(Note: only drawing elements
which are completely
inside the window are
recognised)

Rotate and translate
windowed area

Layering   This is another CAD facility which has played a major role in the development of electronics design. The principle of layering may be understood by considering a number of drawings, each done on a separate transparent sheet. Each sheet could be viewed separately or, alternatively, placed against each other as layers in a stack and viewed collectively.

Similarly, a 2D CAD system can provide a number of drawing *layers* on which separate images may be created. Layering is particularly useful in printed circuit board (PCB) design, where each layer can contain separate

Fig. 4.19 Printed circuit board layering [*Babcock Bristol Ltd.*]

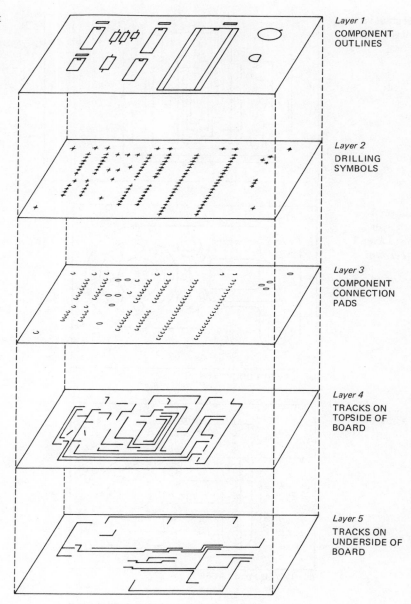

Layer 1
COMPONENT
OUTLINES

Layer 2
DRILLING
SYMBOLS

Layer 3
COMPONENT
CONNECTION
PADS

Layer 4
TRACKS ON
TOPSIDE OF
BOARD

Layer 5
TRACKS ON
UNDERSIDE OF
BOARD

elements of a stacked circuit arrangement. Typical PCB layers are shown in Fig 4.19. It should be noted that this diagram portrays the layers in three dimensions only to illustrate the principle. In fact they would appear on the screen in 2D form, as shown in Fig 4.20.

As with zooming, layering is now successfully applied to all types of drawing and design. For example, in mechanical drawing work, layering is often used for clarity by placing each different aspect of the drawing on a separate layer. Fig 4.21 shows a component drawing with geometric features on one layer, dimensions on the next, and tool-path simulation on another.

Fig. 4.20 Actual screen display of layer 4 in Fig. 4.19

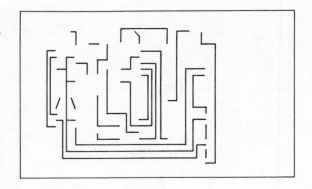

Fig. 4.21 Layer 1 Geometry; Layer 2 Dimensions; Layer 3 Toolpath [*Ferranti Cetec*]

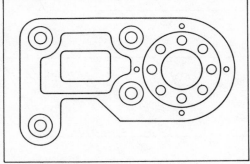

(a) LAYER 1 ONLY

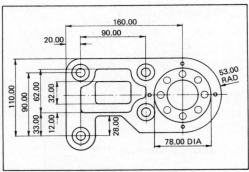

(b) LAYER 1 plus LAYER 2

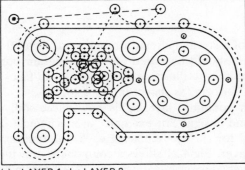

(c) LAYER 1 plus LAYER 3

The number of layers available commonly varies from two to in excess of a thousand, some systems providing an infinite number. The upper range would not be required for the majority of applications, but could be useful where multiple sections are required through a large structure or building.

For viewing layers in combination, clarity is greatly enhanced if a different colour display can be used for each layer. This is an essential requirement when using CAD for pipework layout design.

Layering can also clarify the details of a hard copy plotting if a separate pen is used for each layer. This enables, for example, an engineering drawing to be shown with its geometry and dimensions in either a different colour, or a different thickness, of pen.

4.3 Libraries of Drawing Standards (Macros)

A macro is a subroutine in CADCAM computer software which may be called up for use at any stage in the operation of the program. In effect, a CAD macro is a multiple sequence of graphics routines which may be initialised by a single command.

System macros are part of the CAD software provided by the manufacturer and readily available on the menu. Typical of these are the examples already discussed, such as automatic fillet radii, automatic dimensions, hatching, etc. Most system macros can also be described as *parametric*, which will be defined later in this chapter.

However, an essential feature of CAD systems is the provision for the user to create macros for use in a library of company drawing standards. Libraries of British Standard symbols, such as BS308, Electrical, Welding Hydraulic, etc., may be stored in the computer memory and quickly recalled to the VDU screen when required. Also, libraries of standard components, such as nuts and bolts, bearings, etc., may be compiled. Any drawing, or part of a drawing, may be included in a standards library to eliminate repetitive drawing work. Fig 4.22 shows a typical example. Combinations of standards are endless, and it is a logical progression to extend simple macros into more complex ones, as indicated in Fig 4.23.

Once created, the macro may be stored into the library by a SAVE command at the menu and by inputting a filename in a form which will be recognised by the software operating system. The macro may be recalled onto a larger drawing by a LOAD command and inputting the filename, position required, and any alterations of scale and rotation from the original macro display. The SCALE input will magnify or diminish the complete macro as originally drawn, so that it will only be necessary to draw identical shapes once, whatever their size. For example, if the nut assembly macro of Fig 4.23 were drawn as an M10 size, it could be used on another drawing as an M16 size by inputting a 1.6 magnification scale as shown in Fig 4.24.

If the standards library is to be used efficiently, all the relevant information concerning the original macro drawing should be recorded on a database management system (DBMS), which is further discussed in Chapter 7. Alternatively, the macros may be displayed in simple diagrammatic form on

Fig. 4.22 Macros from standard components library [*Computer Aided Design Centre, Cambridge*]

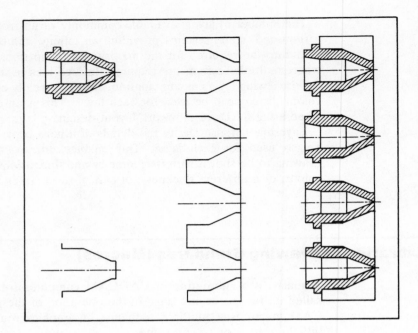

Fig. 4.23 Extended standards

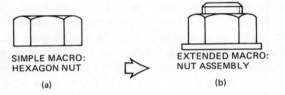

SIMPLE MACRO: HEXAGON NUT

(a)

EXTENDED MACRO: NUT ASSEMBLY

(b)

Fig. 4.24 Loading a standard macro

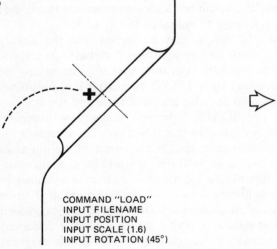

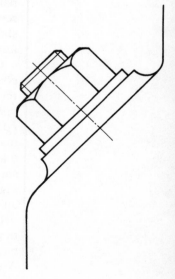

COMMAND "LOAD"
INPUT FILENAME
INPUT POSITION
INPUT SCALE (1.6)
INPUT ROTATION (45°)

command tablet menus if the system has provision for extension menu cards to be made up by the user (see Chapter 2, page 15).

A standards library can also include standard text notes for quick recall onto drawings, and parts lists which may be recalled onto either a graphics screen or an alpha-numeric screen.

Parametric Macros   Although the macros described in the previous section can be changed in scale, every element in the macro is changed by the same proportion, thus keeping the whole shape identical.

However, some CAD systems provide the facility to create "semi-standard" macros with independently variable parameters. Typical examples include shafts, gears, springs, bearing sections, couplings and sprockets. For example, the compression spring section shown in Fig 4.25 would be of little use as a standard macro unless each of its five parameters could be changed separately to accommodate any required size of mean diameter, length, wire size, pitch and internal shaft diameter.

Fig. 4.25 Parametric macro standard

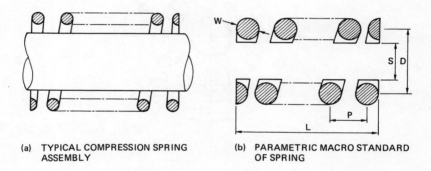

(a) TYPICAL COMPRESSION SPRING
     ASSEMBLY

(b) PARAMETRIC MACRO STANDARD
     OF SPRING

Global Modification of Macros   If a standard ever needs to be changed, this effectively outdates every stored drawing containing the old standard. Global modification facility enables the automatic updating of all these drawings once the new macro has been created. This is another important feature of a DBMS.

4.4   CAD Component Drawing Example

Fig 4.26 shows drawings of an oil pump rotor and its mating cam profile produced on the MEADOS CAD system by Hobourn-Eaton Ltd. The construction involved all of the techniques outlined in this chapter. This example is further discussed in Chapter 6, which deals with the finite stress analysis of the rotor, and in Chapter 9 which deals with the manufacture of the cam profile.

Fig. 4.26a Part display of oil pump CAD assembly drawing [*Hobourn-Eaton*]

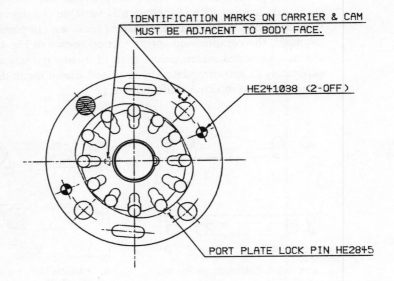

IDENTIFICATION MARKS ON CARRIER & CAM
MUST BE ADJACENT TO BODY FACE.

HE241038 (2-OFF)

PORT PLATE LOCK PIN HE2845

VIEW ON ARROW 'A' WITH COVER REMOVED.

Fig. 4.26b CAD detail drawing of cam ring [*Hobourn-Eaton*]
on page 67 opposite

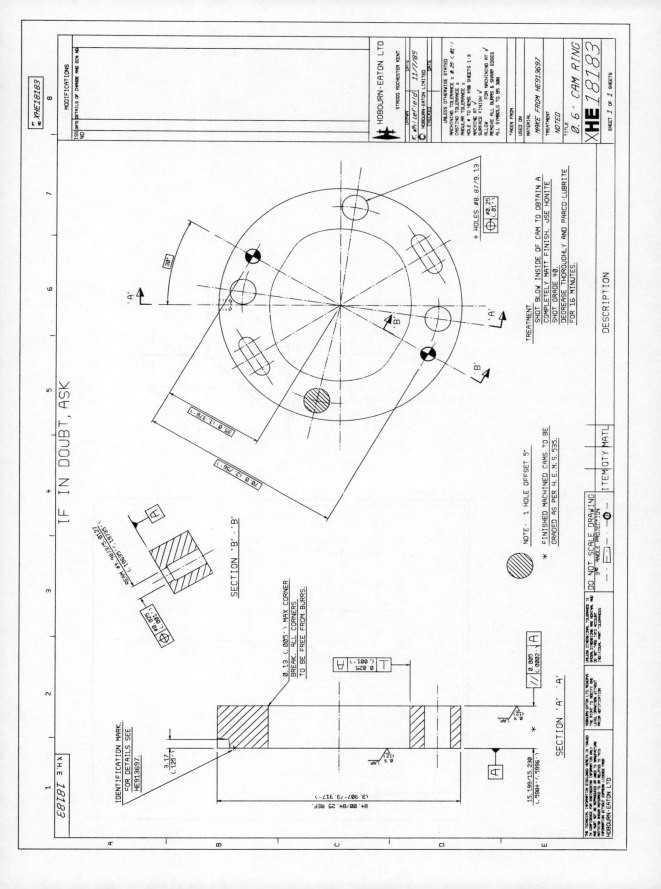

Fig. 5.1

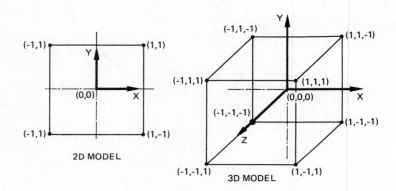

(-1,1) (1,1)

Y

(0,0) X

(-1,1) (1,-1)

2D MODEL

Y

(-1,1,-1) (1,1,-1)

(-1,1,1) (1,1,1)

(0,0,0) X

(-1,-1,-1)

(1,-1,-1)

Z

(-1,-1,1) (1,-1,1)

3D MODEL

Fig. 5.2 Three views
displayed on 2D system

Flat 2D "world"

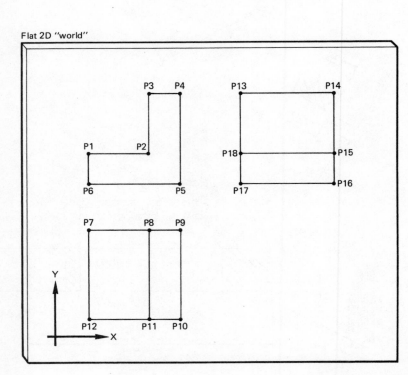

P3 P4

P1 P2

P6 P5

P13 P14

P18 P15

P16

P17

P7 P8 P9

P12 P11 P10

Y

X

Three-dimensional Modelling 5
Techniques

5.1 Features of 3D Systems

A *model* is a mathematical representation of a geometric form which is stored in the computer memory of the CADCAM system. 2D models are recognised by the system as flat frameworks bounded by a number of points which may be defined by X and Y cartesian coordinates.

A 3D model may be held in computer memory by specifying points with a third Z coordinate. Fig 5.1 compares a 2D square model with a 3D cubic model. The 3D cube is imaginary to the extent that it is displayed on a flat screen. However, to the computer memory it is a real 3D shape which is considered as a small element within the boundaries of its vast cubic "world" of mathematical 3D space.

As indicated at the start of Chapter 4, the shapes shown in Fig 5.2 would be recognised by a 2D system as three entirely separate flat frameworks bounded by a total of eighteen points, all contained within a single X–Y plane.

By contrast, a 3D system would recognise these shapes as three views of the same object, contained by twelve points in 3D space (Fig 5.3). For example, once the XY and XZ views have been drawn, the YZ or XYZ views could be automatically displayed. The 3D XYZ view could then be rotated about any chosen axis or transformed using similar techniques to those described for 2D displays in Chapter 4. The sequence would also be reversible, i.e. a 3D view could be drawn first, and then any specified 2D view automatically displayed.

The concept of 3D coordinates means that any additions or alterations specified on one view would automatically be communicated to the others. Some systems have the ability to convert orthographic assemblies into exploded 3D views.

An obvious current limitation of systems with 3D facilities is the very high cost, both of software and the required hardware capacity, the latter due to the heavy demand on computer memory. However, as in many other branches of CADCAM, this will become less of a problem as technology advances.

3D modelling is also time-consuming in man-hours and computer response. However, when considered in terms of the development of the complete product, it can be shown that 3D modelling greatly improves efficiency in many design and manufacturing applications.

3D modelling can be particularly advantageous in the creation of large complex drawings as required for plant layouts, pipework installations and architecture. For example, it is invaluable for ensuring adequate clearance between components. It has also become an important element of integrated CADCAM systems involving tool-path or robotics simulation. Some 3D modelling systems can undertake automatic analysis of physical properties, such as weights, centres of gravity, moments of inertia, and solve geometric problems such as complex blends and interpenetrations.

Since there is the automatic linkage of data between all views, 3D modelling is a suitable choice where large amounts of editing are likely throughout the design process.

The 3D modelling procedures undertaken on CADCAM systems fall into three categories:

WIREFRAME MODELLING
SURFACE MODELLING
SOLID MODELLING

5.2   3D Wireframe Modelling

A wireframe model is described entirely in terms of POINTS and LINES. This is the lowest level of modelling and has serious limitations, most of which derive from the lack of any data regarding faces between lines, and the inability to distinguish between the inside and the outside of a solid object. It is less demanding on computer memory than the other two modelling techniques, and can be adequate for some tasks involving simple shapes.

One of the most common applications of wireframe modelling is the use of 3D tool-path simulation displays for simple machining operations, such as $2\frac{1}{2}$ axis and 3 axis milling. The simpler systems can accommodate only shapes of uniform cross-section. This is sometimes referred to as $2\frac{1}{2}$D GEOMETRY.

The XYZ view in Fig 5.3 is a simple example of a 3D wireframe display. Being of uniform cross-section, this shape would be most easily constructed by first creating the XY view. Depth may be specified by quoting two Z coordinate values at each point. However, non-uniform thicknesses and non-uniform cross-sections are extremely difficult to perceive when working from only one view. In such cases, it is necessary to specify 3D coordinate points on a combination of XY, XZ, YZ, and XYZ views.

Limitations of Wireframe Models

1 *Ambiguity*   One of the greatest disadvantages of wireframe models is the confusion caused by their ambiguity of orientation and viewing plane. For example, the 3D view in Fig 5.3 could be interpreted as a view from

Fig. 5.3 3D display

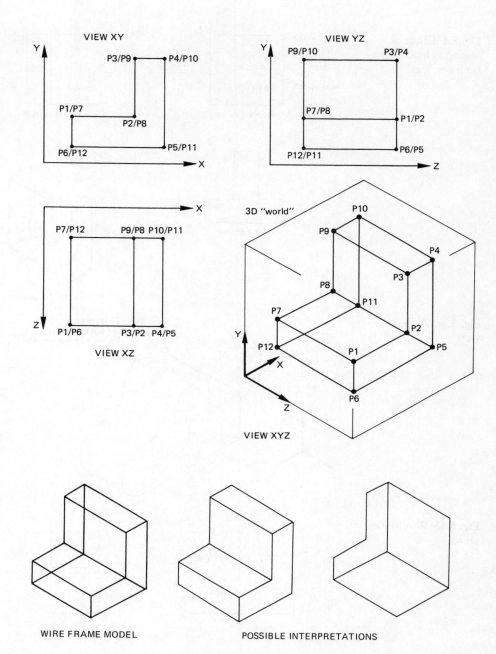

VIEW XY

VIEW YZ

VIEW XZ

3D "world"

VIEW XYZ

Fig. 5.4

WIRE FRAME MODEL

POSSIBLE INTERPRETATIONS

either above or below, as indicated in Fig 5.4. This potentially disastrous effect is a consequence of the basic wireframe principle. Having no perception of solid shape, it cannot distinguish between "visible" and "hidden" edges. Removal of hidden lines can only be undertaken manually, with a separate edit command for each line. Such an arduous task would in fact be self-defeating, since edges which are hidden on one view need to be shown as visible lines on other views. This cannot be accomplished because any line erased automatically disappears from all views (Fig 5.5).

Fig. 5.5 Effect of
removing hidden lines
from one view

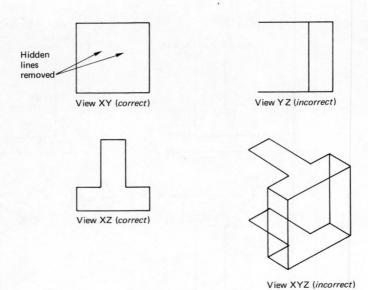

Hidden
lines
removed

View XY (*correct*)

View YZ (*incorrect*)

View XZ (*correct*)

View XYZ (*incorrect*)

Fig. 5.6*a* Actual 3D
view

These profiles
are not recognised
by the wireframe model

Fig. 5.6*b* Wireframe
views

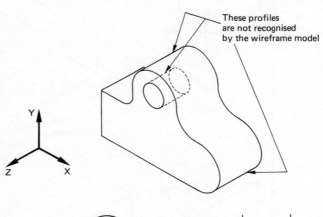

View XY

View YZ

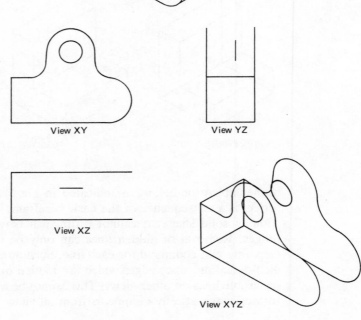

View XZ

View XYZ

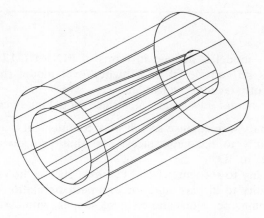

Fig. 5.7 Attempt to indicate curved profile with straight lines

2 *Inability to recognise curved profiles* Longitudinal profiles of cylindrical shapes are not fixed edges between defined points in space. They are seen by the observer as the *silhouette* of a component *face* which could vary in position, depending on the direction of view. Therefore, they are not recognised as wireframe elements and are omitted. Fig 5.6 shows a shape with curved profiles and a blind hole as it would actually appear in 3D, and then contrasts this with the utterly confusing wireframe representations.

It is possible to indicate curved profiles with longitudinal "shade lines" at regular angular intervals. However, these non-existent lines can cause further confusion on a drawing which is already riddled with ambiguities. Non-uniform cross-sections present particular problems (Fig 5.7).

3 *Inability to detect interference between components* Since the wireframe model has no knowledge of surface faces, there can be no provision for automatic detection of unwanted contact between object surfaces. This is a serious drawback in such applications as 3D kinetic analysis of mechanisms, robot simulation, and the design of plant layout and complex piping assemblies. Wireframe also curtails the sophistication of toolpath simulation packages, since tool collisions cannot be automatically detected at the design stage.

4 *Difficulty in calculating physical properties* This is another consequence of the lack of surface data. The correct shape, and therefore the volume, of anything other than very basic components cannot be determined accurately. Properties such as mass, surface area, centre of gravity, or moment of inertia are thus very unreliable.

5 *No facility for automatic shading* Colour tone variation and shadow effect are essential tools of any artist and have become important techniques in 3D modelling. The underlying principle is that *surfaces*, not edges, are shaded. These effects thus cannot be applied in a world which has no surfaces.

5.3 Surface Modelling

A surface model is defined in terms of POINTS, LINES, and FACES. It may thus be considered as a higher-level model than wireframe, and is consequently far more versatile.

The particular advantages of surface modelling over wireframe include:

a) Ability to recognise and display complex curved profiles.
b) Ability to recognise faces, and thus provide the facility of shaded surfaces in 3D.
c) Ability to recognise facial features, such as holes.
d) Ability to display superior tool-path simulations in 3D for multi-axial machining operations and complex shapes, with ease of CNC manufacture interface.
e) Improved facility for simulation of robot handling.

Surface modelling can be undertaken using 16-bit systems but, in the majority of cases, would give most efficiency with 32-bit minicomputer facility.

Although less advanced than solid modelling, surface modelling currently gives the most suitable choice in some applications, particularly those which involve the design and manufacture of complex curved surfaces, such as car bodies.

Types of Surface

1 *Basic Geometrical* Plane surfaces may be easily created by drawing a straight line and then entering a command which *sweeps* an identical line through a specified distance in 3D space (Fig 5.8).

Similarly, cylindrical and conical surfaces may be generated by sweeping circles or arcs through 3D space (Fig 5.9).

Fig. 5.8 Formation of a swept plane surface

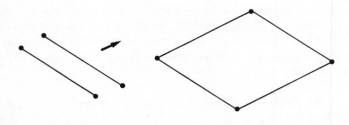

Fig. 5.9 Formation of swept curved surface

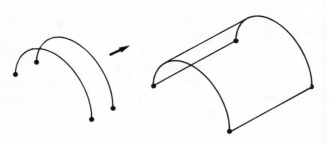

Areas may also be swept into 3D objects, as shown in Fig 5.10. It should be noted, however, that the modelling system does not recognise the resulting view as a solid volume, but merely as seven plane surfaces joined together in 3D space, and bounding an "empty" interior.

2 *Surfaces of Revolution* These can easily be created by commanding a created plane shape to rotate about a defined axis (this procedure may be conveniently thought of as a "rotational sweep"). Again, it must be remembered that only surface areas are generated, not volumes (Fig 5.11).

Fig. 5.10 Swept surface area of 3D object

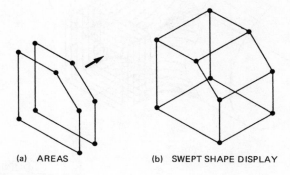

(a) AREAS   (b) SWEPT SHAPE DISPLAY

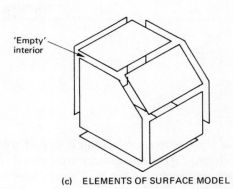

(c) ELEMENTS OF SURFACE MODEL

Fig. 5.11 Surface of revolution

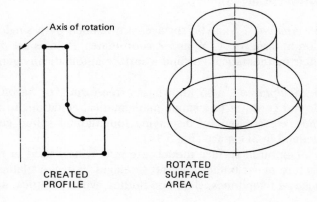

CREATED PROFILE   ROTATED SURFACE AREA

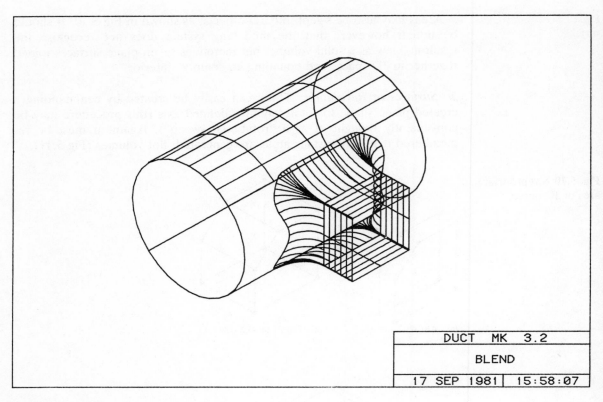

DUCT	MK	3.2
BLEND		
17 SEP 1981		15:58:07

Fig. 5.12 Surface blending [*Delta Computer Aided Engineering Ltd.*]

3 *Blends and Intersections* Blending is one of the most useful techniques in surface modelling. Also, as surfaces are defined, it is possible to establish the intersection of two faces. Fig 5.12 shows how a 3D fillet blend may be created between square and cylindrical surfaces by projecting curved splines from the square to an automatically-generated interpenetration curve on the surface of the cylinder.

4 *Analytic* Analytic surfaces are defined by a single mathematical equation in terms of X, Y, and Z coordinates. Profiles are displayed according to their mathematical law and a surface automatically generated over them.

5 *Sculptured* Also known as "free-form", or "arbitrary", these surfaces do not conform to a single mathematical equation. In their most basic form they are created by displaying longitudinal spline curves between points defined in 3D space (Fig 5.13).

Sculptured surface models are now widely used in the design and manufacture of car bodies, aircraft fuselages, impellor blades, and domestic items such as telephones, shampoo bottles, whisky bottles, and utensil handles.

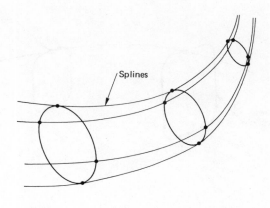

Fig. 5.13 Sculptured surface

Splines

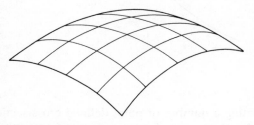

Fig. 5.14 Network of patches on surface

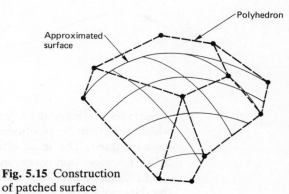

Polyhedron

Approximated surface

Fig. 5.15 Construction of patched surface

Principles of Composite Surface Definition

Advanced surface modellers can fully define a composite surface by considering it to be made up of a network of quadrilateral *patches*, bounded by longitudinal and transverse lines (Fig 5.14).

The shape of each patch is called a *topological rectangle* (i.e. it has four sides which are not necessarily straight or perpendicular). The patch boundaries form continuous curves resulting in a smooth surface across the network. Interpolation is used to define the interior surface of each patch. The patched surface may be displayed on the VDU screen either by splining curves between points, or by creating a polyhedron framework, to which the system will automatically approximate a smooth curved surface (Fig 5.15).

The DUCT Surface Modeller

This system, developed by Cambridge University Engineering Department and marketed by Delta Computer-Aided Engineering, is one of the most versatile and successful surface modellers used in modern CADCAM.

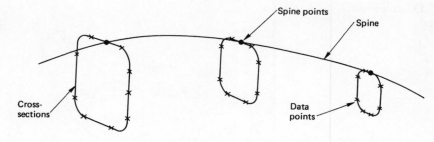

Fig. 5.16 Principle of DUCT surface modeller

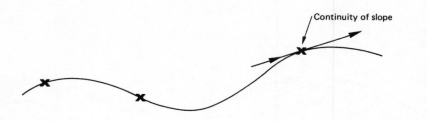

Fig. 5.17 The Bezier curve

Surfaces are formed by creating a number of point-defined cross-sections which may then be positioned and orientated relative to a reference curve called a *spine*. The spine effectively forms the backbone of the shape (Fig 5.16). Cross-section curves may be either open or closed.

The basis of the Duct system is the *Bezier curve*, which is fitted through the data points of the cross-sections by interpolation, thus ensuring smoothness of curve via continuity of slope. The Bezier curve conforms to a parametric cubic law which provides adequate design freedom whilst avoiding the complexity of an excessive number of patches (Fig 5.17).

Once the spine points and data points have been defined, the resulting surface is generated using patches. Fig 5.18 shows typical surface model displays using the Duct system.

Duct automatically calculates cross-sectional areas, surface areas, and volumes, and can undertake optimisation of component weight for both geometry and stress. It has also been designed to provide interface with a finite stress analysis package.

Limitations of Surface Modelling

Despite the many attributes and recent advantages of surface modelling, there remain a number of limitations which can only be overcome by using solid models. These limitations include:

a) No comprehension of solid volume, with resulting ambiguities.

b) Some surface models give unreliable volume data, depending on the accuracy of surface definition.

c) Hidden lines cannot be easily removed, nor internal sections easily displayed.

Fig. 5.18a

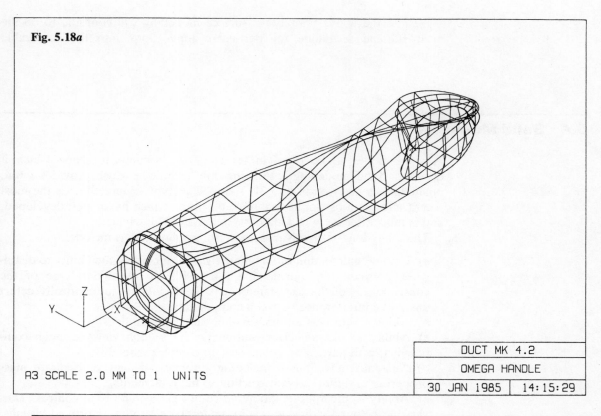

A3 SCALE 2.0 MM TO 1 UNITS

DUCT MK 4.2	
OMEGA HANDLE	
30 JAN 1985	14:15:29

Fig. 5.18b

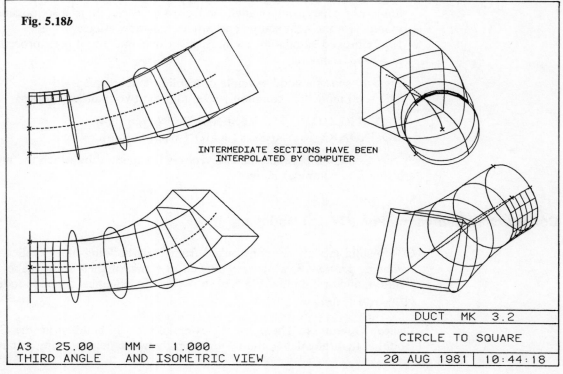

INTERMEDIATE SECTIONS HAVE BEEN
INTERPOLATED BY COMPUTER

A3   25.00   MM = 1.000
THIRD ANGLE   AND ISOMETRIC VIEW

DUCT MK 3.2	
CIRCLE TO SQUARE	
20 AUG 1981	10:44:18

Despite the above limitations, surface modelling will continue to be the most suitable technique for particular applications into the forseeable future.

5.4 Solid Modelling

A solid model is described in terms of the volumetric shape which it occupies. Solid modelling is thus the only technique which provides a full, unambiguous description of a 3D shape. This type of modelling is the most recent and the most sophisticated of the three which have been developed, and is most effectively tackled on systems of 32-bit capacity.

The many long-term advantages in using solid models include:

a) Complete definition of volumetric shape, including the ability to distinguish between the outside and the inside of an object. One of the consequences of the last statement is the facility to automatically detect unwanted interference between components.

b) Ability to provide automatic removal of hidden lines.

c) Ability to provide clear, automatic 3D section views through components, with particular advantages on complex assemblies.

d) Analytical advantages, including automatic display of accurate mass properties and efficient construction of finite elements.

e) Ability to incorporate extensive colour choice and tone control. Thus variable colour shading is readily undertaken to give improved visualisation of shape, components, and cross-sections. It is also possible to manipulate the light source and produce shadow effects.

f) Improved simulation of mechanism dynamics, tool-path procedures, and robot handling.

Fig 5.19 shows a good example of a solid model display.

The solid modellers commonly used fall into two main categories:

CONSTRUCTIVE REPRESENTATION type (C-Rep).
BOUNDARY REPRESENTATION type (B-Rep).

The distinction between the two types is the method by which the models are stored in computer memory.

Constructive Representation (C-Rep) Modelling

C-Rep solid models are constructed from basic building blocks called *solid modelling primitives*, which are defined in terms of their solid shape, size, position, and orientation. Fig 5.20 shows typical examples of solid modelling primitives.

Boolean Operators   These are the essential tools in building up the C-Rep model in that they define the relationships between neighbouring primitives.

Fig. 5.19

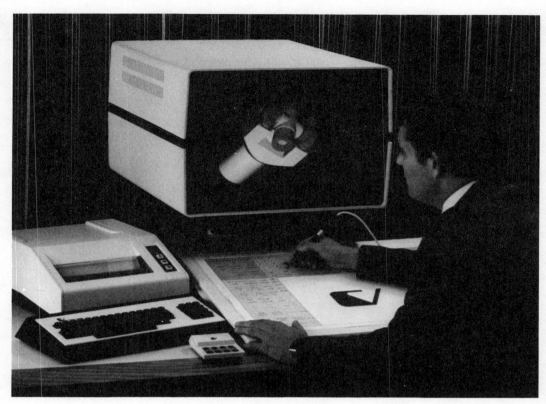

Fig. 5.20 Solid modelling primitives [*Applicon*]

Fig. 5.21 Boolean operations

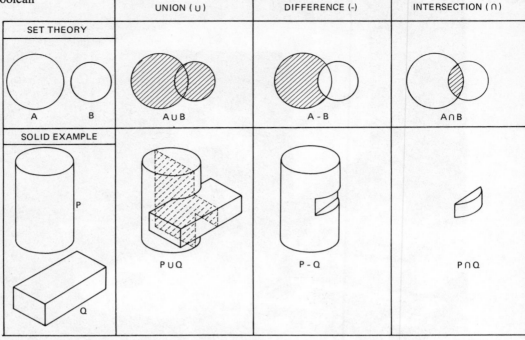

	UNION (∪)	DIFFERENCE (-)	INTERSECTION (∩)
SET THEORY			
A B	A∪B	A - B	A∩B
SOLID EXAMPLE			
P Q	P∪Q	P - Q	P∩Q

Boolean operators are based on algebraic set theory and have particular significance to solid objects which become merged. The three Boolean operators are called *union, difference*, and *intersection*. Fig 5.21 defines these terms and gives a practical solid modelling example against each.

A UNION (∪) defines the space inside the outer boundaries of the combined shape formed when two bodies have penetrated each other. The union of the two dissimilar circles A and B in Fig 5.21 is the shaded area A∪B. Thus a union operation defines a resultant composite shape as a *single* item. The equivalent union of two solid primitives (cylinder P and cuboid Q) is also shown in Fig 5.21. One section is also shown through this union to emphasise that the original profiles of the two shapes are not recognised inside the merged portion since they do not affect the single new shape.

A DIFFERENCE (−) defines the space bounded by the remaining profile of one of the original shapes and the outer boundary of the merged region. One of the difference values of circles A and B in Fig 5.21 is shown as the shaded area A−B. Similarly, one difference between the two solid shapes of this diagram is the slotted cylinder P−Q.

An INTERSECTION (∩) defines the space inside the boundaries of the merged region. The intersection of circles A and B in Fig 5.21 is shown as the shaded area A ∩ B, just as the intersection of P and Q is shown as the solid shape P ∩ Q.

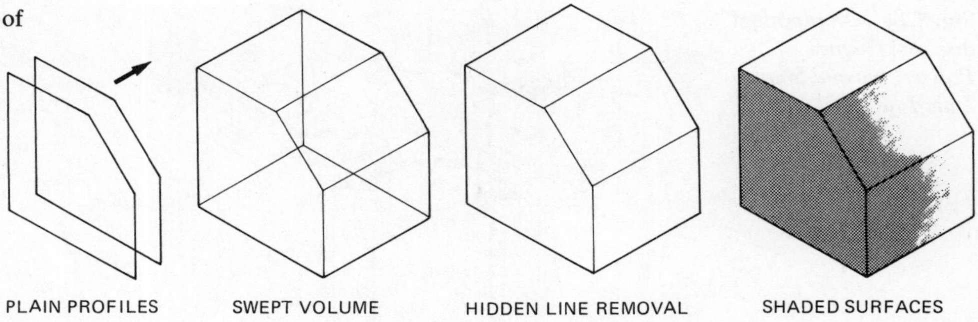

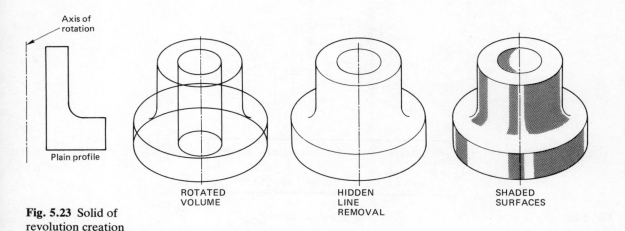

Fig. 5.22 Creation of solid primitive

PLAIN PROFILES   SWEPT VOLUME   HIDDEN LINE REMOVAL   SHADED SURFACES

Axis of rotation

Plain profile

ROTATED VOLUME   HIDDEN LINE REMOVAL   SHADED SURFACES

Fig. 5.23 Solid of revolution creation

Constructing the C-Rep model   Solid primitives may be created by sweeping 2D areas in 3D space as with surface modelling, but with the essential difference that one solid volume is now generated instead of an empty space surrounded by faces. Automatic hidden line removal and shading of surfaces are natural extensions to the solid volume display (Fig 5.22). It is also possible to sweep areas rotationally to produce solids of revolution (Fig 5.23).

The 3D display of the component in Fig 5.24 is shown by kind permission of Thames Polytechnic who created its geometry using the Romulus Solid Modeller package (marketed by Shape Data Ltd). The following is a simplified description of the steps involved in creating such a shape.

1   The component model may be constructed from the primitives shown in Fig 5.25. These are originally created using a mixture of linear and rotational sweeping operations, and may then be stored as parametric macros in the primitives library of the software. Thus primitives (b) and (e) may be categorised as the same standard, i.e. a parametric solid cylinder whose variable dimensions may be specified on recall. Once displayed on the VDU screen, the primitives may be moved to any desired position and orientation.

Fig. 5.24 A component display [*Thames Polytechnic and Shape Data Ltd.*]

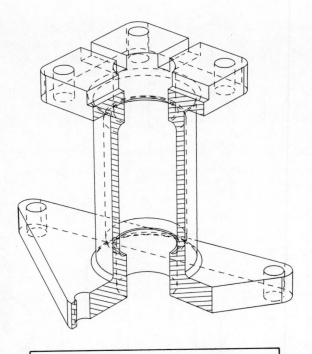

```
ROMULUS 5.2 rev 11: Shape Data Ltd: Sept 85
Scale 4.47214:1
Drawn:  ↑-B2
© SHAPE DATA LTD   24-MAR-1986 15: 5
```

Fig. 5.25

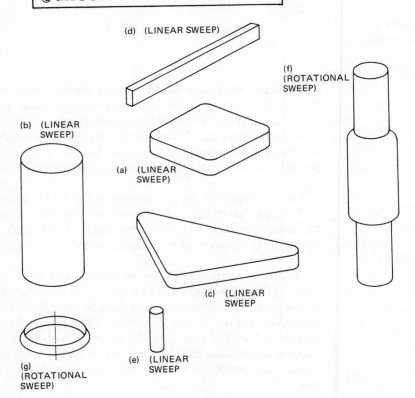

(d) (LINEAR SWEEP)

(f) (ROTATIONAL SWEEP)

(b) (LINEAR SWEEP)

(a) (LINEAR SWEEP)

(c) (LINEAR SWEEP

(e) (LINEAR SWEEP)

(g) (ROTATIONAL SWEEP)

2 The main body is created by union operations between primitives (a), (b), and (c). For each operation the primitives are positioned as required in 3D space and a union command given to the system (Fig 5.26).

3 Similarly, each slot is created by positioning primitive (d) as required over the main body display and selecting a difference command. The same procedure, using difference commands, is then followed to create the drilled holes (e) and the main bore (f). These steps are shown in Figs 5.27, 5.28, and 5.29.

4 A fillet radius is added via a union operation between the main body and primitive (g) (Fig 5.30).

5 The component may be sectioned by using a difference operation with a cuboid primitive, as shown in Fig 5.31. Automatic cross-hatching can be displayed if required.

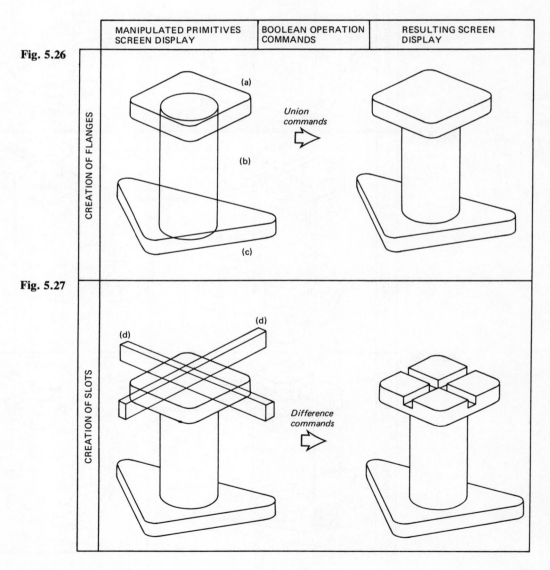

Fig. 5.26

Fig. 5.27

6 Once the 3D model is created then, effectively, so is the detail drawing, since the required number of 2D orthographic views may now be automatically displayed and automatically dimensioned. Fig. 5.32 shows the final views of the component.

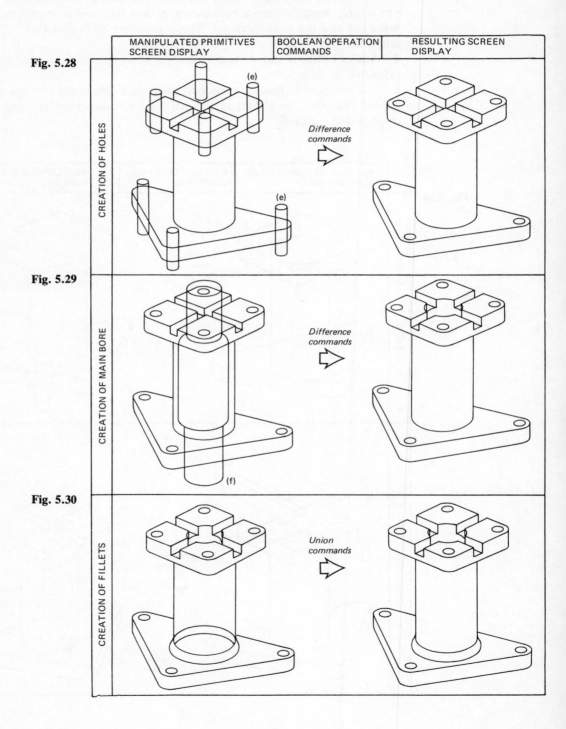

MANIPULATED PRIMITIVES SCREEN DISPLAY	BOOLEAN OPERATION COMMANDS	RESULTING SCREEN DISPLAY

Fig. 5.28 — CREATION OF HOLES — *Difference commands*

Fig. 5.29 — CREATION OF MAIN BORE — *Difference commands*

Fig. 5.30 — CREATION OF FILLETS — *Union commands*

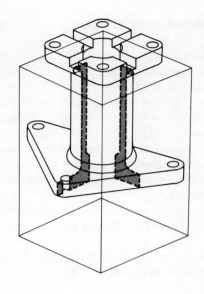

Fig. 5.31 Sectioning by
difference operation
with cuboid

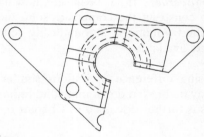

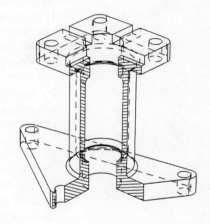

Fig. 5.32 Component
final view [*Thames
Polytechnic and Shape
Data Ltd.*]

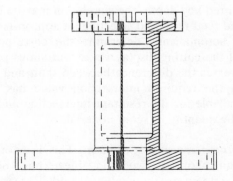

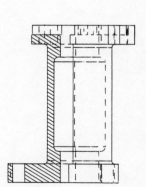

3RD ANGLE PROJECTION

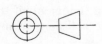

Solid Modelling Using Boundary Representation (B-Rep)

To create models using B-Rep, exactly the same techniques may be used, i.e. primitives may be formed with linear or rotational sweeps, and composite shapes built up using Boolean operations.

However, whereas C-Rep modellers recognise a composite body in terms of the primitive solids from which it was built, a B-Rep modeller recognises that body in terms of the edges and faces which make up its surrounding surface (i.e. its 3D volumetric boundary). Data concerning the boundary representation is structured in terms of its *topology* (which describes the number of faces) and its *geometry* (which describes the shape and position of vertices, edges, and faces).

The main advantage of B-Rep modelling is that boundary profiles may be more easily modified. However, B-Rep systems are more demanding on memory capacity.

Generally, there is little to choose between the two types of modeller, and some systems employ a combination of both.

Applications of Boolean operations

1 *Volume and Mass Properties*   It has been seen how union and difference operations are used to construct the composite solid model. At each progressive step the resultant volume is automatically redetermined, making mass properties instantly available.

2 *Stress Analysis*   Using difference operations similar to those for sectioning, a 3D model may be broken down into solid finite elements for stress analysis purposes. This is further discussed in Chapter 6.

3 *Simulation of Machining Operations*   This is one of the most natural and significant developments of Boolean operations in solid modelling. Metal-cutting techniques such as turning, milling, and drilling may be directly related to difference and intersection operations. For example, Fig 5.33 shows the milling cutter operation for producing a sled-runner keyway in a shaft. Once the shaft and cutter solid models have been positioned on the screen at the required key depth, the simulation may be initiated by quoting the key length and feed rate, and selecting an appropriate menu command. The system will automatically determine the corresponding intersection value and control the cutting display via a continuous program loop which progressively increases the difference between shaft and cutter. The loop is terminated when the required intersection value has been obtained. A display is also available for the resultant intersection and its volume, which is equivalent to the quantity of scrap material.

4 *Detection of Interference or Collision*   This is another natural consequence of Boolean theory. If two solid objects have not penetrated each other, there will be no intersection value. A modelling system can thus check for the existence of intersections between adjacent objects, and issue warning statements if they occur. This is an essential tool for investigating possible collisions of moving objects in robot handling and factory layout

Fig. 5.33 Milling simulation for sled-runner keyway

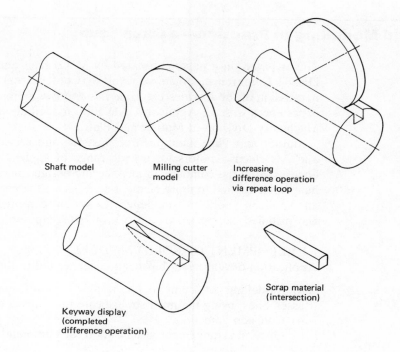

Shaft model

Milling cutter model

Increasing difference operation via repeat loop

Keyway display (completed difference operation)

Scrap material (intersection)

Fig. 5.34 Use of intersections for interference detection

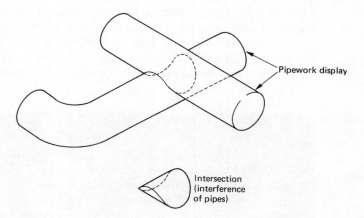

Pipework display

Intersection (interference of pipes)

design. It can also be used to detect unwanted tool collisions in cutting operations, and obstructions in the loci of complex mechanisms.

Intersections can also indicate unwanted interference of mating components in mechanical assemblies, and interference between static components in piping assemblies and plant layout. Through the value of the intersection, the system can also report how much interference has taken place and, consequently, the degree of correction required (Fig 5.34).

5.5 Solid Modelling in Practice—a Case Study

This is based on a paper presented by M. G. Holt and R. A. Jobson at the DES84 Conference, organised by IFS (Conferences) Ltd. Shown by kind permission of the *Engineering Materials and Design* magazine, it outlines the experiences with an Applicon CAD solid modelling system in the Rotating Machinery Division of Mather and Platt.

Mather and Platt manufactures, installs, and services centrifugal pumps and AC electric motors for a wide range of applications. Computers have been used by the company in engineering design for some twenty years and have been applied to finite element analysis for the past seven years. In 1982 an Applicon "Solids 1" modeller 3D system comprising four workstations was installed, supported by a VAX 11/780 computer.

DEVELOPMENT OF SOLID MODELLING
Application development has been concentrated in the following areas:

  a) Modelling of components such as pump impellers and complex assemblies, using the most sophisticated primitives available.
  b) Collision detection.
  c) General arrangement visualisation for pump and motor packaged sets.

The objectives are to influence over 80% of all engineering activity—not just drawing and analysis. The Applicon system fulfils the requirement of an automated draughting capability, whilst the VAX provides the additional capacity for large "number crunching" analysis programs, 3D solid modelling, and comprehensive engineering databases. The VAX and Applicon systems can communicate with each other via an integrated network. Recently, the VAX 11/780 was doubled in capacity, and facilities were enhanced by a second Applicon processor plus two additional workstations.

Fig. 5.35*a*

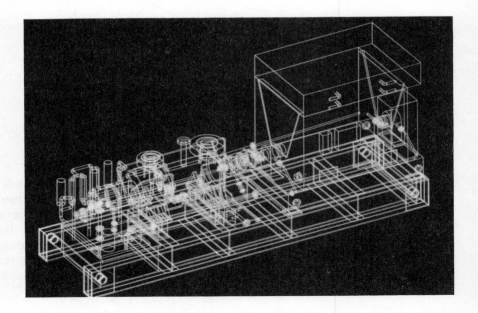

THE CHOICE OF SOLID

The nature of product at Mather and Platt is particularly suited to a 3D solid display. Fig 5.35a shows a typical Mather and Platt assembly displayed in 3D wireframe form. Most of this display is totally unclear and highlights all the ambiguities and shortcomings of wireframes.

Fig 5.35b shows an improved view with hidden line removal, whilst Fig 5.35c shows the superior solid model with shaded faces. Although a surface

Fig. 5.35b

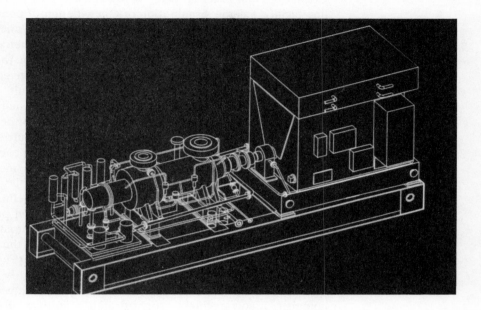

Fig. 5.35c

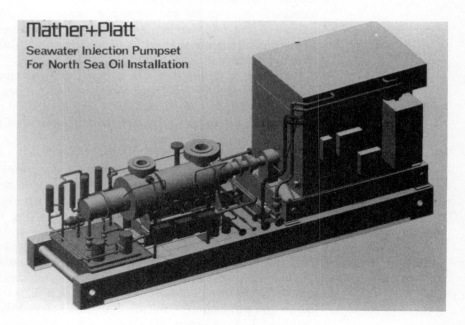

modeller could have given a similar shaded display, it could not have provided the clear 3D views of sectional assemblies, accurate mass property details, and efficient detection of interference, which is commonly required in this company's projects, and which is readily obtainable with a solid modeller.

CONCEPTUAL DESIGN

One of the first practical uses for Mather and Platt's Applicon solid modelling facility was the visualisation of a new design of pump impeller.

The design of impeller geometry is assisted by an interactive graphics program which produces 2D views of the 3D geometry. For the hydraulic engineers this is frequently adequate. However, in the case of the high-speed pump, the impeller design was highly unconventional, causing the interpretation of 2D drawings to be extremely difficult.

When previously faced with problems of design visualisation, the designer would normally have resorted to making a wooden or perspex model. In this case, as computer modelling methods were largely untried, it was decided to commission both a wooden model and a computer-generated 3D model for comparison. The computer model was completed more quickly and for lower cost.

However, both models demonstrated that this preliminary design, whilst theoretically correct, was not suitable for production purposes (Fig 5.36a). The design was subsequently modified using the computer model to express the continually changing thoughts and ideas of the designer, until an analytical and visual optimum had been achieved (Fig 5.36b). Thus solid modelling had easily proved its worth.

In practical terms, the solid modelling techniques used were quite complex, involving highly sophisticated primitives. Each of the impeller blades was modelled as one general surface. This required that parallel sections be defined through the vanes. The computer then automatically blended smooth curves and surfaces between the sections. The hub and the shroud of the impeller are axisymmetric. Therefore it was necessary to define only their sectional profile, which was then rotationally swept into a solid of revolution.

This exercise clearly demonstrated the valuable contribution of 3D computer solid modelling for design visualisation, and has prompted the compilation of an automated procedure for generating solid model representations of all impeller designs, an example of which is shown in Fig 5.37.

PIPING ARRANGEMENTS

The conventional approach to designing and drawing piping arrangements varies according to the complexity of the pipework and the requirements of the customer. In some cases, it is sufficient to represent the pipework schematically and show termination points, leaving the precise routing of pipes to the pipe fitter on final assembly. Other situations demand a fully-detailed isometric drawing to be generated. This involves considerable effort and is only feasible once the design has been settled. It is necessary to consider the problems of clash detection, ease of assembly and maintenance, minimum cost of pipe lengths and fittings, as well as the overall appearance. Given the production demands and time constraints of any conventional drawing office, an optimum design is rarely achievable.

Fig. 5.36*a*

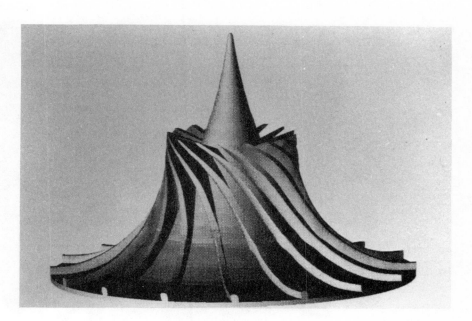

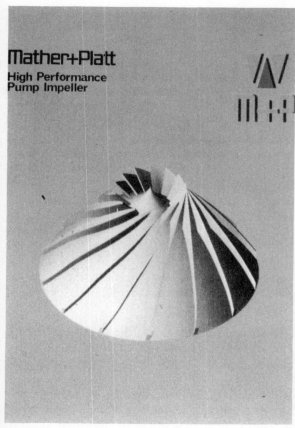

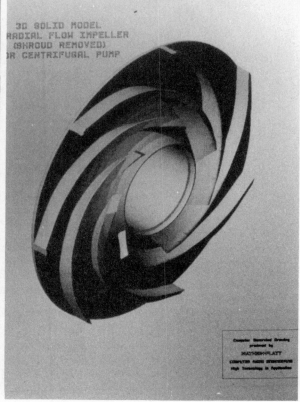

Fig. 5.36*b*

Fig. 5.37

Fig. 5.38

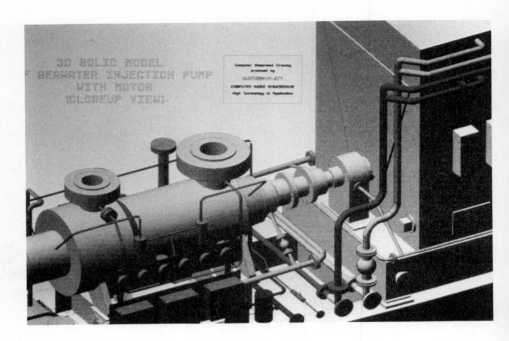

Solid modelling techniques make design modification much easier, enabling a detail layout to be formulated at any early stage, whilst responding to the inevitable changes later in the contract. A good example at Mather and Platt was the design and layout of the ancilliary pipework on a high-performance pump and motor, supplied as a packaged set for a North Sea oil platform (Fig 5.38). This model had the characteristic advantages of possible views from any position or angle, and automatic clash detection. It was also possible to generate pipework cutting lists and detailed dimensioned drawings, directly from the computer model. This permitted prefabrication of pipework, thereby minimising the final assembly and delivery lead time.

DETAIL DESIGN VISUALISATION

The ability to examine a fully-defined solid model representation of assembled components is of considerable assistance at the detail design stage. Two examples at Mather and Platt usefully illustrate this:

1   The shear ring cartridge locking arrangement on the multi-stage barrel casing pump (Fig 5.39a) of the previously described North Sea oil rig package. An appropriately-sectioned model highlights the function of this critical feature (Fig 5.39b).
2   A solid model of a motor rotor (Fig 5.40) was the only means by which the moment of inertia could be accurately predicted. A sectioned view of the model conveniently illustrates the complexity of the assembly.

Fig. 5.39a

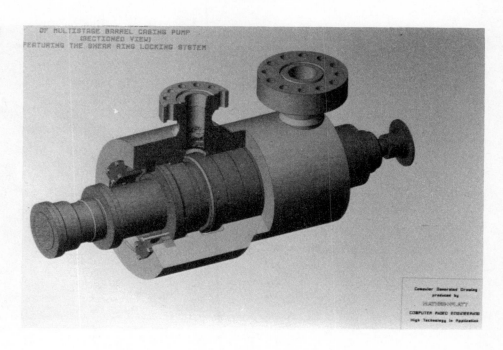

Fig. 5.39b

Fig. 5.40

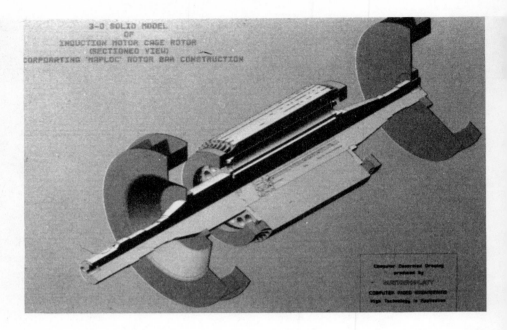

FUTURE DEVELOPMENT

Mather and Platt's commitment to solid modelling during its infancy was based upon the belief that it will become the foundation of the CADCAM systems of the future. The computer-aided engineering approach to the manufacturing industry should see solid geometry as the basis of prototypes, finished designs, analysis, CNC machining, inspection and assembly, and at the heart of the database.

The present construction of primitives is likely to be simplified, either by displaying solids directly, or by the automatic generation of solids from independent orthographic views. Further advances in 3D visualisation could include the development of *holography*, which dispenses with the screen and allows true 3D display.

Finite Element Analysis 6

6.1 Introduction

Finite Element Analysis (FEA) has become one of the most widely-used techniques for analysing mechanical loading characteristics in modern engineering components. Traditional analysis techniques, though theoretically sound, can only be satisfactorily applied to a range of conventional component shapes and specific loading conditions. Unfortunately, the majority of engineering loading situations are not simple and straightforward. Therefore the traditional techniques often need to be modified and compromised to suit situations for which they were not intended. The uncertainty thus created commonly leads to the designer applying excessively high safety factors to the mechanical loads and so to "overdesign" components by specifying either unnecessarily bulky cross-sections or high-quality materials. Inevitably the cost of the product is adversely affected.

FEA allows the designer to effectively analyse complex components by splitting a shape into smaller, simpler *finite elements*. These elements are sometimes referred to as *discrete*, and the process of generating them as *discretizing* the component shape. Typical element shapes are shown in Fig 6.1. The finite elements are then analysed for their strain characteristics, and the results are related back to the whole structure of the component. Each element is bounded by points called *nodes*. The lines crossing through the nodes, and so forming the element shapes, make up the *finite element mesh* (FEM), (Fig 6.2).

The fundamental principles of FEA have been known since the 19th century, but the technique was not widely used until recent years, due to the prohibitive mathematics involved. As will be later discussed, FEA mathematics uses highly complex and repetitive matrix algebra procedures which would be far too time-consuming and error-prone to undertake by conventional means. It was thus not until the development of computers, microprocessors, and CADCAM that FEA could be used to the advantage of the engineer. Clearly, FEA is a classic example of a sound principle, developed before its time and "waiting for computers to come along".

Industrial applications of FEA were pioneered in the 1950s and 1960s by the aeronautical industry, who were quick to realise its potential in aiding the creation of designs with high strength/weight ratios. FEA is now exten-

Fig. 6.1 Typical finite element (discrete) shapes [*FEGS Ltd.*]

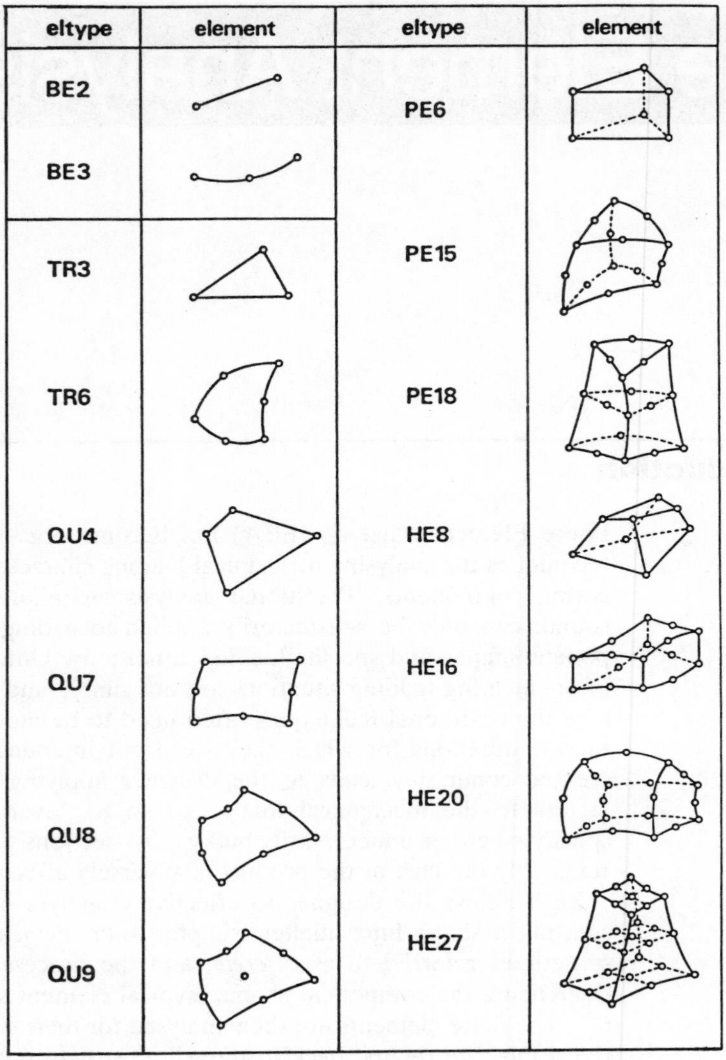

eltype	element	eltype	element
BE2		PE6	
BE3			
TR3		PE15	
TR6		PE18	
QU4		HE8	
QU7		HE16	
QU8		HE20	
QU9		HE27	

sively used, having made particular impact in the automobile industry, which is constantly striving to reduce weight for improved fuel efficiency. While the predominant application has been in stress and deflection analysis, the technique is increasingly being used to solve design problems associated with fluid flow, heat transfer, natural frequencies, electronics, and radiation analysis. Fig 6.3 shows the VDU display of a 3D stress analysis procedure using FEA.

FEA, by its very nature, demands the input of large amounts of data (commonly Mbyte quantities) and produces an even larger amount at output (commonly hundreds of Mbyte quantities). It has thus, until recently, been an exclusive facility for minicomputers and mainframes. However, with the continued advances in microprocessor technology, several good FEA software packages are now available for a range of 16-bit microcomputers.

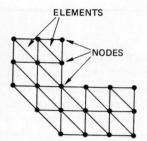

Fig. 6.2 The finite element mesh

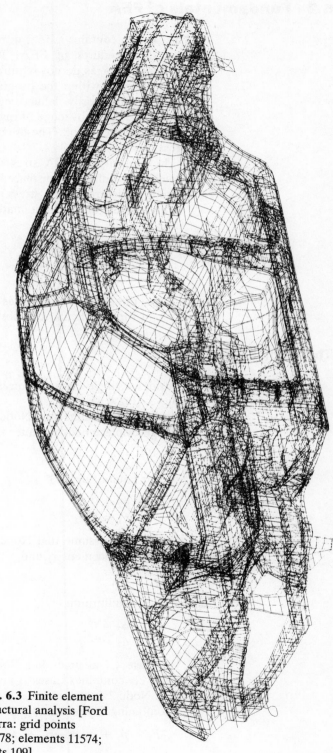

Fig. 6.3 Finite element structural analysis [Ford Sierra: grid points 10078; elements 11574; parts 109]

6.2 Fundamentals of FEA

This section contains a brief introduction to the basic principles and mathematical procedures of FEA. It should be emphasised that most FEA software packages do not require proficiency in these procedures since they are performed within the programs. However, associated terminology can only be satisfactorily defined via such an exercise. The calculations shown assume a basic knowledge of matrix algebra, such as may be obtained from any relevant textbook. The discussion will be confined to the use of FEA in stress analysis.

The majority of FEA stresswork methods are based on using *stiffness values* to establish the displacements at the nodes of the loaded mesh and thereby to determine the stress in each element.

The stiffness of an elastic material may be given as

$F = kx$
where k = stiffness
F = applied force
x = displacement.

While the displacement varies with the applied force, the stiffness remains constant for a particular component.

The Stiffness Matrix

Consider a single element consisting of a thin, light, elastic rod of stiffness value k (Fig 6.4).

In Case A, assume that Node 1 is fixed and that Node 2 is free to move through displacement x_2 under the action of force p_2. Now

$p_2 = kx_2$

and, for equilibrium:

$p_1 + p_2 = 0$
i.e. $p_1 = -p_2$

In Case B, assume that Node 2 is fixed and that Node 1 is free to move through displacement x_1 under the action of force q_1. Now

$q_1 = kx_1$

and, for equilibrium:

$q_1 + q_2 = 0$
i.e. $q_2 = -q_1$

In Case C, assume that Nodes 1 and 2 are both free to move. This effectively combines Cases A and B with resultant forces F_1 and F_2 at Node 1 and Node 2 respectively.

Combining Cases A and B at Node 1:

$$F_1 = p_1 + q_1 = -p_2 + q_1 = -kx_2 + kx_1 = kx_1 - kx_2$$

Fig. 6.4 Thin rod element

CASE A (NODE 1 FIXED)

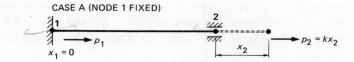

CASE B (NODE 2 FIXED)

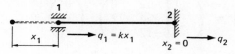

CASE C (NODES FREE)

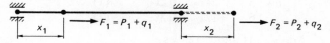

Combining Cases A and B at Node 2:

$$F_2 = p_2 + q_2 = p_2 - q_1 = kx_2 - kx_1 = -kx_1 + kx_2$$

Thus, in summary:

$$F_1 = kx_1 - kx_2$$
$$F_2 = -kx_1 + kx_2$$

This may also be expressed in the matrix form:

$$\begin{pmatrix} F_1 \\ F_2 \end{pmatrix} = \begin{pmatrix} k & -k \\ -k & k \end{pmatrix} \begin{pmatrix} x_1 \\ x_2 \end{pmatrix}$$

↑	↑	↑
Nodal forces	Stiffness matrix	Nodal displacements

The stiffness matrix may be considered as the main building block of all stresswork finite element mesh calculations.

Consider now that we have a mesh whose elements are two thin, light rods of equal stiffness k, connected in series, and subjected to a force at each of the three nodes (Fig 6.5).

Using the same arguments as those in the case of the single element, the following matrix equation may be obtained:

$$\begin{pmatrix} F_1 \\ F_2 \\ F_3 \end{pmatrix} = \begin{pmatrix} k & -k & 0 \\ -k & 2k & -k \\ 0 & -k & k \end{pmatrix} \begin{pmatrix} x_1 \\ x_2 \\ x_3 \end{pmatrix}$$

Fig. 6.5

Example Two thin, light rods of stiffness 12 kN/mm are connected as in Fig 6.5 and subjected to loads of $F_2 = 3$ kN and $F_3 = 6$ kN at Nodes 2 and 3 respectively. The system is fixed at Node 1. Determine the displacements at Nodes 2 and 3.

Solution Using the matrix equation derived from Fig 6.5, and taking x_1 as zero:

$$\begin{pmatrix} F_1 \\ 3 \\ 6 \end{pmatrix} = \begin{pmatrix} 12 & -12 & 0 \\ -12 & 24 & -12 \\ 0 & -12 & 12 \end{pmatrix} \begin{pmatrix} 0 \\ x_2 \\ x_3 \end{pmatrix}$$

i.e.
$$\begin{pmatrix} F_1 \\ 3 \\ 6 \end{pmatrix} = \begin{pmatrix} 0 & -12x_2 & 0 \\ 0 & 24x_2 & -12x_3 \\ 0 & -12x_2 & 12x_3 \end{pmatrix}$$

Thus
$$3 = 24x_2 - 12x_3 \quad (1)$$
$$6 = -12x_2 + 12x_3 \quad (2)$$

Adding (1) and (2) gives

$$9 = 12x_2$$
$$x_2 = 0.75 \quad (Ans)$$

Substituting in equation (1) gives

$$3 = (24 \times 0.75) - 12x_3$$
$$12x_3 = 15$$
$$x_3 = 1.25 \quad (Ans)$$

The displacements at Nodes 2 and 3 are 0.75 mm and 1.25 mm respectively.

The displacements calculated in the above example could be used to calculate stress values via original lengths and Young's Modulus values.

Stiffness Matrix for Practical Elements

Engineering components are, of course, rarely made from simple elements such as the thin rods previously discussed. For areas and volumes, the relationship between force and displacement is considerably affected by the geometry of the element, and is thus not a simple quantity such as the k stiffness value. Therefore the stiffness matrix must be derived from a complex algebraic procedure involving a number of constituent matrices, each of which are of a highly advanced form.

The general expression for the stiffness matrix is given as

Stiffness Matrix $= V \int (B)^t (D) (B)$

where (B) is a matrix describing the element geometry

(D) is a matrix relating stress and strain, which includes Young's Modulus and Poisson's Ratio values

$(B)^t$ is the transpose matrix of (B)

V is the volume of the element.

Element Parameters

Element types may described in terms of

a) SHAPE, via the relative positions of its nodes.
b) The DEGREES OF FREEDOM (i.e. possible directions of movement) of each node.

The total number of degrees of freedom in the mesh gives the size of the stiffness matrix. For example, the first of the thin rod elements considered had one degree of freedom at each of its two nodes and thus gave a two-by-two stiffness matrix. This was extended to a three-by-three matrix for two-rod elements with one degree of freedom at each of its three nodes.

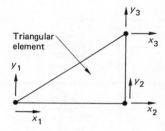

Fig. 6.6 Six degrees of freedom leads to a six-by-six matrix

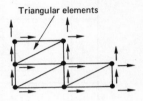

Fig. 6.7 Eight nodes, with two degrees of freedom per node, leads to a sixteen-by-sixteen matrix

If we now consider a simple two-dimensional shape, such as the triangle shown in Fig 6.6, this could have two degrees of freedom at each of its three nodes, which would thus result in a six-by-six stiffness matrix. If this element were part of the simple shape shown in Fig 6.7, the eight nodes would give a sixteen-by-sixteen matrix.

Calculations with a matrix of this size would be extremely involved, time-consuming and error-prone. Given that some complex components and loading conditions can require huge stiffness matrices of many thousands by many thousands, it can thus be appreciated that using FEA to solve engineering problems becomes practically impossible without the aid of computers.

Element Types

Fig 6.8 lists common types of element. These may be broadly classified as:

1 Rod or Beam type The simplest case of this type (Fig 6.8(1)) was the first element discussed in the fundamentals of FEA, with a single linear degree of freedom at each of its two nodes. Rod or beam elements are, in practice, usually more complex than this—a common example being shown in Fig 6.8(2). This is a typical beam bending element with two linear and

Fig. 6.8 Some common elements (DOF = degrees of freedom)

	ELEMENT TYPE	DESCRIPTION	D.O.F.s PER NODE	D.O.F.s PER ELEMENT
1	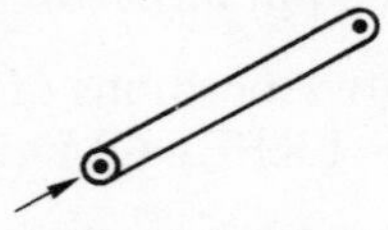	Thin rod; Two-dimensional; Two nodes	1	2
2	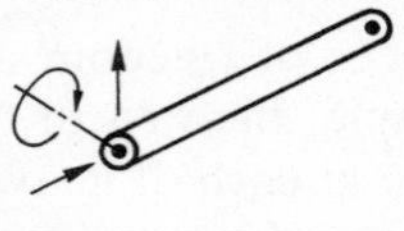	Thin rod; Beam bending type; Two-dimensional; Two nodes	3	6
3	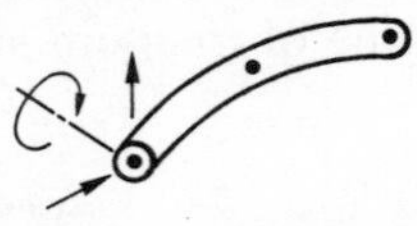	Thin rod; Beam type; Two-dimensional; Three nodes	3	9
4	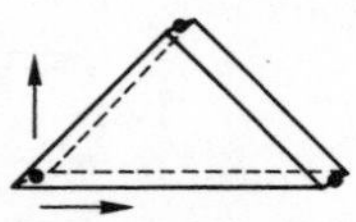	Triangular; Plane stress; Two-dimensional; Three nodes	2	6
5	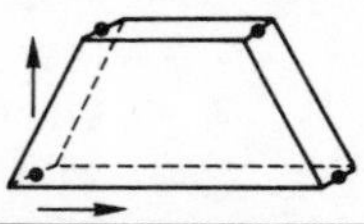	Quadrilateral; Plane stress; Two-dimensional; Four nodes	2	8
6	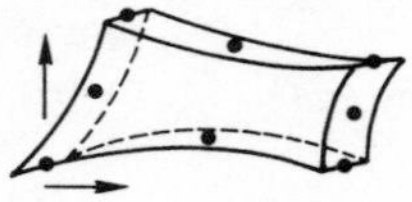	Parabolic; Plane stress; Two-dimensional; Eight nodes	2	16
7	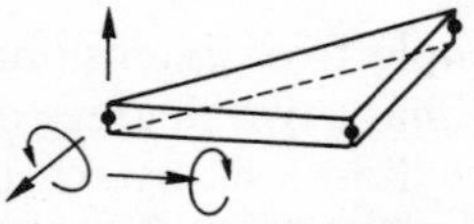	Triangular; Plate bending; Two-dimensional; Three nodes	5	15
8	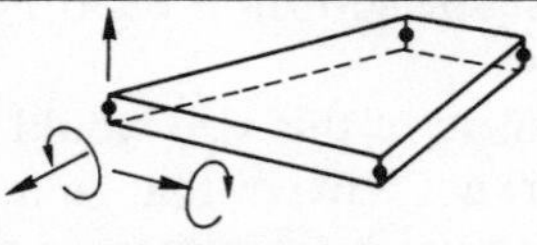	Quadrilateral; Plate bending; Two-dimensional; Four nodes	5	20
9	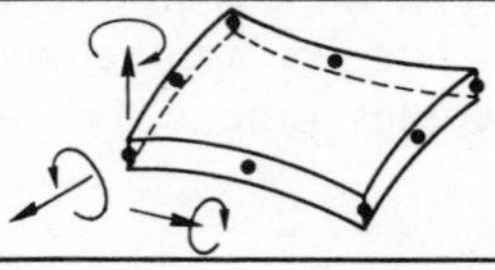	Curved shell; Three-dimensional; Eight nodes	6	48

one rotational degree of freedom per node. A variation on this shape is the curved rod having three nodes per element (Fig 6.8(3)). Rod or beam elements are used for the analysis of plane frameworks and as stiffeners in platework design.

2 2D Plane Stress type These are flat shapes with uniform cross-sections and usually two degrees of freedom per node. They have a regular thickness, which is assumed to be equally displaced about each node. Typical

	ELEMENT TYPE	DESCRIPTION	D.O.F.s PER NODE	D.O.F.s PER ELEMENT
10		Triangular; 3D solid; Linear isoparametric; Six nodes	3	18
11		Tetrahedral; 3D solid; Linear isoparametric; Four nodes	3	12
12		Quadrilateral; 3D solid; Linear isoparametric Eight nodes	3	24
13		3D solid; Quadratic isoparametric; Twenty nodes	3	60
14		Triangular ring; 3D solid; Axisymmetric; Three nodes	2	6
15		Quadrilateral ring; 3D solid; Axisymmetric; Four nodes	2	8
16		Curved sided ring; 3D solid Axisymmetric; Eight nodes	2	16

element cross-sections include *triangular* (Fig 6.8(4)), *quadrilateral* Fig 6.8(5)), and *parabolic* (Fig 6.8(6)). The triangular type is the simplest and least demanding of computer memory, whereas the other two are higher-order elements and are more accurate.

Two degrees of freedom at each node allow direct stresses to be applied to the area contained within the regular thickness, and shear stress to the area of the element shape.

2D plane stress elements may be used for a wide variety of applications involving either regular solids or membrane plate elements for plane plate structures.

3 Plate Bending Elements As in the 2D plane stress type, these are flat elements of regular thickness. They are assumed to be thin-walled and have three linear, and two rotational, degrees of freedom at each node. This combination provides a good model for plate-bending applications, such as floor sections, ships bridge decks, and foundation rafts. Typical plate bending elements are shown in Figs 6.8(7) and 6.8(8).

4 Curved Shell Elements These may be considered as an extension to the plate-bending elements. They have additional nodes to describe a thin-walled 3D curved profile (Fig 6.8(9)). 3D bending stress analysis is available via rotational degrees of freedom along three axes at each node. Typical applications of this type of model include pressure vessels and car bodies.

5 3D Solid Elements This type of element is used for complex three-dimensional components such as those with non-uniform thickness.

3D solid elements may generally be grouped into two families: isoparametric and axisymmetric.

Isoparametric is a term which may also be applied to two-dimensional elements. It describes any element which has the same shape function for its displacement and its geometry. Common isoparametric elements have forces, displacements and fixities considered only at the nodal points and do not contain internal nodes. Three types of *linear solid isoparametric* elements are shown in Figs 6.8(10), 6.8(11) and 6.8(12). These have straight edges joining the nodes. *Quadratic solid isoparametric* elements (Fig 6.8(13)) have edges made up of parabolic curves which are defined via an extra node at the centre of each edge. Typical applications of isoparametric elements include the analysis of such component shapes as valve bodies, pistons, and turbine blades.

Axisymmetric solid elements are formed by specifying revolved cross-sections about a fixed axis. These are extensively used for analysing mechanical components. Typical cross-sections include triangular (Fig 6.8(14)), quadrilateral (Fig 6.8(15)), and the higher-order curved-sided types (Fig 6.8(16)). Common applications of axisymmetric elements include shafts, flywheels, nozzles, pump-casings, impellers, and missiles.

Loading Conditions and Stress Terminology

This section briefly discusses some of the more common types of loading conditions and stress-types. These will be referred to in later case studies of FEA software applications.

Compound Stresses Consider a solid element with mutually perpendicular load components parallel to axes X,Y and Z. Six possible stress components result from this situation, as shown in Fig 6.9. These are classified as:

a) Direct Stresses (i.e. tensile or compressive) in the X,Y, and Z directions (σ_x, σ_y, and σ_z).

b) Shear Stresses in the XY,XZ, and YZ planes (τ_{xy}, τ_{xz}, τ_{yz}).

Fig. 6.9 Compound stresses

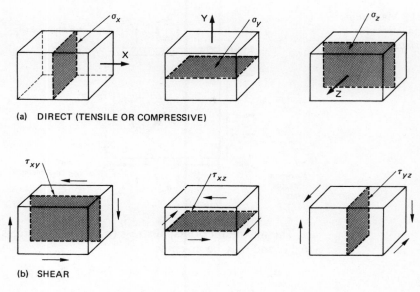

(a) DIRECT (TENSILE OR COMPRESSIVE)

(b) SHEAR

Fig. 6.10 Plane stresses

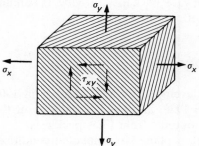

Plane Stress   Plane stresses are often used in two-dimensional FEA work, and may be derived from the loading condition in Fig 6.9, for the special case where

$$\sigma_z = \tau_{xz} = \tau_{yz} = 0$$

Therefore, the stress components are reduced to the XY plane in the form of two direct stresses (σ_x and σ_y), and one shear stress (τ_{xy}) (Fig 6.10).

The resulting two-dimensional stress system may be applied to elements of uniform thickness where out-of-plane stresses are negligible (a common case in engineering applications).

Principal Stresses   Although compound stress components may be analysed separately, their resultant effect on an element could be more critical than individual values.

At any point within an element there will exist mutually perpendicular planes, each with a resultant normal stress. Planes inclined at particular angles will be subjected to maximum normal stress values. These planes are known as *principal planes*, and their resultant stresses are called *maximum principal stresses*.

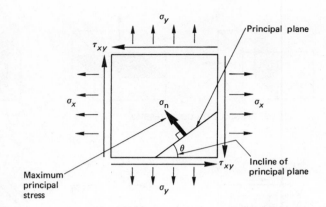

Fig. 6.11 Maximum principal stress for plane stress loading

The maximum principal stress (σ_n) for plane stress loading is shown in Fig 6.11, and may be given as

$$\sigma_n = \tfrac{1}{2}(\sigma_x + \sigma_y) + \sqrt{[\,\tfrac{1}{4}(\sigma_x - \sigma_y)^2 + \tau_{xy}^2\,]}$$

Many FEA software packages provide maximum principal stress values for each element of a mesh display.

The Huber–Von Mises–Hencky Theory

This theory was developed by M. T. Huber in 1904, R. von Mises in 1913 and H. Hencky in 1925, and has become one of the most popular laws for comparing results outputs from FEA packages.

When applied to a plane stress loading condition, the theory states that yielding of the material will begin at a critical equivalent direct stress value:

$$\sigma_v = \sqrt{[\sigma_x^2 - \sigma_x\sigma_y + \sigma_y^2 + 3\tau_{xy}^2]}$$

Thus, when analysing results, it is important to ensure that the σ_v value of any element lies below the yield point of the material to a certain required safety factor.

6.3 Computing Requirements

As already indicated, an encouraging recent trend is the development of FEA packages for simpler 2D, or axisymmetric shapes, which will run satisfactorily on 16-bit microcomputer systems. This has largely been made possible by advances in microprocessor and improved techniques in software generation. Common methods of reducing memory requirements include:

a) Taking advantage of the *banded* nature of the stiffness matrix (i.e. its symmetry about the principal diagonal, with groups of zeros at opposed corners) (Fig 6.12). By ignoring the corner zeros, and using a *half-band-width* value, smaller stiffness matrices may be generated (Fig 6.13). An even

Fig. 6.12 Banded nature of stiffness matrix

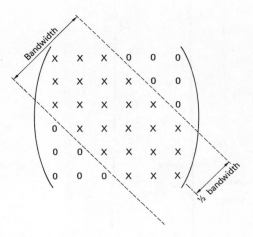

Fig. 6.13 Generation of smaller matrices using half-bandwidth

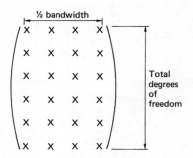

more efficient technique uses a *front solver* subroutine which, in addition to the corner zeros, also ignores a majority of zeros inside the bandwidth. The front solver has the effect of allocating computer core storage in the order in which the nodes are presented for assembly, and thus enables the software to analyse according to element number sequence, rather than node sequence.

b) Solving the equations for each element in turn whilst meanwhile storing the others on disc, and then writing out the reduced equations to disc. *Backsubstitution* is then used with the reduced equations, which are read back into core memory.

Stages in the FEA Program

The procedure in using an FEA program consists of three essential stages:

1 Preparation of the model data (pre-processing).
2 Analysis of the model.
3 Assessment of the results (post-processing).

These stages are illustrated in Fig 6.14.

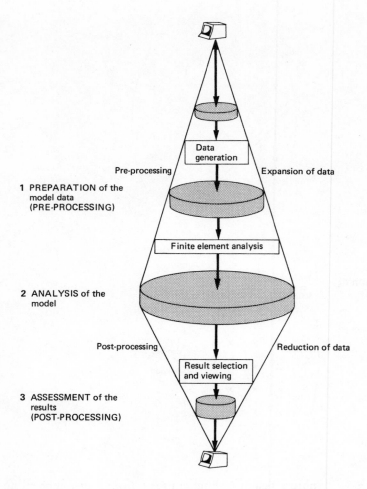

Fig. 6.14 Stages in the FEA program [*FEGS Ltd.*]

Data generation

Pre-processing   Expansion of data

1 PREPARATION of the
  model data
  (PRE-PROCESSING)

Finite element analysis

2 ANALYSIS of the
  model

Post-processing   Reduction of data

Result selection
and viewing

3 ASSESSMENT of the
  results
  (POST-PROCESSING)

The *pre-processor* is a program which enables the engineer to build a geometric model of a component design. From this model, the required mesh of finite elements may be generated (Fig. 6.15*a*).

Required inputs to the pre-processor include:

1 GEOMETRIC PARAMETERS (e.g. type of element, nodal coordinates, variation of mesh intensity). These may be entered directly into the FEA software, or may be obtained via an interface with a CAD draughting or solid modelling package.
2 LOADING CHARACTERISTICS (e.g. magnitudes, positions, and directions of point loads; pressures; thermal loads; centrifugal loads; frequency-dependent forces).
3 BOUNDARY CONDITIONS (e.g. positions and directions of nodal fixities; rotational axes; frictional resistances; prescribed displacements).
4 MATERIAL PROPERTIES (e.g. Young's Modulus; Poisson's Ratio; density; coefficient of friction; coefficient of expansion).

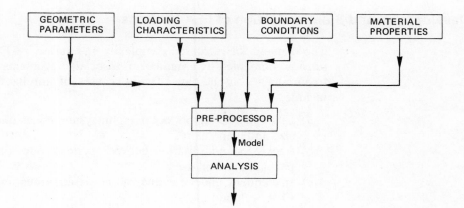

Fig. 6.15a Pre-processing

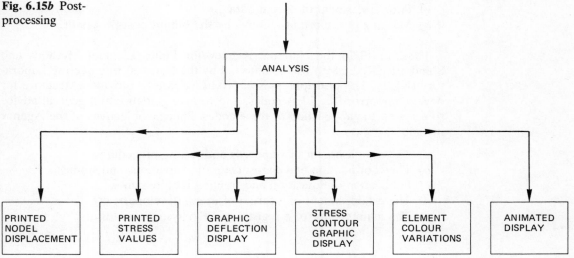

Fig. 6.15b Post-processing

The *post-processor* is a program which provides the engineer with tools to assess the results of the model analysis. Analysed results output from the post-processor may be in either data form (screen or printer) or graphical display (screen, plotter, or printer screen-dump) (Fig 6.15b).

Typical post-processor outputs include:

a) Printed nodal displacement values.
b) Printed element stress values.
c) Graphical display of distorted component mesh under load (with ability to magnify displacements by a stated multiplication factor).
d) Graphical display of stress contours.
e) Colour or tone variation of element display according to stress-range values.
f) Animated displays of moving displacements and varying element patterns for dynamic loading analysis.

The demand for increased complexity and variety of FEA applications has been accompanied by a number of associated problems, which can give rise to unreliable output data. Typical causes of unreliability and inefficiency include:

a) Likelihood of errors occurring in system codes due to their increasing size and complexity.
b) Lack of standardisation between system codes of the many software packages now in use.
c) Inadequate understanding of the assumptions and limitations of the FEA technique.
d) Poor representation of the component by the FEA model.
e) Deficiencies in the individual elements.
f) Selection of unsuitable element types.
g) Poor assessment of output data.
h) Masking of important features by the output post-processor.

Thus, in 1983, the National Agency for Finite Element Methods and Standards (NAFEMS) was established by the National Engineering Laboratory (NEL). The principal aims of NAFEMS are to provide a structure for developing error-free FEA codes, and to give guidance and general advice to users on the application of these codes. Specific objectives of the Agency include:

a) The establishment of standards and testing procedures.
b) The coordination and sponsorship of evaluations and studies.
c) Publication of education and training requirements.
d) The establishment of a forum of users, developers, etc.
e) The maintenance of a register of FEA systems and users.

6.4 FEA Case Studies

FEA CASE STUDY 1: **Plane stress analysis**
This case study is included by kind permission of Mr Ken Kelso, who developed the software package used in the application. The package is called "Trimesh" and is suitable for use on 16-bit microcomputers.
   A simple, two-dimensional component shape has been chosen to ease the explanation of basic principles.

PROBLEM   A component made from 30 mm thick mild steel plate is subjected to the loading shown in Fig 6.16. It is to be hinged at point A and roller-supported at point B. A safety factor of 3 is required on yield strength ($300 \ N/mm^2$). Maximum deflection is to be 0.05 mm.

PROGRAM   Programs are entered by selecting Edit mode from a screen main menu. The first part of the FEA program creates a mesh from

Fig. 6.16

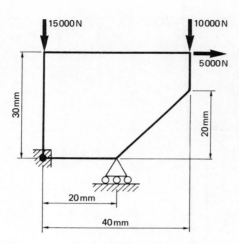

Fig. 6.17 Creation of mesh lines

PROGRAM LINE	DEFINITION
1:M2;0;0;20;0	Mesh line with 2 elements, from X0,Y0 to X20,Y0
2:M3;0;10;30.10	Mesh line with 3 elements, from X0,Y10 to X30,Y10
3:M4;0;20;40;20	Mesh line with 4 elements, from X0,Y20 to X40,Y20
4:M4;0;30;40;30	Mesh line with 4 elements, from X0,Y30 to X40,Y30

triangular elements. The density of the mesh may be controlled by specifying numbers of required elements along a series of lines across the shape. Fig 6.17 shows the first steps in the program. Each mesh-line is specified via cartesian coordinates for start and end points. For example, the first line of the program specifies a mesh-line with 2 elements, starting at point X0,Y0 and ending at X20,Y0.

Having input this data at the keyboard, the main menu is then returned to, and Mesh Generator selected. This automatically creates the finite element mesh and allots a number to each element and node. The created mesh may then be observed by selecting Graphics Module from the main menu, and then Load Mesh and View Mesh from a secondary menu. The screen display of the mesh is shown in Fig 6.18.

Edit mode is then returned to, for the purpose of completing the program. The final program lines are shown in Fig 6.19. Program lines 5 and 6 specify the positions, magnitudes, and directions of the loads. For example, in line 6, L17 specifies loads at node 17, whilst 5000;−10000 specifies rightward (i.e. positive X) magnitude 5000 and downwards (i.e. negative Y) magnitude 10 000.

Program lines 7 and 8 specify positions and nature of restraints. For example, in line 8, R3 specifies a restraint at node 3, whilst 0;1 specifies no restraint in the X direction but a restraint in the Y direction.

Lines 9,10, and 11 specify Poisson's Ratio (0.3 for mild steel), Young's Modulus (207 000 N/mm^2 for mild steel), and thickness (30 mm), respectively.

Fig. 6.18 Display of element numbers and node numbers

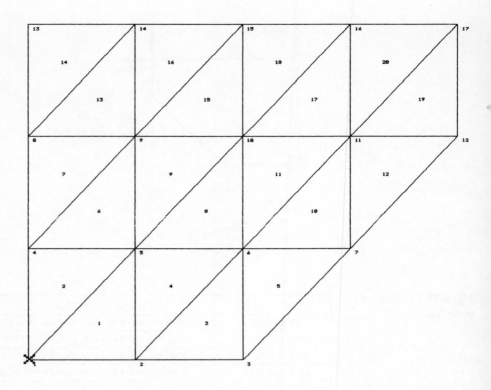

Fig. 6.19 Completion of program

PROGRAM LINE	DEFINITION
5:L13;0;-15000	Load at node 13 (0X,-15000Y)
6:L17;5000;-10000	Load at node 17 (5000X,-10000Y)
7:R1;1;1	Restraint at node 1 (in X and Y directions)
8:R3;0;1	Restraint at node 3 (in Y direction only)
9:P0.3	Poisson's Ratio 0.3
10:E207000	Young's Modulus 207000
11:T30	Thickness 30

ANALYSIS   After completing the program, Analysis Module is selected from the main menu, followed by Analysis Execution from a secondary menu. The software then constructs a stiffness matrix and calculates stresses and deflections.

RESULTS OUTPUT   After the analysis is complete, the software returns to the secondary menu, where Results Output may be selected.

The results output display is shown in Fig 6.20a. In the Nodal Displacements section, it can be seen that the highest deflection value in any direction is 0.023 5925 mm (node 17), which is acceptable for the application.

Fig. 6.20a Results output

```
********----NODAL  DISPLACEMENTS----******

NODE                    X-COMPONENT                              Y-COMPONENT
  1                    4.999909E-27                             2.499905E-27
  2                    9.011428E-04                            -1.423745E-03
  3                    1.545319E-03                            -2.74999E-26
  4                    4.12116E-03                              1.823875E-04
  5                    4.000512E-03                            -1.909977E-03
  6                    3.894297E-03                            -3.42868E-03
  7                    3.644319E-03                            -1.064874E-02
  8                    8.247744E-03                            -1.337814E-03
  9                    8.558688E-03                            -2.444423E-03
 10                    9.004826E-03                            -4.909933E-03
 11                    9.653083E-03                            -1.171918E-02
 12                    9.943171E-03                            -2.180148E-02
 13                    9.525413E-03                            -5.287558E-03
 14                    1.185586E-02                            -3.292295E-03
 15                    1.429822E-02                            -5.801543E-03
 16                    1.725771E-02                            -1.248283E-02
 17                    1.923044E-02                            -.0235925

********----NODAL  REACTIONS----*********

NODE                    X-COMPONENT                              Y-COMPONENT
  1                   -4.99991E+08                             -2.499905E+08
  3                    0                                        2.74999E+09

********----ELEMENT STRESSES----*********

ELEM.       SIGMA                    SIGMA                           TAU
NO.          X-X                      Y-Y                            X-Y
  1        17.1804                 -4.910873                       13.34055
  2        -1.499756                3.325494                       16.15233
  3        -8.74468               -73.59708                        30.03668
  4        -5.734243             -11.78527                         12.58453
  5       -29.08422              -73.69894                        -38.78134
  6        -6.391558             -12.98051                         19.63165
  7        -3.301021             -32.45849                         24.04366
  8       -12.52445              -34.41927                         28.59647
  9         6.501244              -9.112663                        16.66083
 10       -12.99115              -26.05539                         -9.643807
 11         4.637745             -29.27061                        -13.5244
 12        -.7061615             -22.36989                        -32.43159
 13         1.287079             -17.16482                         17.44028
 14        26.05756              -73.94242                         26.05757
 15         4.063904             -17.23716                         22.51435
 16        49.77105               -2.619644                        6.273102
 17         9.534805             -12.94708                         6.332504
 18        61.23575               -8.560181E-02                  -11.04972
 19        -5.62355              -38.76117                         -6.329605
 20        39.66293               -3.908661                       -27.90549


SEMI-BANDWIDTH OF STIFFNESS MATRIX= 14

VOLUME OF PART= 30000
```

In the Element Stresses section, positive SIGMA results refer to tensile stress, and negative SIGMA results refer to compressive stress. The TAU X-Y column refers to shear stresses in the X-Y plane. It can be seen that the two highest stress values are both vertically compressive, and occur in element 5 ($-73.698\,94$ N/mm^2) and element 14 ($-73.942\,42$ N/mm^2). Each stress value displayed is that which occurs at the centroid of the triangular element. Fig 6.20b shows the practical meaning of the three plane stress values displayed for element 14.

Fig. 6.20*b* **Plane stresses in element 14**

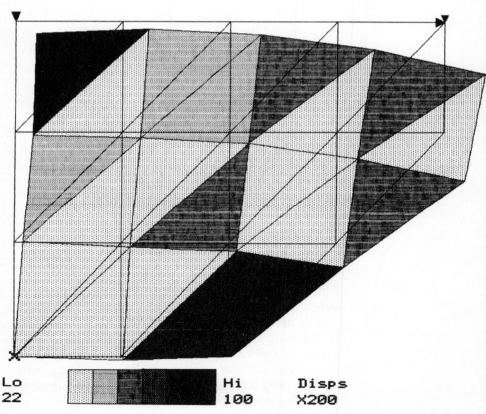

$\sigma_{xx} =$ 26.057 5 6 N/mm² (*tension*)

Centroid

HORIZONTAL STRESS (sigma xx)

Centroid

$\sigma_{yy} =$ 73.942 42 N/mm² (*compressive*)

VERTICAL STRESS (sigma yy)

Centroid

$\tau_{xy} =$ 26.057 57 N/mm²

SHEAR STRESS (tau xy)

The maximum stress of 73.942 42 N/mm² would seem to be permissible for the application, but this is not certain until an equivalent stress of the three is obtained. In most cases, this would require calculating either the maximum principal stress or the Huber–Von Mises–Hencky value for the critical elements. With yield stress being the criteria, it is the latter which would be the most appropriate.

Trimesh enables either principal stresses or Huber–Von Mises–Hencky (σ_v) values to be invoked with simple additions to the program. Alternatively, a quicker procedure is to obtain approximate σ_v values from the graphics display of the analysed mesh.

Fig. 6.21 Deformed mesh display with stress tone variation

Lo 22

Hi 100

Disps X200

GRAPHICS DISPLAY OUTPUT   This may be obtained by first retrieving the previously-created mesh display and then selecting Stress from an accompanying menu display. This invokes a deformed mesh display to a specified displacement magnification, with stresses indicated via colour tone variation at each element (Fig 6.21).

Darker tones indicate higher stresses, and thus, as expected from the results output, the darkest elements are numbers 5 and 14. The key beneath the mesh indicates the range of Huber–Von Mises–Hencky (σ_v) stress values, which ascend to a maximum of 100 N/mm^2 (i.e. this is the approximate σ_v stress value in the critical elements 5 and 14).

As a further explanation, let us check the result by calculating the σ_v value of element 14, using the formula shown on page 108 and the plane stress values from the results output.

$$\sigma_v = \sqrt{[\sigma_x^2 - \sigma_x\sigma_y + \sigma_y^2 + 3\tau_{xy}^2]}$$
$$= \sqrt{[26{\cdot}05756^2 - (26{\cdot}05756)(-73{\cdot}94242) + (-73{\cdot}94242)^2 + 3(26{\cdot}05757)^2]}$$
$$= 100.5 \text{ N/mm}^2 \simeq 100 \text{ N/mm}^2$$

It may thus be concluded that the component has a maximum Huber–Von Mises–Hencky stress of 100 N/mm^2.

Safety factor on yield stress is 320/100 = 3.2, which is adequate for the application.

FEA CASE STUDY 2: **Rotational loading on axisymmetric elements**

PROBLEM   The steel flywheel shown in Fig 6.22a is designed to rotate at 500 rev/min. It is required to determine the critical values and locations of maximum stress due to rotational loading.

Fig. 6.22a Flywheel design

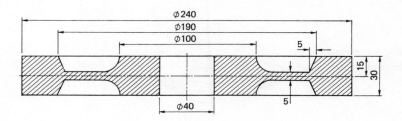

PROGRAM AND ANALYSIS   As in Case Study 1, this analysis was undertaken on the Trimesh package. Fig 6.22b shows the complete program.

Program lines 1 to 14 describe the mesh in the same manner as the previous case study. This time, vertical mesh-lines are used.

Fig 6.22c shows the screen display of the created mesh with element numbers added. Also shown is the axis of rotation (always displayed vertically through the XØ datum), and the centrifugal loads which are automatically applied to each node for a rotational program.

In this program, each element is recognised by the software as a triangular solid of revolution about the Y axis. For example, element 7 is depicted in

Fig. 6.22b Flywheel program

1:M4;20;Ø;20;15	18:R16;Ø;1
2:M4;30;Ø;30;15	19:R21;Ø;1
3:M4;50;Ø;50;15	20:R25;Ø;1
4:M4;50;Ø;50;15	21:R29;Ø;1
5:M3;55;Ø;55;7.5	22:R32;Ø;1
6:M3;60;Ø;60;4	23:R35;Ø;1
7:M2;65;Ø;65;2.75	24:R38;Ø;1
8:M2;70;Ø;70;2.5	25:R42;Ø;1
9:M2;80;Ø;80;2.5	26:R47;Ø;1
10:M3;90;Ø;90;2.5	27:R52;Ø;1
11:M4;95;Ø;95;15	28:R57;Ø;1
12:M4;100;Ø;100;15	29:AXISYMMETRIC
13:M4;110;Ø;110;15	30:PØ.3
14:M4;120;Ø;120;15	31:E207000
15:R1;Ø;1	32:DENSITY=.0000775
16:R6;Ø;1	33:RPM=500
17:R11;Ø;1	

Fig. 6.22c Flywheel mesh display

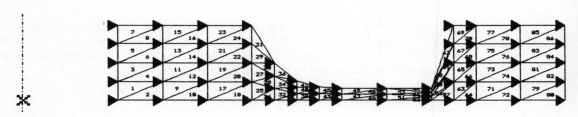

Fig. 6.23 Mathematical model of element 7

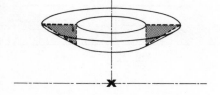

Fig 6.23. Thus it is necessary to specify only the cross-sectional mesh to one side of the axis of rotation. It can also be seen in Fig 6.22c that, area and loading being symmetrical about a radial axis, only half the cross-section need be modelled.

In this example, the nodes along the horizontal radial axis are restrained in the vertical direction only. This gives the nodes a roller-type support, which allows them to be deflected under radial load, whilst simulating a symmetrical mesh and loading condition beneath the support line. Fig 6.24 shows a screen display option which indicates the node numbers and also the

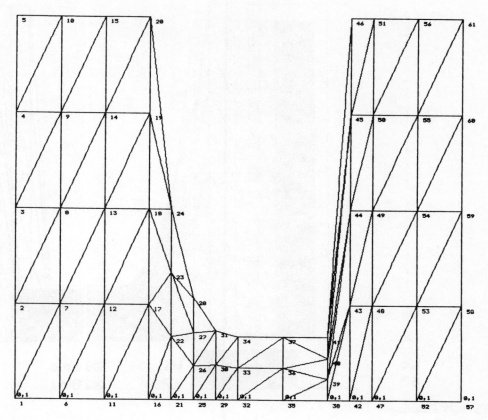

Fig. 6.24 Screen display of nodes roller-type supports (vertical distances magnified 5 times)

roller-type support notations (i.e. $\dot{1};\emptyset$) at the relevant nodes. (For clarity, vertical distance display has been magnified by a factor of five via a variable aspect ratio facility.)

Program lines 15 to 28 specify the node numbers to which the roller-type restraints are applied.

In program line 29, AXISYMMETRIC specifies the type of element. (If no element type is specified, the software defaults to plane stress type.)

Program lines 3Ø and 31 specify Young's Modulus and Poisson's Ratio values, as in the previous case study.

Program lines 32 and 33 effectively specify that rotational loading is required, by quoting the additional parameters of material density and spindle REV/MIN.

Fig 6.25 shows the deformed mesh display, with node displacements magnified by a factor of 200. This display indicates a maximum Huber–Von Mises–Hencky stress of 178 N/mm² at elements 42 and 45.

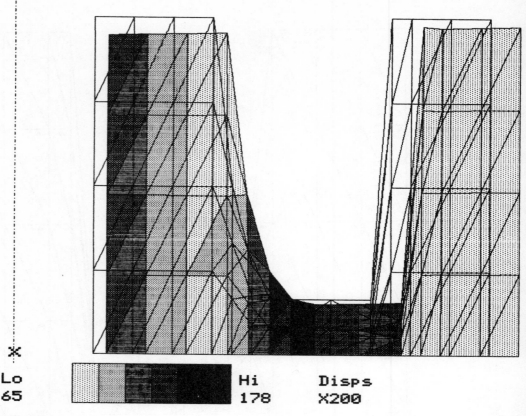

Lo
65

Hi
178

Disps
X200

Fig. 6.25 Deformed
mesh display showing
stress

FEA CASE STUDY 3: **Plane stress analysis of pump rotor via CAD link**
This case study continues an example shown in Chapter 4.

Fig 4.26*a* showed the CAD assembly drawing of a pump rotor and mating
cam profile designed and drawn at Hobourn-Eaton of Rochester. The rotor
is similar in geometry to a spur gear with twelve teeth. It is loosely fitted
onto the drive shaft and driven via a single keyway. Twelve rollers are
positioned between the teeth, acting as vanes (the rollers are also shown in
Fig 4.26*a*).

Stress analysis of the rotor is essential to avoid cracking of the teeth at
higher running pressures. The point of maximum stress is usually situated
near the root of one of the teeth in this type of rotor, but its exact position
and value is difficult to obtain by conventional means, due to the complex
loadings and component shapes.

FEA was thus applied to this rotor using MAEFIN, a 2D FEA package
which links directly with MAEDOS, the 2D draughting package on which
the pump drawings were produced. Ignoring the keyway, all rotor teeth are
identical. However, due to the asymmetric loading, it is necessary to model
at least one quadrant of the complete rotor.

Using the MAEFIN package, the operator may gain direct access to the MAEDOS CAD library files. The required geometry was thus obtained from a layer of the rotor CAD drawing. Fig 6.26a shows the full rotor geometry, from which one quadrant was extracted and the mesh generated.

Distributed oil pressure loading and point loading from the roller was then applied together with the appropriate constraints and material parameters.

Fig. 6.26a Geometry of rotor from CAD library

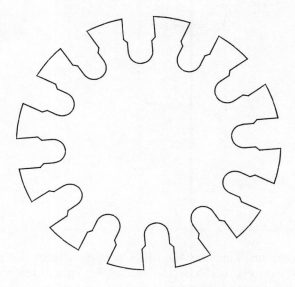

Fig. 6.26b
Displacements display

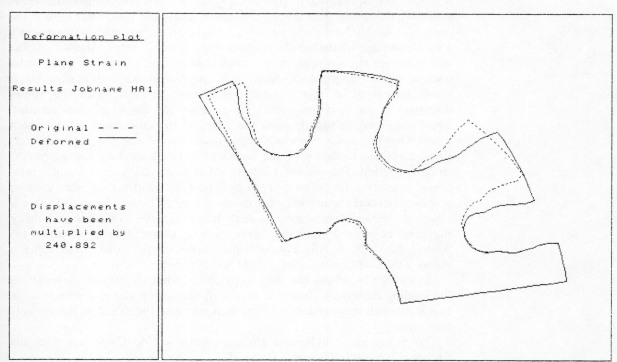

Deformation plot

Plane Strain

Results Jobname HA1

Original – – –
Deformed ——

Displacements have been multiplied by 240.892

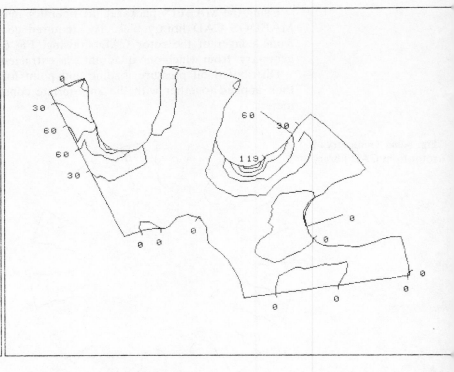

```
Contour plot

Plane Strain

Results jobname HA1

  1st Principal

Function values
  Max    179.280
  Min    -30.312

    Contours
  Max    149.338
  Min      -.371
  Step    29.942
  Number      6
Multiply displayed
values by   1.0000
```

Fig. 6.26c Stress contour display

After invoking the MAEFIN post-processor, the results output may be analysed. Fig 6.26*b* shows the plane strain deformation display with a magnification of approximately 240 on nodal displacements. Fig 6.26*c* shows a display indicating principal stress values across the quadrant. Unlike the previous case studies, stress values are indicated using *stress contours* which may be likened to the height contour lines seen on maps. Stress contours join points of equal stress, so that each contour line represents a particular level of stress across a component. The contours in this display show stress levels increasing at approximately 30 N/mm^2 intervals with the values displayed at the start (or sometimes the start and finish) of each contour. The lines protrude slightly from the edges of the component to provide a marker for the stress value. Critically-loaded areas may be approximately located via the tendency of the contours to be closer together where the stress is higher. The highest contour value displayed is 119 N/mm^2 (positioned near the leftmost root of the rightmost full tooth). One more contour is shown beyond the marker protrusion of the 119 N/mm^2 level (no value is attached to avoid overlapping figures). It may thus be concluded that this is the area of highest principal stress, with a value of approximately 149 N/mm^2 (i.e. 119˙+ 30). The accurate maximum principal stress value is shown at the side of the display (149.338 N/mm^2).

MAEFIN also allows the user to perform "what if" exercises by varying the loading conditions. In this case, the drive loading and pressure distribution were both independently varied to investigate the effect on the areas of high stress.

The pump case study and Hobourn-Eaton's CADCAM activities are further discussed in Chapters 9 and 11.

FEA CASE STUDY 4: **Solid mesh analysis — piston design**

This case study is included by kind permission of FEGs Ltd, and describes the design and analysis of an aluminium alloy piston.

FEGs market a pre-processor (called FEMGEN) and a post-processor (called FEMVIEW), which interface with each other to complete an advanced 3D FEA system. The FEGs system is designed to operate on 32-bit computers.

PRE-PROCESSING

The operation of the FEMGEN pre-processor consists of three main activities:

a) Construction of model.
b) Generation and testing of model.
c) Application of constraints, loads, and properties.

The *geometric model* may be constructed on FEMGEN's advanced solid-modelling facility or may be received via an interface with an appropriate CAD system. It is the former option which was used in this piston design. The model is a hierarchy in which solid bodies are defined in terms of surfaces; surfaces in terms of sides; sides in terms of lines; and lines in terms of points and scalars. All geometric parts are given names, such as P1, S3, etc., so that new objects may be defined by reference to previous ones. For example, a line joining points P5 and P7, could be defined as LINE L4 P5 P7; a solid body surrounded by six surfaces could be defined as BODY B1 S1 S2 S3 S4 S5 S6; and so on (Fig 6.27). All geometric names are chosen by the user. The model is built up on the VDU screen via typical CAD facilities (e.g. digitising tablet, joystick, lightpen) and techniques (e.g. mirroring, replicating, projecting, linear sweeping, and rotational sweeping).

Fig. 6.27a Line definition

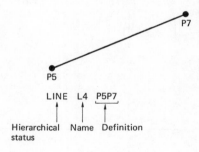

Fig. 6.27b Solid body definition

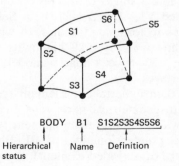

Fig. 6.28 Initial stages of piston design

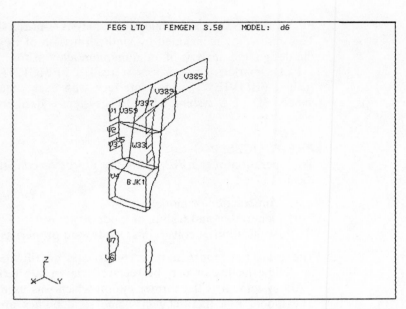

Fig. 6.29 Profile-change sections

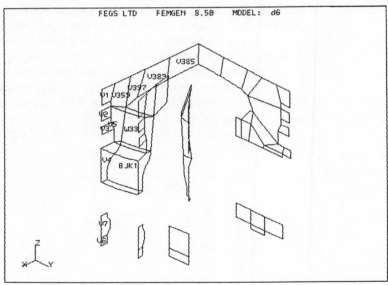

Fig 6.28 shows the initial stages of the piston design. A basic profile of vertical surfaces (named V1,V2,etc.) is created. Selected surfaces are then given rotational sweeps to form solid bodies, of which W33 and BJK1 are shown. The image shown in Fig 6.29 highlights sections that mark the changes in profile. Fig 6.30 shows a quarter model, with completed profiles spanning the swept surfaces.

Mesh generation is then undertaken. Element types are selected from a library and attached to geometrical parts. The FEMGEN element library has already been shown in Fig 6.1. Each element type may be specified by two characters indicating dimensionality (i.e. BE–Beam; QU–Quadrilateral; PE–five-sided element; HE–six-sided element).

Fig. 6.30 Quarter model

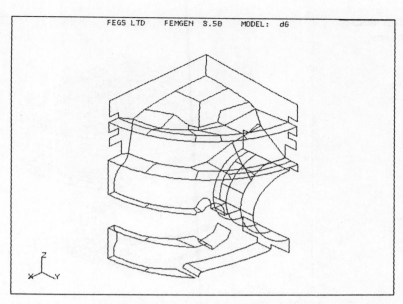

Fig. 6.31 Test mesh on inside surfaces

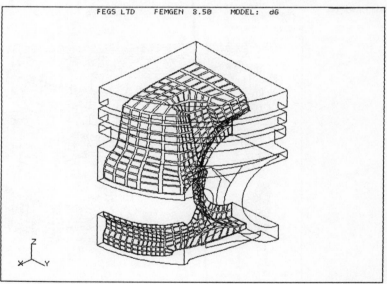

Mesh control may be exercised by using *division* and *bias* parameter adjustment facilities. FEMGEN's mesh generation algorithms scan the geometric model and, for each part that has an element type attached to it, FEMGEN generates appropriate numbers of nodes according to division parameters, spacing them according to bias parameters, and then generates elements of the type attached to that geometrical part. Element types may be attached to any comparable geometrical configuration (i.e. BEs on lines, TRs and QUs on surfaces, and PEs and HEs on solid bodies). Fig 6.31 shows a test mesh on the inside surfaces, undertaken to check the element integrity. Further test meshes on some internal sections are shown in Fig 6.32. These confirm the shape of the solid elements and the distribution

Fig. 6.32 Test mesh on internal sections

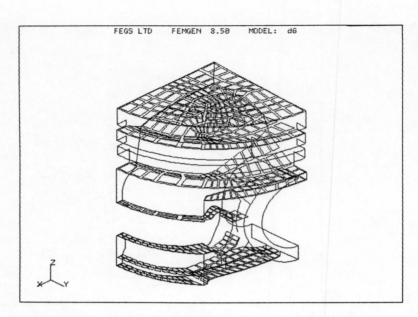

Fig. 6.33 Half model

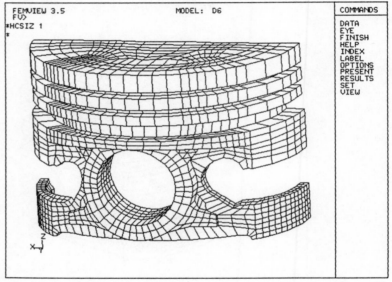

through the body thickness. Once the mesh is satisfactory, the quarter model is mirrored to produce the half-model required for the analysis (Fig 6.33).

Constraints may next be applied to specified nodes, and material properties specified via a materials code database. Fig 6.34 shows both of these options displayed against the relevant parts of the skirt portion of the piston. The *applied loading* is displayed at the appropriate nodes of the skirt in Fig 6.35. Load components may vary in accordance with user-defined data patterns. These loading conditions can then be stored into a library of *load cases*, which may be factored and combined to simulate complex loading patterns in subsequent FEA applications.

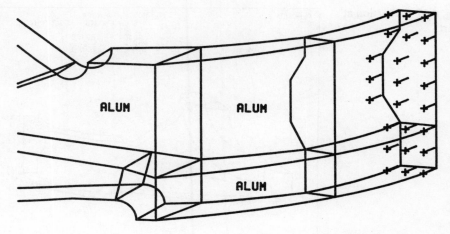

Fig. 6.34 Constraints and materials properties at skirt

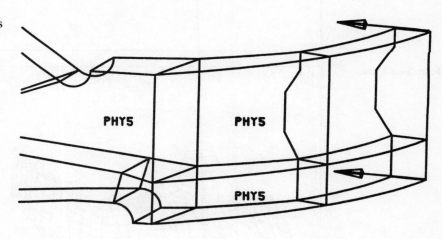

Fig. 6.35 Node loadings at skirt

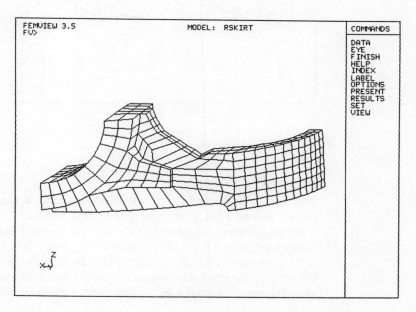

Fig. 6.36 Model subset of skirt

Fig. 6.37 Deflection at skirt

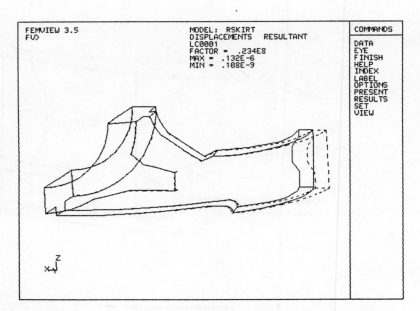

```
FEMVIEW 3.5              MODEL: RSKIRT              COMMANDS
FU>                     DISPLACEMENTS  RESULTANT
                        LC0001                      DATA
                        FACTOR =  .234E8            EYE
                        MAX =  .132E-6              FINISH
                        MIN =  .108E-9              HELP
                                                    INDEX
                                                    LABEL
                                                    OPTIONS
                                                    PRESENT
                                                    RESULTS
                                                    SET
                                                    VIEW
```

Fig. 6.38 Von Mises stresses

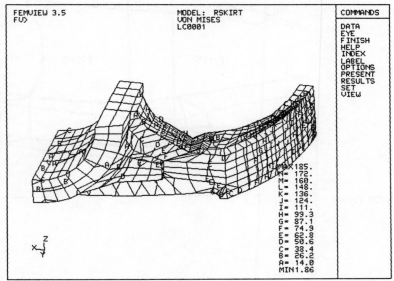

```
FEMVIEW 3.5              MODEL: RSKIRT              COMMANDS
FU>                     VON MISES
                        LC0001                      DATA
                                                    EYE
                                                    FINISH
                                                    HELP
                                                    INDEX
                                                    LABEL
                                                    OPTIONS
                                                    PRESENT
                                                    RESULTS
                                                    SET
                                                    VIEW

                                            MAX185.
                                          N=  172.
                                          M=  160.
                                          L=  148.
                                          K=  136.
                                          J=  124.
                                          I=  111.
                                          H=  99.3
                                          G=  87.1
                                          F=  74.9
                                          E=  62.8
                                          D=  50.6
                                          C=  38.4
                                          B=  26.2
                                          A=  14.0
                                          MIN1.86
```

POST-PROCESSING

The FEMVIEW post-processor allows results of the mesh analysis to be clearly assessed via a series of graphical displays.

Through interactive commands, the user selects a model, a load case, a result type, and a form of graphical component. It is also possible to display only a required subset of the model by specifying a particular range of element faces. Fig 6.37 shows a magnified deflection simulation of the piston skirt (element displayed in dashed lines, with displaced shape superimposed

Fig. 6.39 Von Mises
stress contours

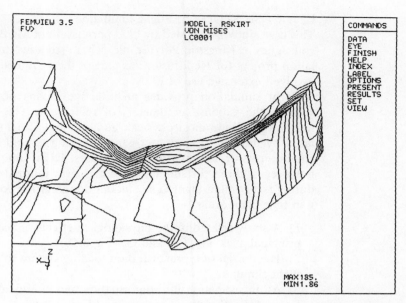

Fig. 6.40

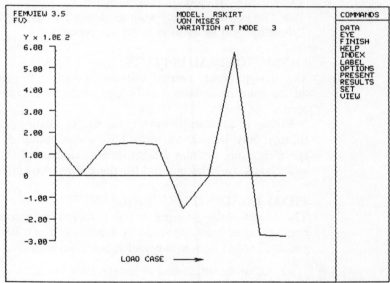

in solid). Fig 6.38 shows Huber–Von Mises–Hencky stress contours on the skirt (values indicated by colour variation). Fig 6.39 shows an enlarged view of the skirt, again with stress contours, but with notation and internal mesh removed. Fig 6.40 shows another results display option. This allows different load cases to be combined and the variations to be graphically displayed for a specified node. Here, the variation of Huber–Von Mises–Hencky failure criteria is shown across ten load cases for Node 3. (Stress values represent an average for the elements which surround the stated node.)

FEA CASE STUDY 5: **Flight simulation**

This case study is included by kind permission of Mr Brian Crawford and his colleagues at Kingston Polytechnic, where students undertook a flight simulation project for Rediffusion, as part of their graduate studies. The project involved extensive use of FEA.

Flight simulation provides an effective means of training young pilots without the expense or dangers of real flight. The present state of high technology allows most physical, audible, and visual sensations to be simulated by the use of computer-generated images and sound effects, and by computer-controlled hydrostatic cylinders. Flight simulation is not complete, however, without the simulation of high gravitational (g) forces experienced during fast combat flight. The student design group concentrated its study of g in four main areas:

1) A study related to the physiological effects of accelerations in the three principal axes, G_x, G_y, and G_z (Fig 6.41)
2) The design of a practical pilot loading system to be incorporated into a flight simulator.
3) An investigation into deformation and energy absorption on a Martin Baker MK.10 ejection seat, using FEA.
4) The construction of a finite element model of a pilot's spine, and the development of an associated pre-processor.

PHYSIOLOGICAL EFFECTS

The design group carried out an extensive literature search and sought advice from prominent members of staff at a number of research establishments.

Effects of acceleration in the G_y and G_x planes are widely acknowledged, though only in general terms. Since the group found no documentation specifying any definite effects, it was concluded that acceleration in these two planes could be ignored for the purposes of flight simulation.

PILOT LOADING (g-CUEING) SYSTEM

The design of the g-cueing system involved the consideration of a number of conceptual designs approved by Rediffusion. To develop the designs into a practical solution, a number of requirements had to be fulfilled:

a) Accurate simulation of acceleration cues.
b) No interference with operation of controls.
c) Lightweight construction.
d) Quick time response.
e) Minimum maintenance requirement.
f) Low cost.

The final design of the g-cueing system is shown in Fig 6.42. It simulates acceleration principally in the $-G_z$ plane and partly in the $+G_z$ plane. The system loads the pilot by a head and torso loader, the necessary force being supplied by hydraulic cylinders via a series of chords and pulleys. The load produced by the cylinders is determined by a microcomputer, which communicates with the flight simulator host computer. The load transmitted to

Fig. 6.41 Physiological effects

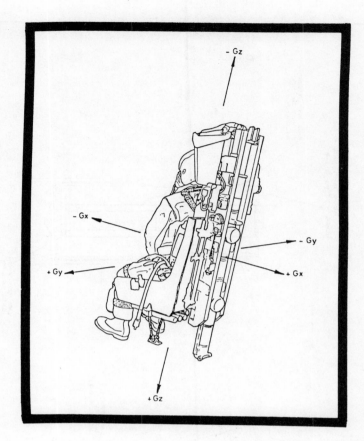

the pilot is then measured by a load-cell which acts as a comparator between the actual load and the desired load.

The *g*-cueing system also incorporates a respirator. By using a small valve, it is possible to simulate the pilot's difficulty in breathing during high-*g* manoeuvres.

FINITE ELEMENT MODEL OF EJECTION SEAT
Fig 6.44 shows the finite element model of a Martin Baker MK.10 ejection seat. This was created for the purpose of investigating the amount of energy the seat absorbed from the pilot. FEA work at Kingston Polytechnic is undertaken on FINEL and LUSAS software systems, running on an integrated college network with mainframe host computer.

FINITE ELEMENT SPINAL MODEL
It was decided to form a spinal model to be run on the FINEL FEA package. The spine consists of twenty-four individual bones called vertebrae, which are separated by fibro-cartilaginous discs. The base of the spine is connected to the pelvis and the top of the head. In addition to this basic structure are the ligaments, articulated synovial facet elements, and viscera (organs and fluids) which also participate in spinal behaviour. The whole mechanism is normally subjected to a variety of shear, axial, and torsional forces.

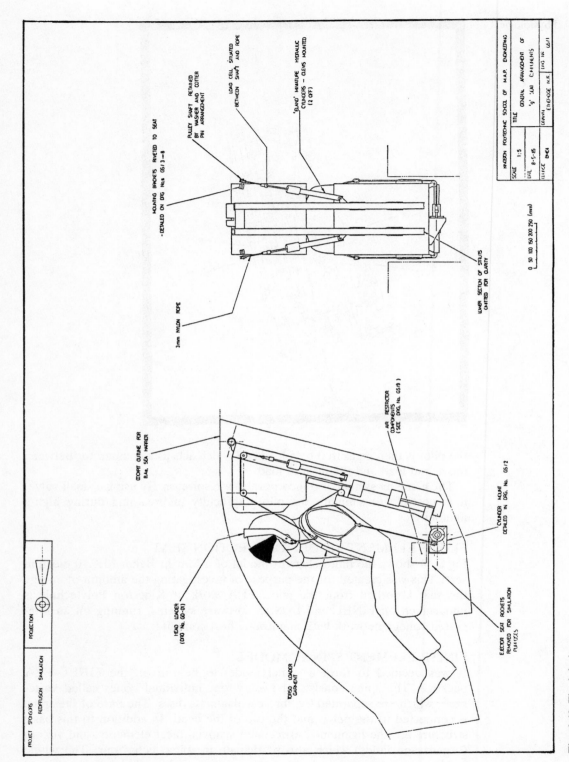

Fig. 6.42 Final design of g-cueing system

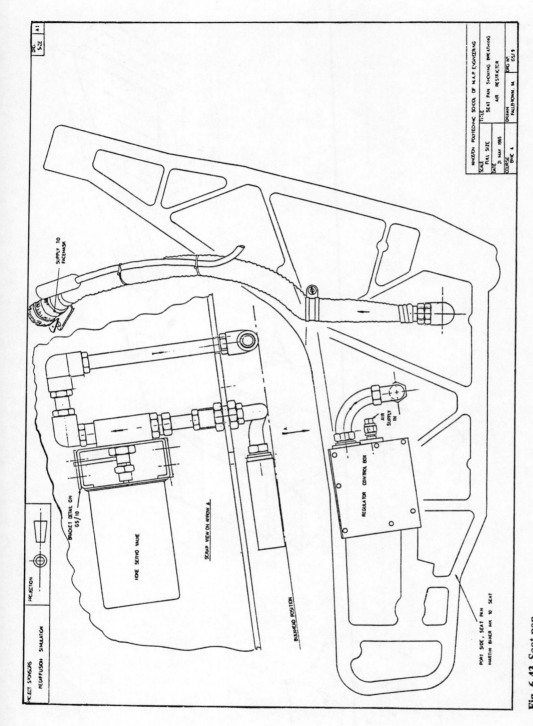

Fig. 6.43 Seat pan showing breathing air restrictor

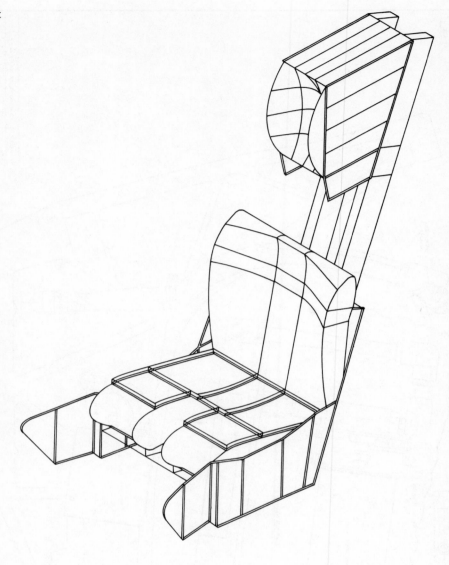

Fig. 6.44 Finite element model of Martin Baker MK 10 ejection seat incorporating seat pan and swabbing

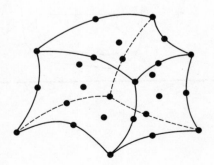

Fig. 6.45 HX27: the six-faced 27-noded element chosen from the FINEL library

134

STRUCTURE OF SPINAL MODEL

The intervertebral discs being the dominant members of the spine's behaviour, the initial approach was to model the vertebrae and discs. Both are modelled from an isoparametric, solid brick element labelled HX27 (six faces, twenty-seven nodes). This was chosen from the FINEL library because of its suitability for dynamic analysis (Fig 6.45).

Using relevant anthropometric data, a spinal model was created (Fig 6.46). The vertebrae and discs are geometrically idealised to reduce the element and hence the computer running time during analysis. Each vertebrae is represented by two regions: one round and the other triangular. The discs are constructed to match the corresponding faces of the vertebrae regions.

FINITE ELEMENT SPINAL PRE-PROCESSOR

The finite element pre-processor has the following features:

1) It allows each vertebra to be modelled using 14 data values, as opposed to 220, if the model had been manually generated.

2) The vertebrae are modelled locally, i.e. with reference to a point on any vertebra, thus allowing movement to any point in space.

3) It allows the spine model to be given any curvature.

4) Any portion of the spine may be formed as an independent model to investigate particular areas of the spinal column (Fig 6.47).

5) The material properties of the discs and vertebrae can be changed and a new model formed.

6) The graphical output from the FINEL package can be controlled quickly and easily.

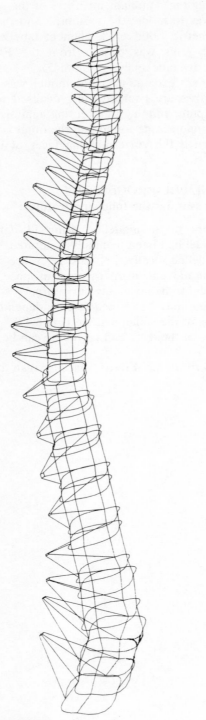 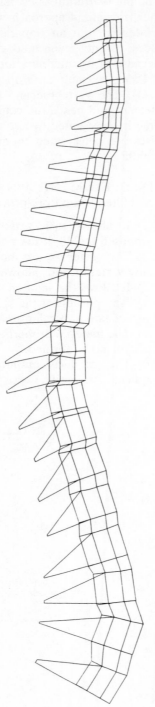 

Fig. 6.46 Finite element
model of spine

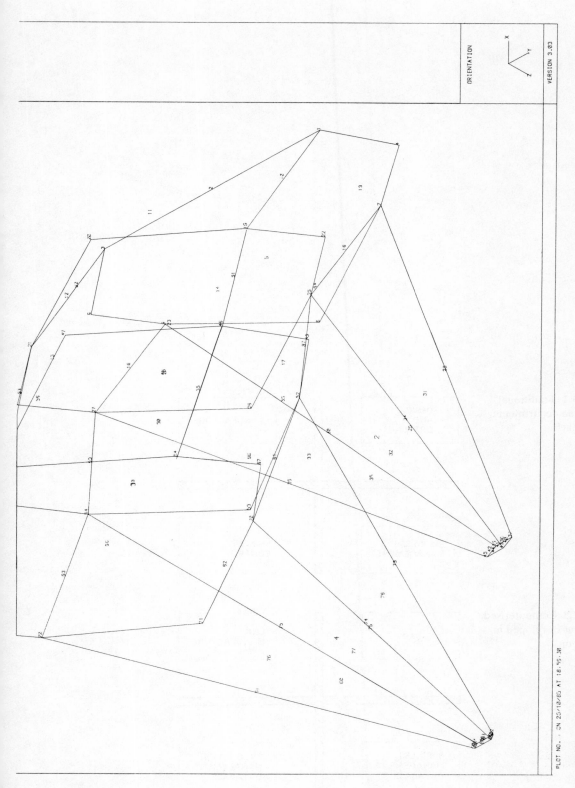

PLOT NO. : ON 29/10/85 AT 18:56:38

ORIENTATION

VERSION 3.03

Fig. 6.47 Portion of spine

137

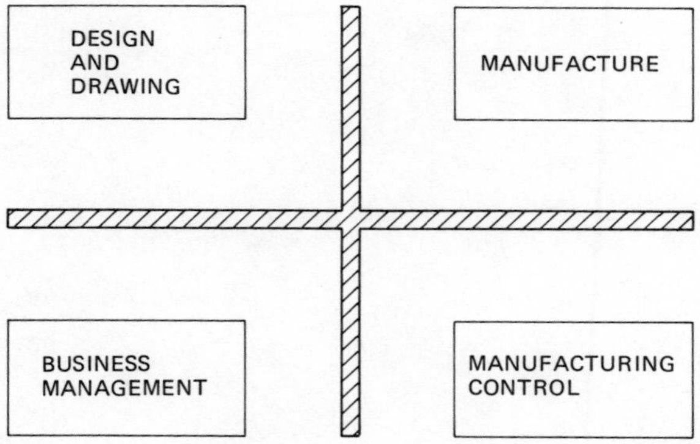

Fig. 7.1 Traditional
isolated departmental
approach

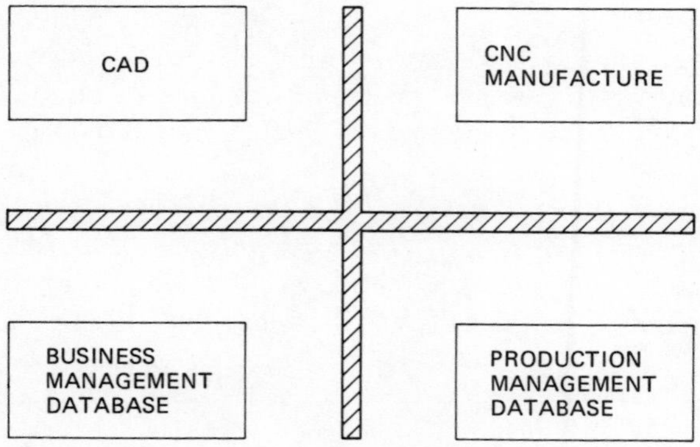

| DESIGN AND DRAWING | MANUFACTURE |

| BUSINESS MANAGEMENT | MANUFACTURING CONTROL |

Fig. 7.2 Computerised
systems developed in
isolation

| CAD | CNC MANUFACTURE |

| BUSINESS MANAGEMENT DATABASE | PRODUCTION MANAGEMENT DATABASE |

Organisation and Planning 7

The full benefits of the CADCAM process will not materialize unless it is part of a structured system in which information is readily available, or automatically transferred, between all departments of the company.

7.1 Traditional Barriers

Good communications is the key to efficient organisation. Traditional design and manufacturing procedures lent themselves to the development of company departments as isolated cells with minimal contact between each other. Information transfer was time-consuming, and good communication became a hindrance to short-term departmental priorities. A common consequence was the temptation to use information which was immediately to hand, irrespective of its current reliability. The system also required repetition of component drawings and recorded data, which led to time-wasting and the progressively increasing likelihood of errors being made.

Unfortunately, these barriers may continue to survive within companies which have supposedly been converted to new technologies. An extreme case is illustrated in Figs 7.1 and 7.2. Fig 7.1 shows possible isolated departmental cells under the broad headings of Drawing and Design, Manufacture, Manufacturing Control, and Business/Finacial Management. Fig 7.2 shows these cells converted into departments with their own computerised facilities, but with no direct communications link between the separate systems. This approach may produce high efficiency in individual departments, but the apparent gains will not be fully reflected in the overall development of the product. Fig 7.2 could also illustrate a classic case of old thought applied to new technology, in which each department chooses a computer-aided system for its own needs with little thought for the overall company benefits. This often results in departmental systems being purchased from different suppliers. These may be totally incompatible and would thus become useless if integration is desired at a later date.

7.2 The Integrated Organisation

Ideal communications can only be achieved if departmental computer-aided systems are linked together in an integrated structure.

An obvious link is between design and manufacture, and a system which can link directly from VDU drawing displays to CNC manufacture could be described as CADCAM. However, further barriers may be created by adopting distinctions such as Graphics Systems and Information Systems (Fig 7.3) or Engineering Systems and Business Systems (Fig. 7.4).

Linking between CADCAM and business/financial systems is still in its infancy and examples, at the time of publication, are rare. The complex technology involved makes integration difficult and costly, particularly in non-turnkey systems. When planning for future integration, it is thus essential to consider the compatibility of hardware and software. If turnkey systems are considered, it is a far-sighted policy to purchase from a supplier of modular units which may be added to and up-dated whilst retaining the links of an integrated system.

Fig. 7.3 Graphics and information divide

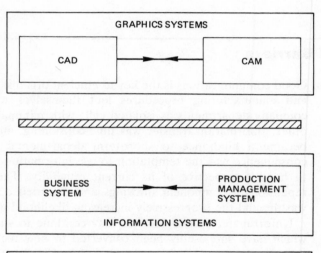

Fig. 7.4 Business and engineering divide

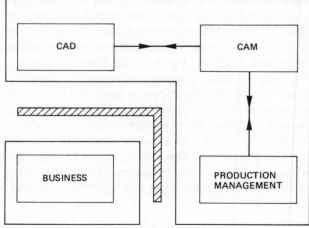

Fig. 7.5 Principle of CIM [*Counting House Ltd.*]

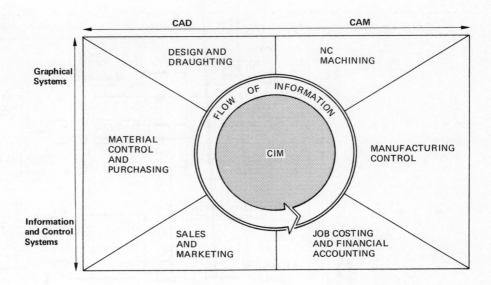

Computer-integrated Manufacture (CIM)

Fig 7.5 illustrates the principle of the ideal *computer-integrated manufacturing* (CIM) system (*courtesy Counting House*). This contains CADCAM and business systems which both operate on the same compatible range of processors, and thus allows direct links between CADCAM, business information, and control.

The philosophy of this CIM system is that of greater efficiency via a flow of consistent product and business information. Such an integrated system can allow, for example:

a) Design engineers to access up-to-date information on standard components, raw materials costs, and tooling.
b) Production managers to control complex projects on a real-time basis.
c) Contracts managers to obtain rapid and accurate status reports.
d) Accountants to have immediate cost information on individual jobs.
e) The company to react more quickly to particular customer requirements.

Fig 7.6 shows the Counting House linked system in more detail. Fig 7.7 shows two possible hardware arrangements.

Database Management System (DBMS)

A CADCAM database is a collection of product-related data which is designed to be used through a variety of associated application programs.

A *database management system* (DBMS) is a sophisticated program, or linked suite of programs, which provides storing, sorting, searching, interrogating, structuring, and up-dating facilities for product information.

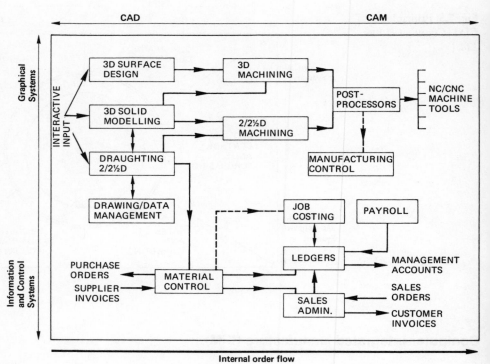

Fig. 7.6 CIM: the Counting House Linked System

Efficient management of data is a vital ingredient of the CADCAM process. A good DBMS will ensure that:

a) All data concerning the product is shared and readily available to everyone involved.
b) All data is reliable and easily updated.

Linking of Data The engineering drawing and its associated data effectively govern all subsequent activities involved with the development of the finished product. In a traditional organisation, prints of the completed drawing will be made and sent to many different departments, including

a) Sales, for quotations.
b) Production drawing office, to design jigs, fixtures, and special tooling.
c) Manufacturing control, to draw up bills of material, quote stock material sizes, decide on manufacturing procedures, and compile production planning sheets.
d) Purchasing, to order new material stock or specially bought-out items, such as bearings or oil seals.
e) Manufacturing, who would also require copies of production planning sheets and fixture drawings.

The system requires several re-draws of the original design and repetition of recorded data. Retrieval of information is only possible by each department keeping their own libraries of drawings, drawing prints, and individual versions of largely identical data.

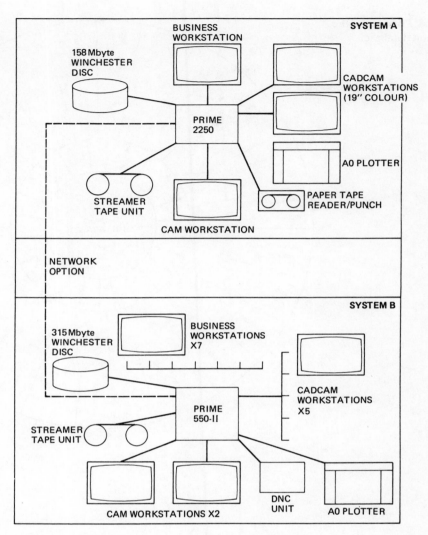

Fig. 7.7 Two possible hardware configurations of Counting House Linked Systems

Under the ideal DBMS, the drawing and its associated data need be created only once, and kept as a computer model in a single library which is easily accessible to all departments. Fig 7.8 shows the concept of a centralised CADCAM DBMS, operating via a *common database*, which contains all company data and is managed by a single program.

Another approach is a *networked system*, in which individual databases are interfaced to provide a data exchange facility such as the "information flow" of the Counting House system.

In theory, the information exchange capabilities of the DBMS are limitless. For example, many systems have direct linkage between bills of material (BOMs) and the CAD drawing library, so that, once the designs have been drawn and given coded filenames, components are automatically listed on an appropriate BOM. The information can be simultaneously conveyed for automatic up-dating of stock control, materials scheduling and

Fig. 7.8 Principle of the common database

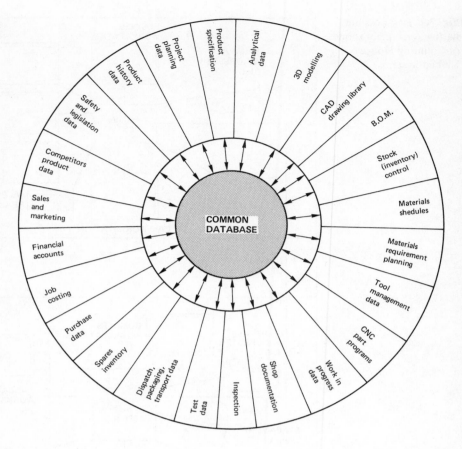

planning, tool requirements, job costing and purchasing. Automatic monitoring of stock can be undertaken via direct access to drawing data so that if, say, a design required a certain size and material of cylindrical bar, then the stock level would be accordingly adjusted with automatic re-purchasing once it had fallen below a critical quantity. If a designer chose a size of stock which was not readily available (i.e. not available at all, very expensive, or on long delivery), this could be automatically communicated via the VDU and perhaps the nearest two available alternatives supplied.

Although some of the instances outlined must be considered to be futuristic they do serve to illustrate the principle and objectives of the ideal DBMS. Integrated systems require advanced programing and high storage capacity. Particular difficulties arise in introducing a common DBMS into an organisation using older CADCAM systems with individual, and unrelated, computer stores and databases. However, most modern CADCAM systems are being developed to make provision for the integrated DBMS.

Fig. 7.9 Database
components

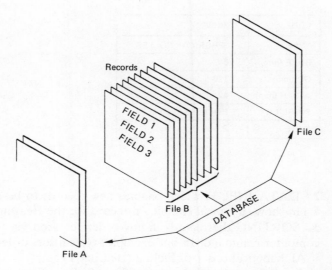

Fig. 7.10 Record
configuration (mask)

FIELD NO	FIELD TYPE	FIELD TITLE	FIELD CONTENTS
1	C	CODE	
2	C	TYPE	
3	N	BORE (mm)	
4	N	OD (mm)	
5	N	WIDTH (mm)	
6	C	SUPPLIER	
7	D	DATE	

Database Principles and Operations

A database may be conveniently thought of as a vast computerised filing
cabinet containing the following sub-sections:

a) FILES of information, each relating to a different category of data.
b) RECORDS inside each file. Every record of the file will be of identical
configuration.
c) FIELDS of specific data on each record.

Typical database operations include:

1 MASK CREATION, which allows the user to design the configuration
of the record (referred to as the mask) according to company requirements.
The number of fields per record, the maximum number of characters per
field, and the type of field, will be specified during the mask creation
process. To illustrate the principles of databases, Fig 7.10 shows the record
mask of a very simple database file entitled Bearings, which could be used to
record relevant data of all the bought-out ball and roller bearings appearing
on a company's mechanical assembly drawings. Each field describes a
different bearing parameter and could be *character type* (containing alpha-
numeric data with no mathematical significance); *numeric type* (containing
numeric data of mathematical significance); and *date type*.

Fig. 7.11a Completed record

CODE	SR6821Z
TYPE	SPHERICAL ROLLER
BORE (mm)	80
OD (mm)	120
WIDTH (mm)	42
SUPPLIER	ROLLERBALL PLC
DATE	2.8.86

2   DATA INPUT, which enables new records to be added to the file. Fig 7.11a shows a typical completed record for the Bearings file.

3   SORTING the records in any order required via the action of a simple computer command. In our example, typical sort orders could include:

Alphabetical order of Field 2 (Bearing Type);

Ascending numerical order of Field 3 (Bore Size);

Calendar order of Field 7 (Drawing Completion Date).

4   INTERROGATING, or "*browsing-through*", the records in the order sorted.

5   EDITING, or updating, the field contents of a particular record. Also, *global editing* may be undertaken. In our example, a global command to "Change all records with a value of 52 in Field 5, to 50 in Field 5" would effectively modify all bearings with a width of 52 mm to a 50 mm width.

6   SEARCHING, which is one of the most important facilities of the database. Individual records, or groups of records, may be quickly retrieved by quoting field numbers and field contents. Search types (again, with reference to the Bearings database) could be classified as:

a) SPECIFIC SEARCH, e.g. a command such as F1 = 63Ø4, might be used to find the records containing the bearing code number 6304 in Field 1.

b) WILDCARD SEARCH. This type of search has already been discussed during descriptions of operating system software in Chapter 3. It is used to find classified groups of records by quoting particular parts of field contents, e.g. a command such as F2 = *ROLLER* might be used to find all records containing the word "roller" in Field 2 (i.e. all the records containing various types of roller bearing).

c) MATHEMATICAL SEARCH, using algebraic operators, such as EQUAL TO, NOT EQUAL TO, GREATER THAN, or LESS THAN. For example, a command such as F4<15Ø might be used to find all records containing numbers less than 150 in Field 7 (i.e. all the records of bearings with outside diameters less than 150 mm).

d) COMBINED FIELD SEARCH. This is a more complex type of search in which fields may be linked together via logical operators such as AND and OR. For example, a command such as

(F1 = *BALL*) AND (F3<6Ø) AND (F6 = BRB LTD) AND (F7>Ø1 − Ø1 − 8Ø)

might be used to find all records with the word Ball in Field 2 AND numbers less than 60 in Field 3 AND BRB LTD in Field 6 AND dates after 01–01–80 in Field 7 (i.e. all the records of ball bearings with bore sizes less than 60 mm supplied by BRB LTD after the start of 1980).

As a further example, a command such as

(F4>3ØØ) OR (F5>8Ø)

might be used to find all records which either have numbers greater than 300 in Field 4 OR have numbers greater than 80 in Field 5 (i.e. all the records of bearings which either have outside diameters greater than 300 mm or have widths greater than 80 mm).

Once the required records have been found they may be browsed-through using the Interrogate facility, and in whatever order is required using the Sort facility.

7.3 Project Management and Planning

The creation of the product is unlikely to be successful unless every stage in its development is carefully planned and efficiently managed from the initial design concept to the delivery of the finished article.

A well-organised Computer-Integrated Manufacture (CIM) system can help to achieve the desired objectives. Fig 7.11b (taken from an article by M. J. Plowman of IBM in the *Numerical Engineering* magazine) shows how project management fits into the complete product development plan.

Typical examples of project stages are as follows:

a) Formulation of design specification from market requirement data.
b) Design concept, possibly with the aid of solid or surface modelling.

Fig. 7.11b Product development process block diagram showing interaction of processes and data [*M.J. Plowman (IBM) and Numerical Engineering*]

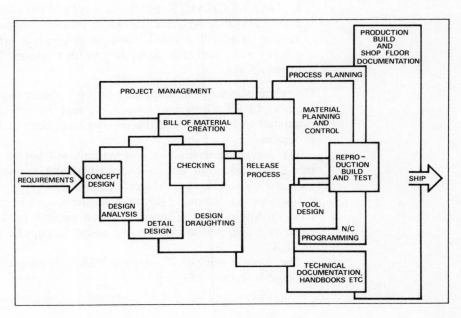

c) Analysis using, for example, finite element analysis (FEA) software, ergonomic packages, and cost-optimisation packages.
d) Analysis of mechanisms and tool-paths using a mixture of 3D kinetics and solid modelling.
e) Detailed design of components and assemblies with the aid of 2D or 3D draughting software and standard components macro libraries.
f) Control, release and distribution of engineering information via the DBMS.
g) Computer-Aided Production Management (CAPM), including process planning, material and stock control, and DBMS interface with commercial software financial analysis.
h) Design of tooling, CNC part-programming and machining tests, and robot programming.
i) Prototype testing and pre-production runs.
j) Product documentation, manuals and user guides via DBMS.
k) Production build, shop floor documentation, and computer-aided inspection.
l) Packaging and transport documentation.
m) After-sales service and data retrieval.

The above activities should be considered neither as rigid disciplines nor as "serial steps" in the overall program. The ideal CIM system and project plan will ensure that many of the required tasks are intermeshed or undertaken in parallel to provide the optimum use of man-power, material, tooling, and machines.

Project Planning Techniques

Two common techniques used in project planning are

1 GANTT CHARTS, which are a type of bar-chart construction.
2 NETWORK ANALYSIS, which involves arranging engineering activities in graphical network form to establish a *critical path* of highest-priority tasks and thus accurately predict intermediate and overall completion dates.

Complete planning exercises may be undertaken using established systems such as PERT (Program Evaluation and Review Technique), which is estimated to have reduced the development time of the US Navy's Polaris programme by two years.

The foregoing techniques and systems will not be specifically defined in this publication, but are fully described and applied in *The Engineering Design Process* (Hawkes/Abinett, Longman).

Many project planning software packages have been developed for use in CIM DBMS systems. These are soften suitable for the full range of CPU capacity types, and are commonly based on popular planning systems such as PERT.

The plotted output of a typical PERT-based project-planning software package is shown in Fig 7.12.

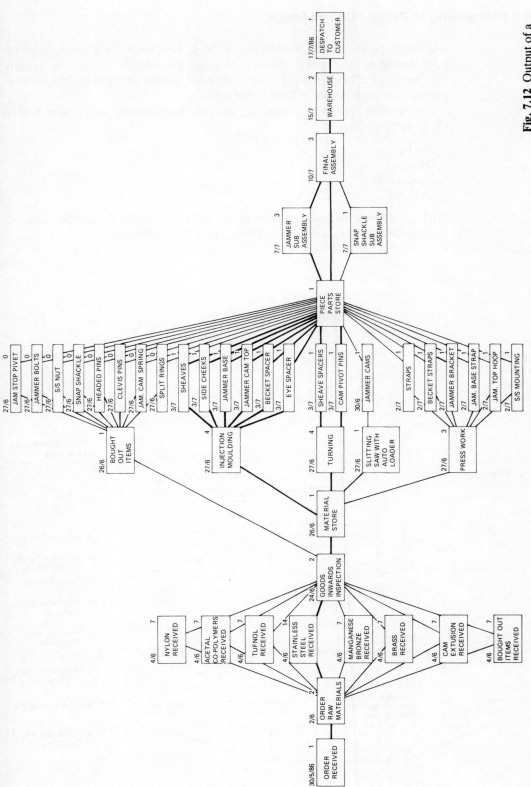

Fig. 7.12 Output of a PERT-based project-planning software package [*Micro-Planning Software Ltd.*]

Information Processing in Project Development

Successful project management in a CIM system requires a wide range of information to be readily available through the DBMS. *Total Information Processing* (TIP) is the term used to describe a fully integrated information exchange system within a CIM organisation.

Information required during the project development may come under the broad headings of

Market
Design
Production
Delivery.

Fig 7.13 shows a detailed analysis of the information which may be required via the DBMS at various stages throughout the project.

Fig. 7.13 Total information processing [*Mackintosh International and Cranfield Institute of Technology*]

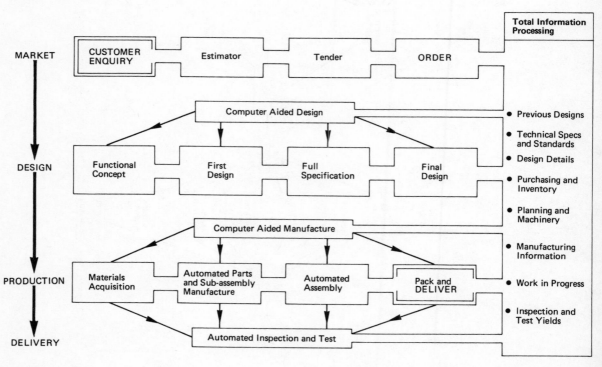

The Systematic Design Process in the CIM Structure

Chapter 1 of *The Engineering Design Process* describes the principles of the Systematic Design Process in detail. The essential elements of the process are derived from a *primary need* for a product according to market trends. From the primary need, a *design specification* is formulated. A number of *initial design solutions* are then conceived, synthesised, and analysed according to the requirements of the specification. These solutions are then compared and evaluated according to such criteria as function, cost, novelty, safety, appearance, and serviceabilty. The comparison and evaluation will result in a *chosen solution* which will ideally incorporate the best aspects of each initial solution.

In the traditional system, designers spent a high proportion of their time searching for information. Fig 7.14 shows how the systematic design process may be transformed in a CIM system by ready access to information through the DBMS and by previously discussed elements of CADCAM.

Fig. 7.14 Information access in the systematic design process

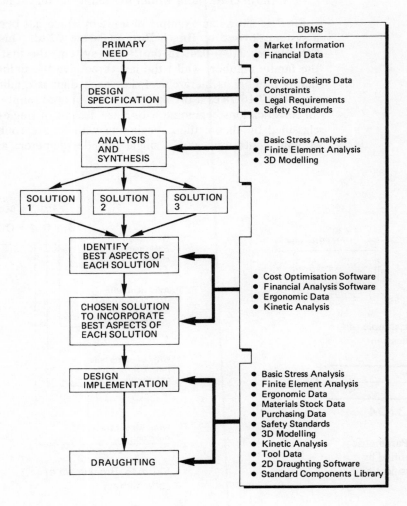

Classification and Coding

A modern approach to the classification and coding of designed items is an essential prerequisite to CADCAM and the efficient DBMS. Such an approach provides true standards and a direct link between the computer drawing and such DBMS files as Bills of Material (BOMs) or stock control data.

Without standardisation and retrieval facility, the advantages of CADCAM may be limited. For example, there is no value in producing a drawing at increased speed if a functionally identical item already exists in the system.

An effective CADCAM standard coding system requires:

a) IDENTIFICATION of each part or assembly according to permanent parameters such as shape or function. The identification would not include parameters which might vary, such as production technique or the product it is part of.

b) CLASSIFICATION of the item into a family of similar items.

c) CODING the item within the family so that it has a unique identity.

Fig 7.15 shows an example of an item which has been coded according to a system devised by Birsch Birn & Partners Ltd. This item is identified by the number 3104–024. In the Birsch system, the first four digits represent the family number, whilst the last three give the unique identification. The family number is hierarchical, i.e. each digit is qualified by the preceding one. Fig 7.16 gives a breakdown of the quoted number. This indicates that all classifications beginning with 3 are designs of single-piece parts which are classified by shape; those beginning with 31 are round axial items with a straight centre-line and a single outside diameter; and so on, with each

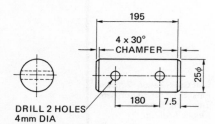

DRILL 2 HOLES
4mm DIA

Fig. 7.15 Example of part classification

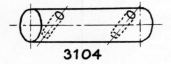

3104

Fig. 7.17 Parametric shape identified by family classification 3104

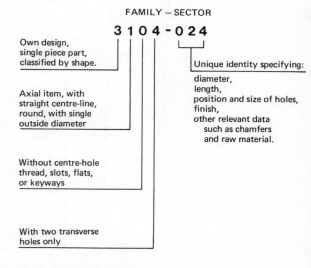

FAMILY — SECTOR

3 1 0 4 - 0 2 4

Own design, single piece part, classified by shape.

Axial item, with straight centre-line, round, with single outside diameter

Without centre-hole thread, slots, flats, or keyways

With two transverse holes only

Unique identity specifying:

diameter,
length,
position and size of holes,
finish,
other relevant data
    such as chamfers
    and raw material.

Fig. 7.16 Breakdown of code number

successive digit representing a more specialized family group. Thus 3104 represents a standard shape with enough identity to be created as a parametric macro in a CAD library (see Chapter 3). This shape is shown in Fig 7.17. The last three digits (024) specify the unique parameters of the item, such as diameter, length, position and size of holes, material, and finish.

Fig 7.18 shows the design cycle after such a classification and coding system has been introduced, and the various savings which may be achieved. Even when a completely new design has to be introduced, savings may be achieved in departments such as production planning because the new design may be compared with similar items in its family.

Fig 7.19 shows another example of standardization achieved through the Birsch system.

Fig. 7.18 Design cycle in classification and coding system

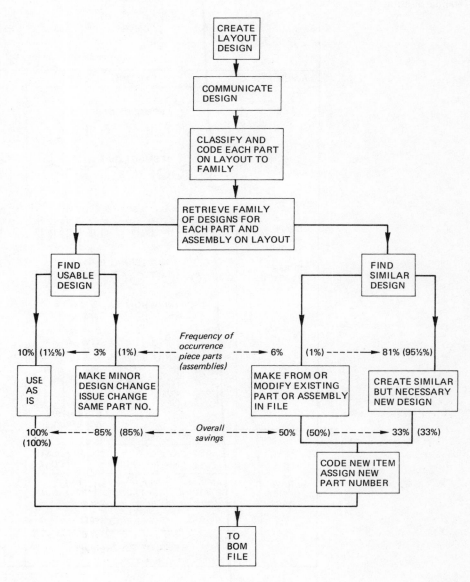

When used via a DBMS, this coding system becomes a powerful retrieval tool. If the equivalent of what is being searched for is available, then details are readily provided, otherwise the nearest two items are displayed.

Coding and classification is also an essential feature in computer-aided process planning systems, as outlined in the next section.

Fig. 7.19 Design control for variety reduction and standardisation

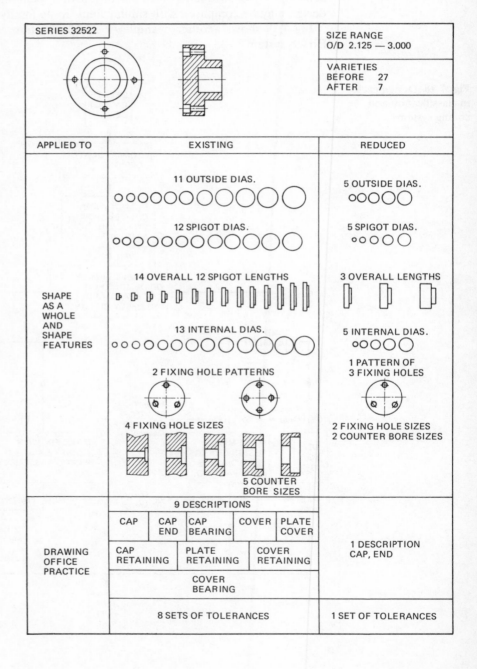

Computer-aided Process Planning (CAPP)

Process planning involves defining the operations required in the manufacture of a product. More specifically, this could involve such decisions as

a) Types of manufacturing process required.
b) Sequence of operations.
c) Machining speeds, feeds and operation times.
d) Tooling requirements.
e) Work-holding arrangements.
f) Machine selection and routing requirements.

Fig. 7.20 Product development via CAPP

Fig. 7.21 Database structure of a CAPP system [*Methods Workshop (Engineering) Ltd. and Delta Computer Aided Engineering Ltd.*]

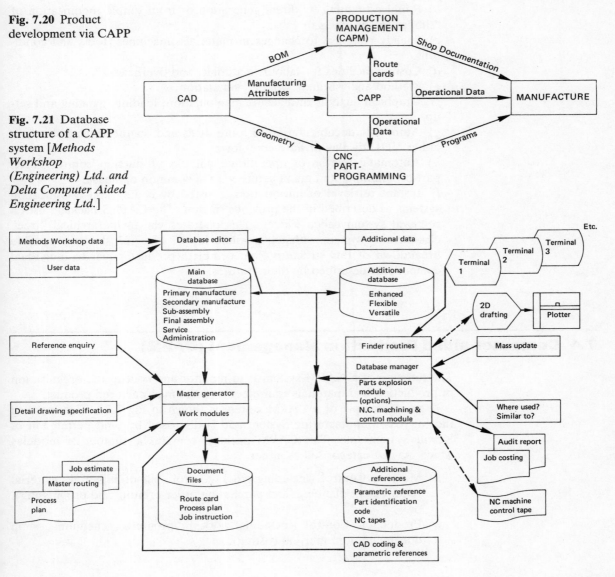

An interactive CAPP system, used in conjuction with a DBMS, computerises routine data-gathering, helps automate manufacturing decision-making, and makes available more of the planner's time for methods improvement and cost-reduction programmes.

Fig 7.20 shows how CAPP fits into the development of the product in a CIM organisation, and effectively provides the vital interface between design and manufacture.

A more comprehensive representation is shown in Fig 7.21. This shows the inputs and outputs to a common database using a commercial CAPP package called CAPES (Computer-Aided Planning and Estimating System). A system such as this can provide the following facilities:

a) "Where-used" capability, allowing the user to list parts and operations using specific machines, materials and tools from files within the database.

b) Rapid estimating by direct generation or from simple modification of "similar-to" products or jobs.

c) Speedy response to changes in materials, machines, tools and conditons.

d) Costing facilities for labour, materials, and overheads.

e) Method analysis and "what-if" simulation.

f) Graphical analysis of machine manipulation, loading, gauging and set-up.

g) Automatic documentation of route cards and operation plan sheets in either VDU display or hard-copy form.

h) Automatic release of operational data to production control, CNC part-programing, and manufacture via the common database.

i) Instant retrieval of information, assisted by coding and classification systems as described in the previous section. The CAPES package uses a retrieval system called Finder. This operates via an hierarchical "tree" classification system with ten possible levels. Fig 7.22 shows a possible breakdown of this structure from complete product down to individual components described by their features.

7.4 Computer-aided Production Management (CAPM)

The function of a CAPM system is to monitor and control the organisation of production and materials rquirements of the manufactured product.

A good example of a CAPM system is shown in Fig 7.23. This is called the Micross Manufacturing System and is discussed by kind permission of Kewill Systems plc. This CAPM package contains a number of modules which may be categorised as either

a) Material Control (including stock control, bill of material, material requirement planning, and purchasing order printing and progressing), or

b) Production Control (including work in progress, scheduling, shop documentation, and job costing).

Fig. 7.22 Breakdown of component structure

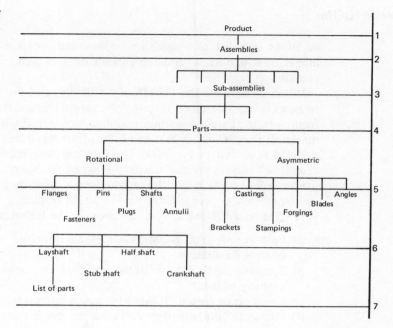

Fig. 7.23 A CAPM system: the Micross Manufacturing System [*Kewill Systems plc*]

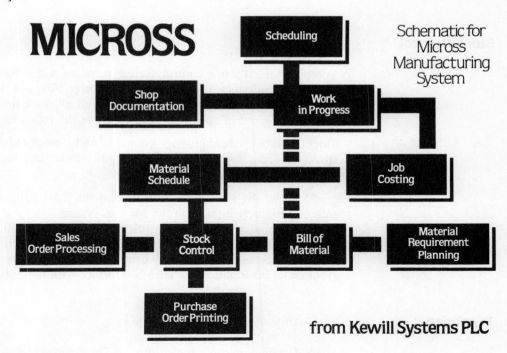

Bill of Material (BOM)

A BOM is a list of assemblies, compound components, component elements, raw materials, and bought-out items which make up the complete product.

When created via the DBMS of a CIM system, the BOM allows the user to quickly explode down through the various levels of product constituents, from intermediate components and assemblies (high level) down to raw materials (low level). A Works Order print-out of the high-level contents in a BOM is shown in Fig 7.24. This lists the intermediate components of a "roadster" bicycle produced with the aid of the Micross CAPM system. The works order is effectively the instructions for the shop floor to manufacture or assemble whatever is listed on the BOM display.

A CIM-based BOM system can provide the following facilities:

a) Fast creation of BOMs via DBMS interface with CAD and stock control databases.
b) Simplification of new BOM creation by rapid cross-reference with existing BOMs.
c) Creation of costed BOMs with automatic updating of current costs.
d) Accurate and efficient updating of stock records via stock control interface.
e) Automatic issuing of works orders to production control via the DBMS.
f) The creation of "Trial Kitting Lists" to determine if sufficient stock is available to meet the requirements of the works order. This helps to minimise shortages and work in progress.

Stock Control

A computer-aided stock control system provides a database record of the movement of all stock in and out of the stores. Via the VDU, it accepts enquiries and produces reports on the status of all stock items.

The stock record of each item could include the following information:

Stock number; description; stock-on-hand; stock-on-order; allocated stock; re-order level; lead time; supplier code; bin location; material, labour, and overhead cost; selling price.

Fig 7.25 shows the stock record display for the front light of the previously mentioned roadster bicycle on the Micross system.

Such a computerised stock control facility helps to minimise stock levels and redundant stock; provides faster updating of stock records and early warning of shortages for assembly programmes; and allows instant access to current order information via DBMS interface with the purchasing system.

Purchase

A CAPM system incorporated within a CIM organisation can provide direct

Fig. 7.24 Works order from roadster bicycle BOM

```
KEWILL SYSTEMS LIMITED                    M I C R O S S                    DATE: 16.12.80

BOM230                          W O R K S   O R D E R   E N Q U I R Y             PAGE:   1
                                ==============================================

WORKS ORDER NO ........  WO2              DUE DATE ................  16.12.80

ASSEMBLY STOCK NO ......  R2600 1000-000  QUANTITY ORDERED .........     200

DESCRIPTION ............  ROADSTER 1000 26in   QUANTITY OUTSTANDING .....   200

COMPONENT                           STOCK    STOCK    TRAN         QTY    DUE
STOCK NUMBER    DESCRIPTION         ON HAND  ON ORDER CODE    QTY  OUTST  DATE
_____

FR 1000-000     FRAME ASSY (R1000)   160              ALE    200   100   021280
                                                      ALI    100

WA 1000-000     WHEEL ASSEMBLY (26in) 428    265      ALE    400   200   021280
                                                      ALI    200

AC 1000-100     FRONT LIGHT          110     35       ALE    200   100   021280
                                                      ALI    100

AC 1000-200     REAR LIGHT (Red)     321              ALE    200   100   021280
                                                      ALI    100

AC 1000-300     REAR REFLECTOR (Red) 200              ALE    200   100   021280
                                                      ALI    100

AC 1000-400     TOOLKIT              275              ALE    200   100   021280
                                                      ALI    50
                                                      SHE    50    50

AC 1000-500     SADDLEBAG            475     250      ALE    200   100   021280
                                                      ALI    100

                *** End of Order ***
```

links between CAD, stock control and purchasing departments through the DBMS.

Designers can thus have ready access to purchase data files for raw materials and bought-out items. Typical purchase information could include: item availability, cost, and delivery; alternative suppliers; and previous purchase history. Designs may therefore be efficiently optimised at an early stage in the process.

Standard purchase notes may be printed and dispatched via interface with stock control data. Fig 7.26 shows the purchase order form for the bought-out electrical items of the Micross roadster bicycle example. Listed information includes: item descriptions, quantities, supplier, unit prices, carriage price, date ordered, date due, and delivery instructions. Once the item has been delivered, the form may be modified to include the date of receipt and the information returned to the database as a "goods received" file. The REC (received) dates of the roadster form reveals that two of the ordered items have been delivered, although the QTY OUTST (quantity outstanding) column indicates that these were not supplied in the full quantities required.

Fig. 7.25 Stock record
for roadster front light

```
KEWILL SYSTEMS LIMITED          M I C R O S S          16.12.80

SCS210                    S T O C K   E N Q U I R Y
                          =========================


STOCK NUMBER:    AC 1000-100         FRONT LIGHT
----------------------------------------------------------------

   PRODUCT GROUP CODE ..... 5000        ISSUES LAST YEAR ....... 1250
   UNIT OF MEASURE ........ EA          ISSUES THIS YEAR ....... 1686
   BIN NUMBER ............. DB1039      ISSUES LAST PERIOD .....   98
                                        ISSUES THIS PERIOD .....  675

   STOCK-ON-HAND ......... 12210.3
   STOCK-ON-ORDER ........ 18039.7      SELLING PRICE ..........  5.45
   ALLOCATED STOCK ........   115       STANDARD COST ..........  3.85
   SHORTAGES .............     0        AVERAGE COST ..........   1.98

   RE-ORDER LEVEL ........   200        MATERIAL COST ..........  1.98
   RE-ORDER QUANTITY ......  500        LABOUR COST ............  0.00
   LEAD TIME (WEEKS) ......    3        OVERHEAD COST ..........  0.00
   SUPPLIER CODE ......... LUCAS
                                        ABC CODE .............. A
   FREE PHYSICAL STOCK .... 12095.3


   ------------------------------------------------------------

   BATCH  TRANS DOCUMENT DATE    QTY    QTY  REC'VD DUE   INTERNAL SUPP ORD
   NUMBER CODE  NUMBER                 OUTST PRICE  DATE  DOC.NO.  CODE STAT
   ------------------------------------------------------------

   1000   ORD   PO1024 311080   500     35          121280 AW/1234 LUCAS PST2
   1003   ALE   AL1002 051180   150    115          010181
   1006   ISS   IS4050 041180    15
   1007   RET   RS6600 051180     5                                LUCAS
   1008   REC   PO1024 041180   265          3.85          AW/1235
   1009   ALI   AL1002 051180    35                        AX/1234
   1009   ISS   801436 041180    50
   1010   REC   PO1024 041180   200          3.85          AW/1236
   1026   ISS   C12345 011180   500
```

This type of computer-aided purchasing system also enables engineers to compile priority lists for the purchase of items, and so assist in bringing forward the implementation of the works order.

Material Requirement Planning (MRP)

The function of MRP is to take the total sales and production demand, explode it through the BOM structures and, not only calculate the requirement for new purchase orders and works orders, but also identify any existing orders which need to be brought forward, delayed, or cancelled. In a CAPM system, MRP should link directly with BOM data and stock

```
KEWILL SYSTEMS LIMITED          M I C R O S S - 3.03              DATE: 26.01.84

POS200                     O R D E R   E N Q U I R Y              PAGE:    1
                           =========================
                                                                 Int.Ref: IR.1234
  ORDER NUMBER   1001                                            Req.No.: RQ.9632
  --------------------
                                   TRANS            QTY   UNIT   DUE  INTERNAL SUPP ORD
  STOCK NUMBER DESCRIPTION    UOM  CODE  DATE   QTY  OUTST PRICE DATE DOC.NO.  CODE STAT
  ----------------------------------------------------------------------------------------

   Item No.  1
   AC 1000-100  FRONT LIGHT    EA  ORD 161280   100   25   3.85 160181 WO1023 LUCAS P
                                   REC 160181    75        3.85          1001

   Item No.  2
   AC 1000-200  REAR LIGHT (Red) EA ORD 161280  120   85   2.61 160181 WO1023 LUCAS P
                                   REC 160181    35        2.61          1001

   Item No.  3  1.5v Batteries
                suitable for use in
                the above items.
                               EA  ORD 161280   220  120   0.25 160181 WO1023 LUCAS

   Item No.  4  Carriage
                                   ORD 161280     1    1  15.00         5001   LUCAS

   Item No.  5  Delivery Instructions
                ---------------------
                The above items should
                be marked for the
                attention of E.J.BLOGGS.

                Delivery should be made
                to GATE No. 5.

                          ***   End of Order   ***
```

Fig. 7.26 Purchase order form for electrical bought-out items of roadster

control to obtain the necessary information. Fig 7.27 shows the Stock Requirements Profile for the Micross roadster. This includes every exploded element of the product and suggested works orders for the manufactured components.

MRP ensures that supply and demand are related as closely as possible and helps to optimise stock levels. It can also improve service to the customer by providing the ability to quote more accurate delivery dates.

Work In Progress (WIP) and Scheduling

WIP and workcentre scheduling are essential components of production control. They effectively enable production resources to be described in terms of people and machines. In a CAPM system, WIP and scheduling packages receive information from the BOM and MRP files via the DBMS.

Works orders for the product are supplied by the BOM. The priority of

161

Fig. 7.27 Stock requirements profile from MRP for roadster

```
KEWILL SYSTEMS LIMITED                        M I C R O S S                              DATE: 16.12.80

MRP300                          STOCK REQUIREMENTS PROFILE - ACTION REPORT                PAGE: 1
                                ================================================
```

STOCK NUMBER DESCRIPTION	UOM	LEAD TIME (wks)	ROL	ROQ	TRAN CODE	DOCUMENT NUMBER	DUE DATE	QUANTITY	PROJECTED STOCK	---SUGGESTED ORDER--- QUANTITY	DATE	DOC. NO.
AC 1000-100 FRONT LIGHT	EA	3	200	500	Opening Stock				210			
					ORD	PO1024	12.12.80	35	245			
					ALE	AL1002	01.01.81	115	130			
AC 1000-200 REAR LIGHT (Red)	EA	3	200	500	Opening Stock				421			
					ALE	AL1002	01.01.81	50	371			
AC 1000-300 REAR REFLECTOR (Red)	EA	4	244	1000	Opening Stock				300			
					ALE	AL1002	01.01.81	75	225			
AC 1000-500 SADDLEBAG	EA	5	250	800	Opening Stock				575			
					ORD	PO1098	01.02.81	250	825			
FA 1100-000 FRAME (26in)	EA	5	194	1000	Opening Stock				180			
					ORD	WO1256	15.01.81	40	220			
					ORD	ZP00001	20.03.81	1000	1220	1000	13.02.81	ZP00001
					ALE	ZW00004	20.03.81	1000	220			
FP 1400-200 RUBBER FOOT PAD	EA	4	238	1500	Opening Stock				465			
					ALE	ALS500	15.12.80	35	430			
FR 1000-000 FRAME ASSY (R1000)	EA	4	100	250	Opening Stock				260			
					ORD	ZW00004	17.04.81	1000	1260	1000	20.03.81	ZW00004
					ALE	ZW00002	17.04.81	1250	10			
FR 2000-000 FRAME ASSY(Jun.Roadster)	EA	5	75	150	Opening Stock				100			
					ORD	ZW00003	17.04.81	900	1000	900	13.03.81	ZW00003
					ALE	ZW00001	17.04.81	1000	0			
FR 2100-000 FRAME (20in)	EA	3	200	500	Opening Stock				150			
					ORD	ZP00002	13.03.81	1000	1150	1000	20.02.81	ZP00002
					ALE	ZW00003	13.03.81	900	250			
HB 1200-000 HANDLEBAR ASSEMBLY	EA	5	150	350	Opening Stock				65			
					SHE	SH1005	04.11.80	50	15			
					ORD	ZW00005	06.11.80	350	365	350	02.10.80	ZW00005
					SHE	SH1000	06.11.80	64	301			
					ORD	WO1022	15.12.80	50	351			
HB 1200-100 HANDLEBAR	EA	5	100	250	Opening Stock				40			
					ORD	ZP00004	02.10.80	500	540	500	28.08.80	ZP00004
					ALE	ZW00005	02.10.80	350	190			
					SHE	SH1005	04.11.80	50	140			
					SHE	SH1000	06.11.80	15	125			
PA 1400-000 PEDAL ASSEMBLY	EA	5	244	1200	Opening Stock				200			
					ORD	WO1022	15.12.80	85	285			
PB 1400-100 PEDAL BODY	EA	3	150	500	Opening Stock				3			
					ORD	ZP00003	04.11.80	500	503	500	14.10.80	ZP00003
					SHE	SH1005	04.11.80	25	478			

each works order, originating from MRP, indicates the sequence for scheduling each workcentre to finite capacity. Fig 7.28 shows a bar-chart schedule display of the current weekly work load for one workcentre using the Micross system.

The WIP package monitors the progress of all jobs by showing partial completions and outstanding jobs through screen enquiries and VDU display reports.

Shop Documentation

CAPM systems can provide a complete set of shop documentation for every item produced in a company.

162

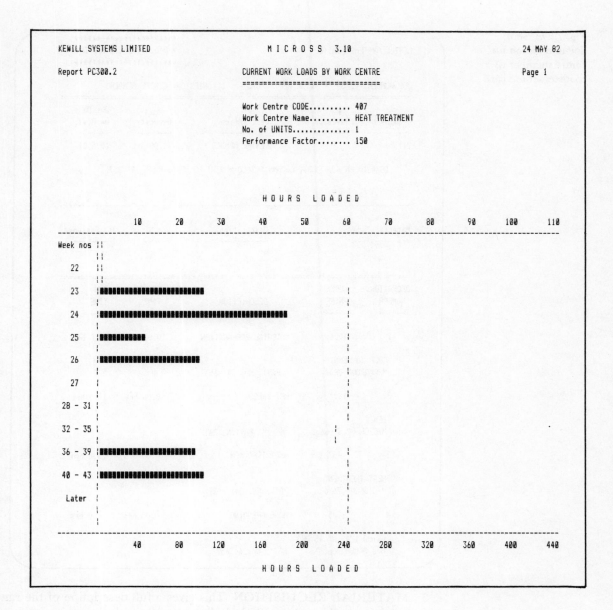

```
KEWILL SYSTEMS LIMITED              M I C R O S S   3.10                    24 MAY 82

Report PC300.2                  CURRENT WORK LOADS BY WORK CENTRE           Page 1
                                =====================================

                          Work Centre CODE.......... 407
                          Work Centre Name.......... HEAT TREATMENT
                          No. of UNITS.............. 1
                          Performance Factor........ 150



                              H O U R S   L O A D E D

              10    20    30    40    50    60    70    80    90    100   110
         -----------------------------------------------------------------------
Week nos !!
         !!
  22     !!                                        :
         !!
  23     :██████████████████████                   :
         :                                         :
  24     :█████████████████████████████████████    :
         :                                         :
  25     :███████████                              :
         :                                         :
  26     :██████████████████████                   :
         :                                         :
  27     :                                         :
         :                                         :
28 - 31  :                                         :
         :                                         :
32 - 35  :                                    :
         :                                         :
36 - 39  :████████████████████                     :
         :                                         :
40 - 43  :████████████████████                     :
         :                                         :
 Later   :                                         :
         :                                         :
         :                                         :
         -----------------------------------------------------------------------
              40    80    120   160   200   240   280   320   360   400   440

                              H O U R S   L O A D E D
```

Fig. 7.28 Work centre scheduling

A CAPM shop documentation package can include the following elements:

1 ROUTE CARD. This gives a list of the various manufacturing processes required to produce a component, the sequence of processes, times, and allotted workcentres for each process. The route card information could be received via associated CAPP software and WIP through the DBMS.

2 OPERATION CARD. This gives a more detailed description of each operation including the people allotted to set up the process and undertake the manufacturing operation. Again, its direct source of data would be the WIP package and CAPP.

163

Fig. 7.29*a* Shop
documentation for
centre member of
roadster: route card

```
 KEWILL SYSTEMS LIMITED                        ************************
                                               * R O U T E   C A R D *
                                               ************************

 JOB NUMBER: 22759    NETWK REF:  0-0    DESCRIPTION: CENTRE MEMBER
 ====================================================================

                                                          Due Date
 Drawing No.   Revision No.    Description      Quantity   ww.d.yy
 -----------   -----------     -----------      --------   -------
 241657                        CENTRE MEMBER      1200     10.5.81

     BS 4360 GR 43A  12MM X 75MM X 3650 = 9 WT.-2.85KG. PATT 241 657


     -----------------------------------------------------------------


 Material Code                 Description      Grn.No.   Qty Consumed
 -------------                 -----------      -------   ------------



 ====================================================================
 OPERATION    WORK                             SET-UP      RUN
 NUMBER       CENTRE          DESCRIPTION        TIME      TIME
 ------       ------          -----------        ----      ----

    1          1006       MATERIAL PREPARATION  0.00 hrs  14.0 hrs

         CROP TO LENGTH 15.7/16"
         M/C GROUP CP46         PATT. NO. 241 657

    2          1004       HOT PRESS             0.00 hrs  10.0 hrs

         BEND
         M/C GROUP SU No.6          PATT.No.241 657

    3           407       HEAT TREATMENT        0.00 hrs  24.0 hrs

     HEAT TREATMENT
     M/C GROUP 76          PATT. No. 241 657

    4          1005       HAND GRINDING         0.00 hrs   6.0 hrs

         GRIND 1/4" AT 45 DEG
         M/C GROUP HG63        PATT. No 241 657
```

3 MATERIAL REQUISITION. This gives a full description of the raw
material for each component, including overall stock dimensions, mass,
material, and drawing number. Its source of data is WIP via the BOM and
stock control.

Fig 7.29 shows the route card, operation card, and material requisition for
the centre member of the Micross roadster.

Fig. 7.29*b* Shop documentation for centre member of roadster: operation card

```
                                    *********************************
KEWILL SYSTEMS LIMITED              * O P E R A T I O N   C A R D *
                                    *********************************

JOB NUMBER: 22759    NETWK REF:  0-0    DESCRIPTION: CENTRE MEMBER
=================================================================
Drawing No.   Revision No.   Description         Quantity
-----------   -----------    -----------         --------
241657                       CENTRE MEMBER          1200
-----------------------------------------------------------------
Operation     Work                            Set-up       Run
Number        Centre         Description      Time         Time
------        ------         -----------      ----         ----
   1          1006        MATERIAL PREPARATION  0.00 hrs    14.0 hrs

      CROP TO LENGTH 15.7/16"
      M/C GROUP CP46          PATT. NO. 241 657
=================================================================
SETTER:                      **SET-UP TIME**
  Date   ON   OFF  : Date   ON   OFF  : Date   ON   OFF  : TOTAL
  ----   --   ---  : ----   --   ---  : ----   --   ---  : -----
                   :                  :                  :
                   :                  :                  :
                   :                  :                  :
=================================================================
OPERATOR:                    **RUN TIME**
  Date   ON   OFF  : Date   ON   OFF  : Date   ON   OFF  : TOTAL
  ----   --   ---  : ----   --   ---  : ----   --   ---  : -----
                   :                  :                  :
                   :                  :                  :
```

Fig. 7.29*c* Shop documentation for centre member of roadster: material requisition

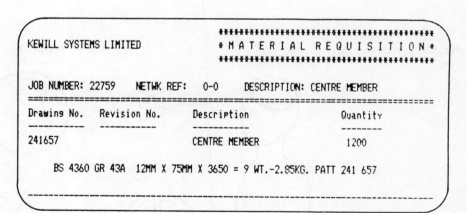

```
                                 ********************************************
KEWILL SYSTEMS LIMITED           * M A T E R I A L   R E Q U I S I T I O N *
                                 ********************************************

JOB NUMBER: 22759    NETWK REF:  0-0    DESCRIPTION: CENTRE MEMBER
===========================================================================
Drawing No.   Revision No.   Description         Quantity
-----------   -----------    -----------         --------
241657                       CENTRE MEMBER          1200

    BS 4360 GR 43A  12MM X 75MM X 3650 = 9 WT.-2.85KG. PATT 241 657

    ---------------------------------------------------------------
```

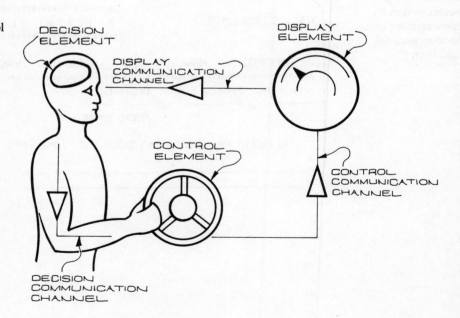

Fig. 8.1 Typical control loop

Ergonomic Applications   8

Ergonomics is the scientific study of the relationship between people and their working environment. Typical considerations include workspace, heat conditions, lighting, fellow colleagues, tools, machines, and methods of organisation and production.

This subject, critical to the needs of modern society, has traditionally been denied its required status in design priorities. CADCAM systems have now given the designer a powerful tool which allows human aspects to be assessed at the same early stage that the functional aspects are considered.

Anthropometrics is one of a group of scientific disciplines that come under the general heading of Ergonomics, and may be defined as the listing of data information on human body size.

Ergonomics and anthropometrics have previously been discussed in *The Engineering Design Process* and *Engineering Design for Technicians* (Hawkes/Abinett, Longman). A brief revision of these subjects will now be undertaken.

8.1 The Man—Machine Relationship

Any person who operates a machine may be considered as part of a closed *control loop* system in which he or she receives and processes information, and then acts on it. A typical control loop is shown in Fig 8.1.

Information (e.g. the speed of a machine) is sent to the operator from a *display element* via the display communication channel. A display is any source of information aiding the operator in the control of the machine. Typical displays include dial gauges, digital readouts, and warning lights.

The information from the display is passed to the control mechanism of the brain via the optical and nervous system where it is processed in order to arrive at a decision in relation to the required performance. The decision is then communicated to the control element via the mechanical leverage system of the human bone and muscle which makes up the decision communication channel.

A *control* is any device which regulates the action of a machine. Typical controls include handwheels, handles, levers, control knobs, pedals and push buttons. The effect of the action of the machine will be registered on the display via the control communication channel, and the loop is thus completed.

The efficiency of the control loop will be affected by various internal and external factors. The display element should be easily and accurately readable, and have a movement which is compatible with the movement of the control. The position of displays should be such that they can be communicated to the operator with the minimum of physical effort. The display communication channel should have a direct line of path to the decision-making organs and be free from interference such as glare on an illuminated panel. The operator must be physically and mentally capable of making the required decision under satisfactory working conditions. The decision communication channel should provide easy access to the control and be free from interference. The control element should be of suitable size, easily operated, and give compatibility with the display. The control communication channel must be a reliable mechanism.

External factors such as heating, lighting, noise, ventilation, physical obstructions, and fellow colleagues must also have a considerable effect on the control loop.

8.2 The "Average" Person

Physically, people vary in size, weight, strength and shape, and in their abilities to see and hear. As a yardstick, the ergonomic designer could therefore consider the use of average human data. However, anyone with a knowledge of statistics will realise that a simple average or *mean* value can be very misleading and may require further analysis regarding the scatter from this value.

Where only mean values are considered, it is likely that only about half the population under consideration is satisfied by a given design. Thus to ensure that a broad range of population is accommodated, human data which deviates from the mean is often accounted for.

Human data is best analysed by considering a *normal distribution curve* or *Gaussian curve*, which plots stated sizes against percentage of population with that size. Fig 8.2 shows the normal distribution curve for the height of clothed men in the UK.

The *standard deviation* σ may be considered as the average amount of scatter above or below the mean height value. It can be assumed to represent about 34% of the population. Thus, the average scatter above or below the mean is equivalent to 2σ, or 68% of the population.

Population proportions are often expressed as *percentiles*. For example, staying with Fig 8.2:

Mean height value (1737 mm) = 50th percentile

i.e. 50% of the male population have this height or above.

Mean − σ = 50% − 34% = 16th percentile

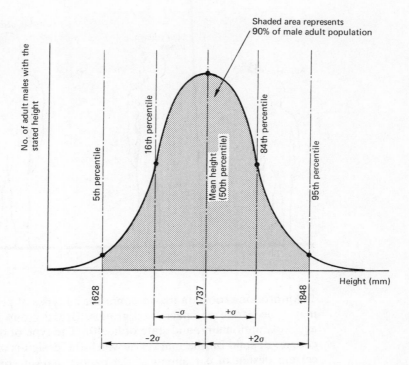

Fig. 8.2 Normal distribution curve for heights of adult males

Shaded area represents 90% of male adult population

No. of adult males with the stated height

5th percentile

16th percentile

Mean height (50th percentile)

84th percentile

95th percentile

Height (mm)

1628

1737

1848

$-\sigma$ $+\sigma$

-2σ $+2\sigma$

i.e. only 16% of the male population have less than this height.

Mean + σ = 50% + 34% = 84th percentile

i.e. 84% of the male population have less than this height.

Further analysis reveals that double the average scatter above or below the mean (i.e. mean value $\pm 2\sigma$) gives the 5th and 95th percentiles, i.e. only 5% of the population do not exceed the 5th percentile height (1628 mm) but 95% do not exceed the 95th percentile height (1848 mm). The 5th and 95th percentile values thus cover a range equivalent to 90% of the male population.

When considering the full range of population for a design, it is thus common practice to take the 5th and 95th percentiles as the lower and upper limits of consideration (see Fig 8.3). In most cases it would not be practical or economic to consider 100% of the population by catering for people at the extremes, and attempts to do so could drastically limit the efficiency of the design for the majority of people.

8.3 Anthropometric Data

In anthropometrics, the human data considered is entirely that of body size. This subject thus becomes a scientific discipline in its own right due to the immense variety of dimensions which exist.

Fig. 8.3

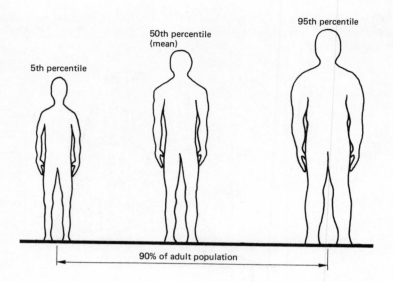

Anthropometric data may account for all types of people, or alternatively, may concentrate on specialised groups. Broad group headings may include age, sex, nationality, and state of health. The type of data chart used will, of course, depend on the market at which the design is aimed. For example, a certain design of car aimed at the export market could be assumed to be used by adult men and women of a wide range of nationalities. However, a design of children's toy car or disabled person's car would require specialised data.

Traditionally, charts of anthropometric data have been used, but these can only give a rough guide in determining sizes on a design, and are subject to serious limitations. One of the particular difficulties in complying with anthropometric data is in obtaining reliable values of arc movements for the human frame. This problem can be partially overcome by using the charts in conjunction with pin-jointed scale manikin models of the mean, lower percentile and higher percentile values of human frame size. To manipulate these against a flat drawing surface, these manikins have commonly been made in two elevations of 2D, from cardboard or plastic. However, these mediums give a very inaccurate representation of actual human body movements and the results obtained are generally unsatisfactory.

8.4 Computer-aided Man—Machine Modelling

The infinite variety of human limb sizes and arcs of movement can only be efficiently analysed by using CADCAM software.

One of the most successful of these application software packages is called SAMMIE and is marketed by Prime Computers. The system is written in standard Fortran IV with a modular format allowing special-purpose application programs to be run. It is available for a range of 32-bit computers.

An important feature of the SAMMIE system is that it allows human forms to be modelled three-dimensionally, together with equipment and buildings. The models may be manipulated on the screen with the object of evaluating the physical interaction between the person and the workplace, or between the person and the worktask. SAMMIE may also be used for studying human-machine interactions such as in robotics design.

General-purpose Facilities

The basis of the SAMMIE system is a layered (or hierarchical) data structure which allows a 3D scale representation of the workplace to be created, stored, retrieved and displayed. This data structure may be manipulated to

a) Build a 3D model of the workplace.
b) Place a model of a person within the workplace.
c) Display and view the model in a variety of ways.
d) Interact with the model to modify it and carry out evaluations of human factors.

The man-model can be based on any available population data. Limb lengths are variable, as are body shapes, so that a wide variety of human physiques may be modelled. Joint movement constraints are also provided to limit man-model postures to those which are physically possible.

System Features

1 The Man-model   The man-model within SAMMIE uses a set of 21 links, with 17 pin-joints to represent the major limbs of the body. To provide more realism, flesh contours have been added to the rigid link model. It is these flesh contours which are displayed to allow assessment of whether the person can comfortably fit into the current workspace.

Any range of percentile variation may be obtained, including flesh contours as well as limb lengths. Fig 8.4 shows an extreme range of 98% population from 1st percentile (short and thin *ectomorth*) to 99th percentile (tall and fat *endomorth*).

2 Layered Data Structure   3D models of any complexity may be built from a range of primitives, such as cuboids and prisms, or alternatively they may be created by definition of vertex, edge, and face for irregular solids. These solids are placed in a data structure in such a way that the mechanical or logical relationships between objects can be modelled. The layers of the hierarchical data structure may be stacked to any required level.

An example of SAMMIE's hierarchical model approach is shown in Figs 8.5–8.9, which concern the design of a straddle carrier (a device for moving containers around ports and stacking them as required). Fig 8.5 shows the full perspective side elevation of the carrier (cab at upper left-hand corner). Fig 8.6 shows a zoomed-up side elevation of the cab, with a seated driver of average height and build. Fig 8.7 shows a zoomed-up side elevation of the cab control panel (the diminished view of the panel may be seen above the driver's head in Fig 8.6). The panel and associated instruments may be interactively moved in space as one level of hierarchical layer (Fig 8.8). Alternatively, the individual instruments, being on a lower level of hierarchical layer, may be re-arranged on the panel (Fig 8.9).

3 Displaying and Viewing the Model The 3D models may be viewed either isometrically or in perspective.

Essentially, the engineer using SAMMIE specifies a *centre of interest* on the model and a *viewing point* in terms of model coordinates. The view displayed on the screen is the centre of interest as seen from the viewing

Fig. 8.4 Man model anthropometric data range

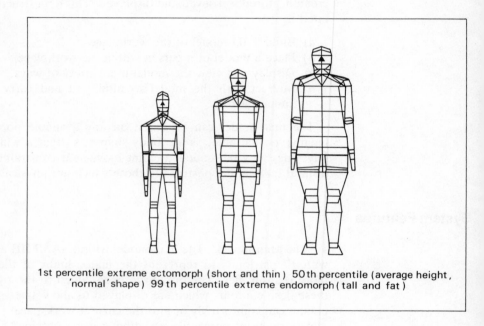

1st percentile extreme ectomorph (short and thin) 50th percentile (average height, 'normal' shape) 99th percentile extreme endomorph (tall and fat)

Fig. 8.5 Straddle carrier: side elevation

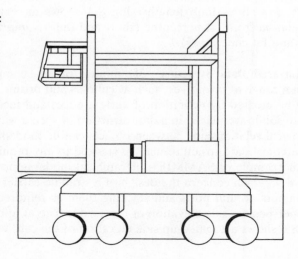

point. By moving the viewing point, the engineer may obtain a 3D view from any position outside or inside the model space. In this way it is possible to "walk around" or "enter" the model.

The viewing point may be situated at the position of the person's eyes, thus allowing the view of the centre of interest as "seen" by the man-model, to be displayed. Fig 8.10 shows the driver's view from the straddle carrier (in perspective) by specifying the viewing point as the drivers eyes, and the centre of interest as the corner of floor and wall directly ahead of the line of motion.

Normally the display is of wireframe form to give fast response times. However, the mathematical model is solid, thus allowing hidden line removal when required. This facility is shown in the office furniture layout of Fig 8.11.

Fig. 8.6 Straddle carrier cab

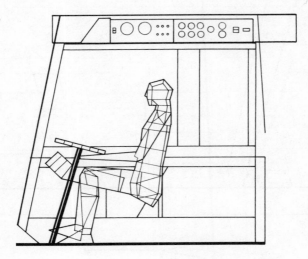

Fig. 8.7 Instrument panel

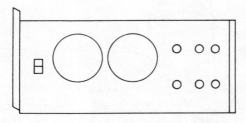

Fig. 8.9 Independent rearrangement of instruments on panel

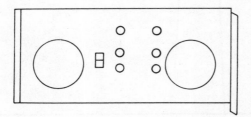

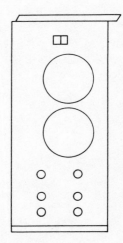

Fig. 8.8 Movement of complete panel and instruments

173

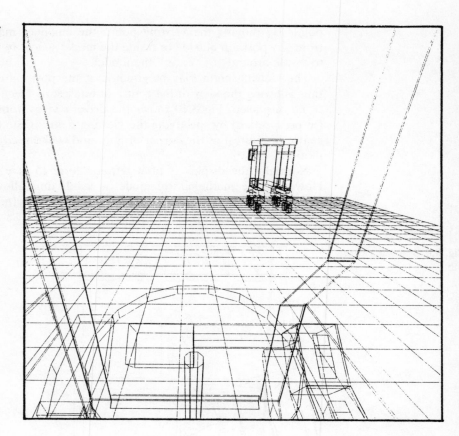

Fig. 8.10 Driver's view from straddle carrier

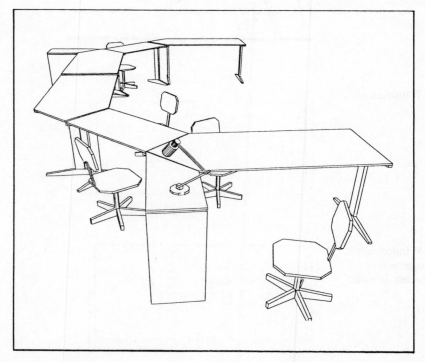

Fig. 8.11 Office furniture layout (hidden lines removed)

4 Human Factors Evaluation The main aspects that can be examined using SAMMIE are VISIBILITY, REACH, ACCESS, and WORKING POSTURES.

As already demonstrated in Fig 8.10, SAMMIE can provide views of the workplace model as seen by the man-model. Also, by applying a regular mesh over the visual field, "blind spots" may be easily quantified.

Another option is a "mirror facility" which provides reflected views such as would be seen, for instance, by a person using the rear view mirror of a car. Up to sixteen mirrors of varying focal lengths may be examined in this way (Fig 8.12).

Reach tests may be requested to points along a path or over surfaces. The results may be displayed indicating either maximum or comfortable reach areas. A typical example of a reach test display is shown in Fig 8.13, which is a further examination of the control panel in the previously described straddle carrier. Fig 8.13 shows a shaded area indicating that which could be comfortably reached by a 95th percentile height man.

It is possible to specify limb movements, head movements, etc., within the workspace. Furthermore, it is possible to link together a sequence of limb movements into a single command. Access to the workplace may be

Fig. 8.12 Driver's view of the mirror on a Leyland bus

Fig. 8.13 Results of a reach test on straddle carrier instrument panel

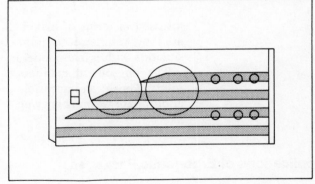

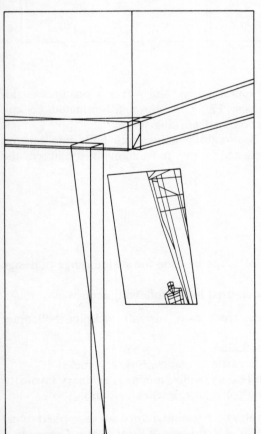

Fig. 8.14 Simulated cockpit situation: man in a confined working space (hidden lines removed)

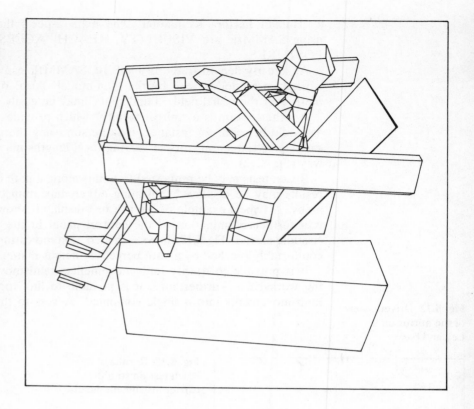

assessed in terms of maximum operator size, and working postures evaluated by reference to joint angles. Fig 8.14 shows a simulated cockpit situation with a man-model in a confined working space.

The pin-jointed man-model has realistic constraints built into various joints. Thus if an impossible sequence of limb movements is attempted, the appropriate warning is given.

Applications of Ergonomic Packages

Software packages such as SAMMIE can be used for a wide range of design studies in a number of fields.

SAMMIE itself has already been used in the following areas:

a) Transportation (cars, buses, truck cabs, aircraft cockpits, helicopter interiors, spacecraft).
b) Robotics handling and installation.
c) Materials handling (straddle carriers, cranes, fork lift trucks).
d) Manufacturing (production line assembly, mining machinery layout).
e) Interiors (office layouts, control rooms, kitchen layouts).

Chapter 10 gives further examples of ergonomic software as applied to car design in a case study of the CADCAM process at Ford Motor Company.

Aspects of CAM 9

The purpose of this chapter is to discuss in detail some of the topics which may be included under the broad heading of Computer-Aided Manufacture (CAM).

9.1 Numerical Control (NC)

NC is a technique which controls the actions of machines via instructions in the form of an alpha-numeric code. The coded instructions are supplied to the machine in *blocks* of information. Each block is interpreted by the NC machine as an instruction to perform a single operation. For example, a typical instruction block could command an NC machine to move a spindle relative to the workpiece through a stated distance and direction, and at a stated spindle speed and feed rate. Typical NC applications include turning, milling, flame-cutting, welding, pressing, and punching.

An NC program is a set of instruction blocks which commands the NC machine to carry out a specific task. The most common of such tasks is the complete machining of an engineering component, or *part*. This type of NC program is thus called a *part program*, and is one of the main ingredients of the CADCAM process.

Traditional NC machines contain no local intelligence and thus their part programs have to be fed into them manually—usually in the form of punched paper tape. Working from a paper drawing of the designed component and from planning sheets, the part-programmer writes out the program blocks for the required machining operations by hand. This is usually done at a location remote from the NC machine. The program is then copied on the keyboard of a manual paper punch machine which converts every character of the program (letter, number, or punctuation mark) into a row of punched holes on a paper strip. Each successive row has a particular pattern representing a binary code number for the NC language character typed in. Once the program is punched out, the reel of paper is extracted from the punch machine and fed into the *machine control unit* (MCU) of the NC machine. Having no memory, the MCU can read only single blocks of

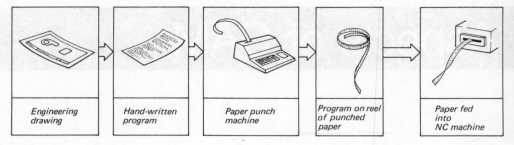

Fig. 9.1 Stages in traditional NC part programming

instructions, with the respective machining operations taking place after each block has been read.

Any number of identical components may thus be produced using the same NC paper tape, which may be stored for future use.

Coding Systems

The ASCII Code   This has already been mentioned in conjunction with CAD systems (Chapter 2). It is also the principal coding system for NC and CNC applications. ASCII (American Standard Code for Information Exchange) uses seven-bit binary numbers to represent all alpha-numeric characters in the part-program language.

The International Standards Organisation (ISO) recommends a subset of the ASCII code for NC and CNC applications and this ISO code is specified in BS 3635 Part 1:1972. The full ISO character set, binary representations, and decimal equivalents are shown on page 24.

When using paper tape, a punched hole represents a binary digit 1 and the absence of a hole represents a binary digit 0. Fig 9.2 shows the punched-tape representation for the typical part-program instruction block:

NØ15 GØØ X2ØØ Y-348 MØ3

This diagram, in fact, shows eight columns (or tracks) of punched holes. The eighth bit (leftmost track) is used as a *parity check* to detect possible errors during data transmission, and does not form part of the coded instruction. Between tracks 3 and 4 there is a stream of smaller *feed holes* which exist purely to help transport the tape and do not represent a binary digit. All numeric signals have binary 1 at tracks 5 and 6. Thus the seven-bit code for a figure "one" is 0110001; for a figure "two" it is 0110010; for a figure "three" it is 0110011; and so on. All letter signals have a binary 1 at track 7 and otherwise ascend from binary "one" (A) to binary "twenty six" (Z). Thus the seven-bit code for a letter A is 1000001; for a letter B it is 1000010; and so on.

It should be noted that the numbering system is not strictly a binary format. Numeric data is communicated in decimal form with each decimal digit recognised by a binary code. This is known as *Binary Coded Decimal* (BCD).

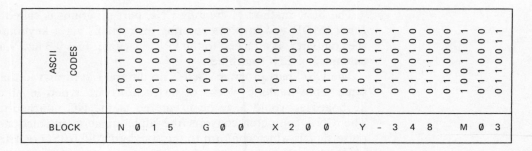

| BLOCK | N | 0 | 1 | 5 | | G | 0 | 0 | | X | 2 | 0 | 0 | | Y | - | 3 | 4 | 8 | | M | 0 | 3 |

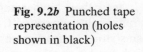

Fig. 9.2a Typical part-program instruction block

Fig. 9.2b Punched tape representation (holes shown in black)

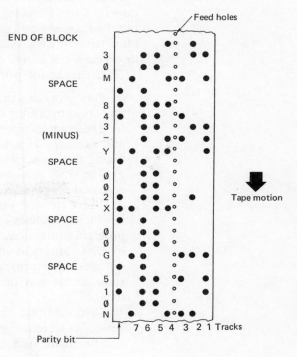

The EIA Code The EIA (Electronic Industries Association) code was popular before the present ISO code had been devised. Adopted by the American Standards Association, it is based on a similar seven-bit code. Most modern NC and CNC machines will accommodate either of the two coding systems.

9.2 Computer Numerical Control (CNC)

CNC embraces the essential principles of traditional NC, but employs a dedicated *stored program* computer to perform the basic NC functions. The computer is housed within the machine control unit and allows part programs to be created via its software and stored in its memory.

The basic method of creating CNC part programs is called *Manual Data Input* (MDI) and involves entering instructions via a keyboard which, like the computer, is attached to the CNC machine. Figs 9.3 and 9.4 show typical examples of CNC machines.

The CNC part program itself is no different in format to that of NC. The same alpha-numeric blocks of instructions are typed in at the computer keyboard as would have been entered at the NC punched-tape machine. The CNC computer converts the alpha-numeric instructions into binary pulse signals which conform to the standard ASCII/ISO or EIA NC codes.

Once created, the part program may be executed any number of times directly from memory. It may then be permanently stored on traditional punched paper tape (automatically generated from the CNC computer) but most modern CNC systems store part programs on magnetic tape cassettes or on magnetic floppy discs similar to those used in CAD applications.

CNC has the following advantages over traditional NC:

a) Part programs may be entered, and edited, directly at the machine unit, thus bypassing the initial paper-punching process.

b) The complete part program may be stored in the computer memory and executed as a full production cycle instead of the machine undertaking single operations after each block has been read.

c) The CNC part program need be loaded only once for any number of repeated program executions required.

d) The CNC software may contain automatic procedures for common machining routines ("canned cycles"), which may be actioned via simple program instructions.

e) CNC programs may include subroutines for repeated machining sequences. Once programmed, these may be repeatedly recalled at any later stage in the part program, thus eliminating the need to input identical data.

f) CNC software may include tool-compensation facility which allows versatility of tool size in producing a particular component. For example, a cutter path for a machined profile may be automatically offset to suit any size of tool quoted.

g) Similar shapes may be parameterised into one CNC part program, with individual dimensions varied as required, in the same manner as the creation of a parametric macro drawing standard for a CAD library.

h) CNC allows direct communication with other computer systems such as CAD databases, direct numerical control (DNC) host computers, and CAPM systems.

The CNC Part Program

The object of this section is to give an insight into the structure of the CNC part program, its associated terminology, and standard language codes. Part programming is a highly skilled occupation requiring a wealth of manufacturing knowledge, much preparatory work, and knowledge of proving techniques. Full instruction in writing part programs is thus beyond the scope of this book, and will require further reading and practical training.

Fig. 9.3 CNC lathe with multi-tool turret (note the attached control unit with computer keyboard and display) [*N.C. Engineering Ltd.*]

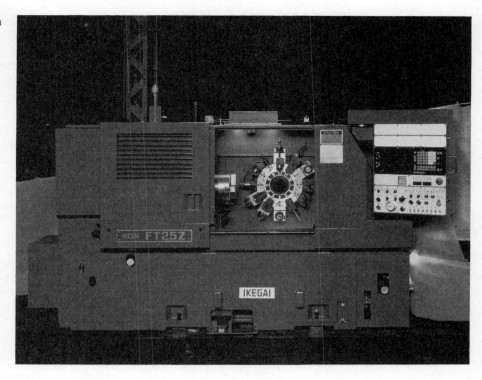

Fig. 9.4 CNC vertical machining centre [N.C. Engineering Ltd.]

Fig. 9.5 Extract of part program for slot-milling operation (speeds and feed data omitted)

		PART-PROGRAM EXTRACT				INTERPRETATION
NØØ6	GØØ	X3Ø	Y2Ø	Z6Ø	MØ3	SPINDLE ON, RAPID MOVEMENT TO POINT1 (AT Z6Ø)
NØØ7				Z1	MØ8	RAPID DOWNWARDS MOVEMENT TO Z1, COOLANT ON
NØØ8	GØ1			Z-1Ø		FEED LINEAR INTERPOLATION TO Z-1Ø (DEPTH OF CUT)
NØØ9		X16Ø				FEED LINEAR INTERPOLATION TO POINT2.
NØ1Ø		X13Ø	Y5Ø			FEED LINEAR INTERPOLATION TO POINT3.
NØ11	GØØ			Z1		RAPID UPWARDS MOVEMENT TO Z1 AT POINT3
NØ12		X1ØØ	Y11Ø			RAPID MOVEMENT TO POINT4 AT Z1.
NØ13	GØ1			Z-8		FEED LINEAR INTERPOLATION TO Z-8 (DEPTH OF CUT)
NØ14	G17					SET X-Y PLANE FOR CIRCULAR INTERPOLATION
NØ15	GØ3	X5Ø	Y6Ø	IØ J-5Ø	MØ9	ACW CIRCULAR INTERPOLATION TO POINT 5, COOLANT OFF
NØ16	GØØ			Z6Ø	MØ5	RAPID UPWARDS MOVEMENT TO Z6Ø AT POINT 5, STOP SPINDLE
NØ17		XØ	YØ		MØ2	RAPID MOVEMENT TO XØ,YØ AT Z6Ø, END PROGRAM

An extract from a simple CNC part program for a slot-milling operation is shown in Fig 9.5. This contains commands in language which conforms to BS 3635. Most CNC control units operate with the majority of these commands although each make of machine is likely to include many additional non-standard variations.

As previously stated, each line in the program is called a *block*, which is made up of a number of commands. Each command consists of a capital letter called an *address*, followed by a numerical value which makes up the complete command *word*. The arrangement of words in the block conforms to a standard order called a *format*.

Each block commences with a *block sequence number* which always starts with a capital N address (such as NØØ6 in the first block of the program shown).

COMMON G-CODES	
G00	RAPID TOOL MOVEMENT
G01	LINEAR INTERPOLATION
G02	CW CIRCULAR INTERPOLATION
G03	ACW CIRCULAR INTERPOLATION
G04	DWELL
G17	CIRCULAR INTERPOLATION (X-Y PLANE)
G18	CIRCULAR INTERPOLATION (Z-X PLANE)
G19	CIRCULAR INTERPOLATION (Y-Z PLANE)
G30	SERIES FOR MIRROR IMAGE
G33	SCREW-CUTTING
G40	SERIES FOR CUTTER COMPENSATION
G70	INCH UNITS
G71	METRIC UNITS
G80	CANCEL CANNED CYCLE
G81-G89	CANNED CYCLES
G90	ABSOLUTE COORDINATES
G91	INCREMENTAL COORDINATES

Fig. 9.6a

COMMON M-CODES	
M00	PROGRAM STOP
M01	OPTIONAL STOP
M02	END OF PROGRAM
M03	SPINDLE ON (CW)
M04	SPINDLE ON (ACW)
M05	SPINDLE OFF
M06	TOOL CHANGE
M07	MIST COOLANT ON
M08	FLOOD COOLANT ON
M09	COOLANT OFF
M10	CLAMP ON
M30	REWIND TAPE

Fig. 9.6b

The block sequence numbers in Fig 9.5 are sometimes followed by G-CODE PREPARATORY FUNCTIONS which instruct the machine to change its mode of control. For example, the GØØ function of block NØØ6 instructs the spindle to begin rapid movement. Common G-code functions are listed in Fig 9.6a.

Words commencing with X, Y, or Z addresses command spindle movement in the designated direction relative to its axis. (Additional letters are used if the spindle has more than three axes of movement.)

Words commencing with I, J, or K addresses specify the arc centres when using *circular interpolation* (i.e. multiple spindle action resulting in a circular feed machining path). The numerical values following I, J, or K, represent the incremental distance of the arc centre relative to the arc starting point in the X,Y, and Z directions respectively.

Some of the blocks in the slot-milling program end with M-CODE (miscellaneous) FUNCTIONS. For example, the MØ3 function of block NØØ6 instructs the spindle to be switched on. Common M-code functions are listed in Fig 9.6b.

Other standard letter addresses include: T (tool identification); S (spindle speed specification); and F (feed rate specification).

Once entered, a word is assumed to remain unchanged in the next block unless otherwise stated, and thus need not be repeated.

The instruction blocks in Fig 9.5 may be summarized as follows:

Block NØØ6 causes the spindle to switch on (MØ3), and rapidly moves it (GØØ) to point 1 (X3Ø,Y2Ø).

Block NØØ7 moves the spindle rapidly downwards to a 1 mm clearance from the top of the workpiece (Z1) and switches on the coolant (MØ8).

Rapid movement and X,Y coordinates are unchanged from the previous block and are thus not included in this block.

Block NØØ8 provides LINEAR INTERPOLATION (GØ1), i.e. straight-line feed movement, downwards to 10 mm cutting depth (Z−1Ø).

Block NØØ9 provides linear interpolation (unchanged from previous block) to point 2 (X16Ø).

Block NØ1Ø provides linear interpolation to point 3 (X13Ø,Y5Ø).

Block NØ11 provides rapid movement (GØØ) upwards to 1 mm work clearance (Z1).

Block NØ12 provides rapid movement to point 4 (X1ØØ,Y11Ø).

Block NØ13 provides linear interpolation (GØ1) downwards to 8 mm cutting depth (Z−8).

Block NØ14 instructs the machine to change to circular interpolation mode (G17).

Block NØ15 provides anti-clockwise circular interpolation (GØ3) to point 5 (X5Ø,Y6Ø), with arc centre X coordinate at starting point 4 (IØ, i.e. zero X increment from current position) and arc centre Y coordinate at 50 mm below starting point 4 (J−5Ø, i.e. −5Ø Y increment from current position).

Block NØ16 rapidly (GØØ) retracts the spindle upwards to its starting clearance height of 60 mm above the workpiece (Z6Ø) and stops the spindle (MØ5).

Block NØ17 rapidly returns the spindle to its starting datum point (XØ,YØ) and ends the program (MØ2).

This program uses ABSOLUTE COORDINATE dimensions from the datum position. Alternatively, it could have been written with IN-CREMENTAL COORDINATES which specify each dimension as the distance moved from the last coordinate position. An absolute mode may be changed to incremental with a G91 command, and reverted to absolute mode with a G9Ø command.

Axes of Movement

Both the complexity of the part program, and the versatility of form in the finished component, are influenced by the maximum number of axes along which the tool can move relative to the workpiece at the same time. Fig 9.7 shows the most common types of axial movements available in CNC machines.

a) 2D AXIS CONTROL machines provide programmable tool movement along two axes simultaneously. Typical CNC applications include turning and flame cutting.

b) $2\frac{1}{2}$D AXIS CONTROL provides programmable tool movement along three axes but allows simultaneous movement along a maximum of only two axes per operation. It is commonly used for basic 2D milling profiles which require programmable depth, such as slots and pockets.

c) 3D AXIS CONTROL machines provide programmable tool movement along three axes simultaneously. It may be used to cut complex 3D

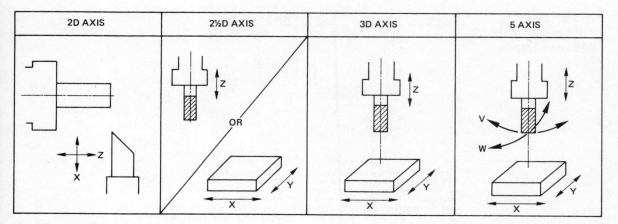

2D AXIS	2½D AXIS	3D AXIS	5 AXIS
	OR		

Fig. 9.7 Axes of movement

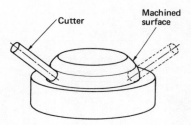

Cutter   Machined surface

Fig. 9.8 Sculptured surface with five-axis milling cutter

profiles but is limited by its inability to vary the tool angle relative to the workpiece during operation.

d) 5 AXIS CONTROL machines provide programmable tool movement along three axes simultaneously and also allow programmable angular movement of the tool spindle axis. This enables the tool spindle to remain normal to the work surface at all times. Sculptured 3D surfaces often require bull-nose milling cutters in their manufacture. Satisfactory surface finishes on such profiles can be achieved with fewer cutter passes when using 5-axis control than with a 3-axis machine (Fig 9.8).

Program Features

1 Canned cycles, or fixed cycles, are automatic procedures for common operating routines which may be actioned from a single program command and thus save a great deal of time and effort. The nature of the canned cycle will depend on the type of CNC application. Fig 9.9 shows some of the canned cycles available on a typical 3-axis CNC milling machine.

2 Program loops may be used to minimise laborious programming steps (e.g. a number of identical drilled holes each at an equal incremental distance apart). A simple command may be included which tells the computer to "jump back" to the repeated command for a stated number of times after each increment has been actioned (Fig 9.10*a*).

Fig. 9.9 Typical milling canned cycles [*Bridgeport Textron Ltd.*]

Cycle 1: Drill/Peck Drill

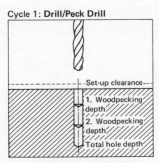

From the set-up clearance plane, either the total depth or first depth is drilled at a programmed feed rate. The spindle then retracts to the set-up clearance position in rapid traverse. Where a peck drill cycle is required this procedure is repeated for subsequent peck depths until the total hole depth is achieved.

Cycle 3: Slot milling

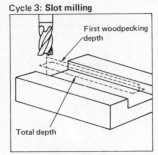

The cutter sinks in at half the programmed feed rate to the final depth or first peck depth. A pass through the centre is then made and this is repeated until the final depth is achieved. The slot is then contour-milled to the final depth.

Cycle 2: Tapping

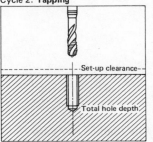

From the set-up clearance plane, the total thread depth is achieved at programmed feed rate. The spindle then retracts to the set-up clearance position at the same programmed feed rate.

Cycle 4: Pocket milling

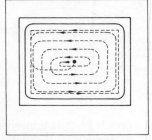

The cutter initially sinks in to the centre of the pocket, at half the programmed feed rate, to the final depth or first peck depth. The cutter then steps over parallel to the edges of the pocket approximate 80% of the cutter diameter and produces a picture frame type cycle. These operations are repeated until the final dimensions of the pocket are achieved. The cutter returns to the centre and subsequent peck depth repeat operations are carried out until the desired pocket depth is obtained.

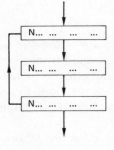

Fig. 9.10a Program loop

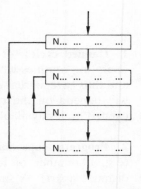

Fig. 9.10b Nested loop

Complex "loops-within-loops" may also be included in a program. Such a sequence is called a *nested loop* (Fig 9.10b).

3 As in CAD software, a CNC program **macro** is a subroutine which actions a number of operations in response to a single command. CNC macros, like loops, are used to control repetitive manufacturing operations. Unlike loops, a macro, once written, begins with a sequence number outside the main structure of the program and may be called up at any stage in the program when required (Fig 9.11).

A macro may be either:

a) *System type* (i.e. integral with the system software), or
b) *User-defined* (i.e. individually programmed by the user).

System macros will be contained within a database library and may be called up and actioned via single commands within the part program. Thus they perform a similar function to that of canned cycles. However, whereas the term "canned cycle" normally refers to fixed subroutines contained within the core memory of the CNC machine, system macros are usually taken to be contained within disc package software.

User-defined macros may also be entered as standards into a database library for use in any future part program, or alternatively they may be created as an integral section of a single part program.

Parametric macros are used for producing repeated shapes with similar features but whose individual dimensions and specifications (i.e. parameters) may be altered as required each time they are called up (Fig 9.12).

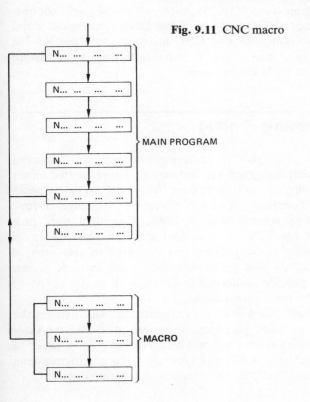

Fig. 9.11 CNC macro

MAIN PROGRAM

MACRO

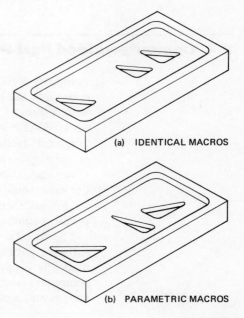

Fig. 9.12 Machined component using macros

(a) IDENTICAL MACROS

(b) PARAMETRIC MACROS

9.3 Direct Numerical Control (DNC)

Manual data input at the CNC keyboard has the disadvantage of rendering the machine inoperable whilst the program is being entered and edited.

In a DNC system the part program may be created on a host computer which then downloads the data directly to the CNC machine. Several CNC machines may accommodated in this way from one host computer and may all be running whilst part programs are being produced.

DNC particularly lends itself to computer-aided part programming techniques and graphical simulation of production processes. Also the host computer may receive data from other computer systems such as CAD and production management via a common database. DNC thus becomes a vital component in a linked CADCAM system and in a computer integrated manufacturing (CIM) organisation (Fig 9.13).

Fig. 9.13 Principle of DNC

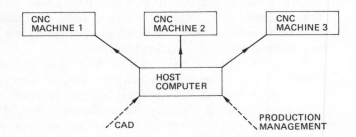

RS-232 interface   Serial transmission (p.23) involves a single-cable connection between host computer and workstation. Most DNC systems use serial transmission between host computer and CNC machines, and the RS-232 standard governs the format and speed of data transmission, hardware configuration, and required cable connections.

9.4 Computer-Aided Part Programming (CAPP)

Although DNC may be undertaken by entering part program language codes into the host computer, programs are increasingly being created either with a direct CADCAM link or with "user-friendly" CAPP software packages. CAPP packages commonly employ simplified language forms, graphical techniques, or a combination of both. Graphical part programming is undertaken on VDU screens and is often referred to as *Graphical Numerical Control* (GNC). Graphical systems can also provide dynamic tool-path simulations and production data such as cycle times. CAPP software can also provide additional facilities, such as the ability to perform complex trigonometrical calculations.

The specific CAPP format will depend on the company which writes the software package. However many packages are based on the APT (Automatically Programmed Tools) system and will be compatible for a range of computers and CNC machines. APT is effectively both a programming system and a part-programming language, which is internationally used.

Structure of CAPP Software

Most CAPP software packages are divided into three main sections (see Fig 9.14):

Geometry definition.
Manufacturing processor.
Post-processor.

Fig. 9.14 Stages in computer-aided part programming (CAPP)

1 GEOMETRY DEFINITION involves breaking the component shape up into its primitive geometric elements. In the APT system, these primitives include points, lines, circles, planes, cylinders, cones, and spheres.

Fig 9.15 shows a possible APT procedure for defining the geometry of the slots in the milling exercise which was previously shown in Fig 9.5. For example, line 3Ø of the program defines PT1 as a point with cartesian coordinates X=30, Y=20, and Z=−10. Line 6Ø defines L1 as being a straight line passing through points PT1 and PT2. Line 7Ø defines C1 as a circle whose centre is PT6 and whose circumference passes through PT4.

Fig. 9.15 Slot-milling geometry definition using APT

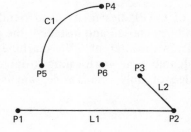

30	P1=POINT/30,20,-10
35	P2=POINT/160,20,-10
40	P3=POINT/130,50,-10
45	P4=POINT/100,110,-8
50	P5=POINT/50,60,-8
55	P6=POINT/100,60,-8
60	L1=LINE/PT1,PT2
65	L2=LINE/PT2,PT3
70	C1=CIRCLE/CENTRE,PT6,PT4

2 The MANUFACTURING PROCESSOR uses the geometry definition to generate the data required to produce the component. Typical data entered at this stage includes size of cutting tool, spindle speeds, and feed rates. In an APT program, the following lines could be included:

11Ø CUTTER/15
115 $PINDL/1ØØØ,CLW
12Ø FEDRAT/3ØØ

Line 11Ø selects a milling cutter of 10 mm diameter.
Line 115 selects a spindle speed of 1000 rev/min in a clockwise direction.
Line 12Ø selects a feed rate of 300 mm/min.

Information regarding direction of tool movement and required cutter path will also be input to the manufacturing processor. For example, linear interpolation of the lower milled slot in Fig 9.5 could be achieved via the following two lines in an APT program:

    145   GORGHT/L1,PAST,P2
    15Ø   GOLFT/L2,PAST,P3

Line 145 instructs the cutter to go right along straight line L1 until it is past point P2.

Similarly, line 15Ø gives an instruction to go left along straight line L2 until point P3 is past.

3 The POST-PROCESSOR is that part of the CAPP software package which converts the English-like statements of a language such as APT, into coded instructions which may be understood by the CNC machine (i.e. G-codes, M-codes, etc.). Up until this stage, the CAPP language remains the same for any make and model of CNC machine. However, because different machine tool manufacturers vary slightly in their functional interpretation and format of G-codes and M-codes, the post-processor has to be a unique piece of software, suitable for a specific CNC machine. To sell their product, the CAPP software writers must therefore make available a wide range of post-processors to suit popular CNC machine models, or be prepared to write them on request. However, this should not greatly affect software costs as post-processors are comparatively simple programs.

The chief advantage of CAPP lies in its user-friendliness and versatility. Once the software has been chosen and installed, the part-programmer does not have to be familiar with different CNC machine systems and complex codings, or waste valuable time performing arduous calculations. CAPP requires the knowledge of only one simple language and sound manufacturing experience.

Examples in Computer-aided Part Programming

The cases to be discussed are extracts from part programs using a CAPP software package called PEPS, produced by N. C. Riter Ltd. PEPS uses the GNC principle of progressive graphical displays to build up the geometry definition. Geometric construction displays are shown with arrows to define their direction. For example, typical displays for a line and for a circle are shown in Fig 9.16.

Constructional elements are displayed via simple keyboard commands, such as P (point), C (circle), T (tangential, i.e. in the same sense of

Fig. 9.16

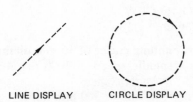

LINE DISPLAY   CIRCLE DISPLAY

direction to an adjacent element), A (anti-tangential, i.e. in the opposite sense of direction to adjacent element), B (angle in degrees).

EXAMPLE 1: **Simple 2½ axis milling profile**

Fig 9.17*b* lists some of the lines and interpretations for milling the component shown in Fig 9.17*a*.

Lines Ø1Ø to Ø16 define the geometry of the shape. As each geometry command is entered, the corresponding construction is simultaneously displayed on the screen. Fig 9.18 shows the completed geometry display.

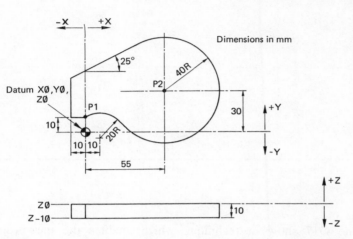

Fig. 9.17 Required component and extract from program

LINE NO.	PROGRAM	INTERPRETATION
Ø1Ø	P1 Ø 10	POINT 1 AT X=Ø, Y=1Ø (Z ASSUMED TO BE AT Ø)
Ø11	P2 55 3Ø	POINT 2 AT X=55, Y=3Ø
Ø12	S1 V-1Ø	STRAIGHT LINE 1, VERTICAL AT X=-1Ø
Ø13	S2 H1Ø	STRAIGHT LINE 2, HORIZONTAL AT Y=1Ø
Ø14	C1 P2 4Ø	CIRCLE 1, CENTRE AT POINT 2, RADIUS 4Ø
Ø15	S3 B25 TC1	STRAIGHT LINE 3, AT 25° AND TANGENTIAL TO CIRCLE 1.
Ø16	C2 LAC1 P1 3Ø	CIRCLE 2, LEFT ANTITANGENTIAL TO CIRCLE 1, PASSING THROUGH POINT 1, RADIUS 3Ø.
Ø17	INPUT 'ENTER VIEW REQUIRED' \$1	COMMAND TO DISPLAY 'ENTER VIEW REQUIRED' AT VDU. \$GIVES LABEL TO OPERATOR'S REPLY
Ø18	IF \$1='XY' VIEW XY	COMMAND TO DISPLAY 2D VIEW (XY PLANE) IF 'XY' IS INPUT AT KEYBOARD
Ø19	IF \$1='XYZ' VIEW XYZ	COMMAND TO DISPLAY 3D VIEW (XYZ PLANE) IF 'XYZ' IS INPUT AT KEYBOARD
Ø2Ø	K1 P1 AS2 TS1 TS3 TC1 AC2 P1 EK	CUTTER PROFILE KURVE 1, STARTING AND ENDING AT POINT 1. EK TERMINATES THE KURVE
Ø21	FRO X-30 Y80 Z50	STARTING POINT OF CUTTER FROM COORDINATES SHOWN. (Z VALUE TO BASE OF CUTTER)
Ø22	TOOL1 D1Ø	TOOL 1, DIAMETER 1Ø
Ø23	SPI 125Ø	SPINDLE SPEED 125Ø rev/min
Ø24	FED V1ØØ H175	FEED RATE, 1ØØ mm/min VERTICALLY, 175 mm/min HORIZONTALLY
Ø25	CLE 3	MOVE MILLING CUTTER TO 3mm CLEARANCE ABOVE WORK PIECE
Ø26	RAP GOTO X-8Ø YØ	RAPID TOOL MOVEMENT TO X-8Ø, YØ
Ø27	GOTO Z-1Ø	SINK MILLING CUTTER INTO WORKPIECE AT 1ØØ mm/min to 1Ø mm DEPTH
Ø28	OFF L2 PRO TK1	MOVE CUTTER ALONG PROFILE OF KURVE 1 TANGENTIALLY AT 2mm OFFSET
Ø29	OFF LØ PRO TK1	AS LINE Ø28 BUT WITH ZERO OFFSET (i.e. FINAL CUT)
Ø3Ø	RET	RETURN MILLING CUTTER TO ORIGINAL Z POSITION
Ø31	GOH	GO HOME (i.e. RETURN CUTTER TO ORIGINAL X, Y POSITION)

Fig. 9.18 Completed
geometry display

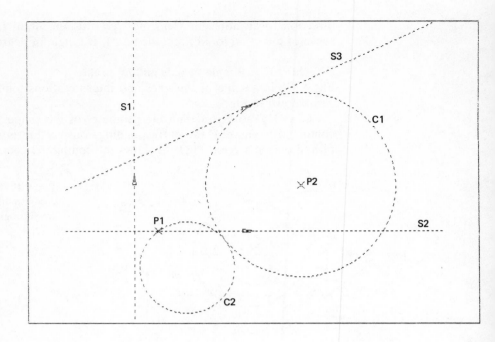

Line Ø17 shows a technique which enables the part-programmer to display text messages to the program user, whose reply is then labelled with a "dollar" sign. In this case, the message ENTER VIEW REQUIRED will appear on the screen after the geometry has been displayed. The operator's reply will be recognised by the computer as $1. Lines Ø18 and Ø19 give the user the option of either an XY plane view (2D plan) or an XYZ plane view (isometric) depending on whether the reply ($1) is XY or XYZ respectively.

The next stage is to define the cutting profile of the component (called a KURVE in the PEPS system). This is shown in line Ø2Ø, which labels the kurve as K1 and specifies each geometric element in order and direction as they appear in a clockwise sense around the kurve. For example, the straight line S3 conforms to the clockwise sense of the kurve and is thus listed as TS3 (tangential), whereas the line S2 is opposed to the clockwise sense, and is thus listed as AS2 (antitangential). All kurves must begin and end with a defined point. The command EK (End Kurve) signifies that the kurve routine is completed. Fig 9.19 shows the XY plane view of the completed kurve.

Lines Ø21 to Ø31 define the tool size, tool movements, spindle speeds, and feeds required to mill the component along K1. In lines Ø28 and Ø29, the command PRO TK1 tells the milling cutter to travel tangentially around the profile of K1 at the stated offset value. Each offset automatically compensates for the size of the tool. For example, the command OFF LØ (offset zero) in line Ø29 will in fact offset the spindle centre at the tool radius value of 5 mm from the kurve.

Figs 9.20 and 9.21 shows the displayed kurve and tool-path simulations for the XY plane and XYZ plane display options respectively.

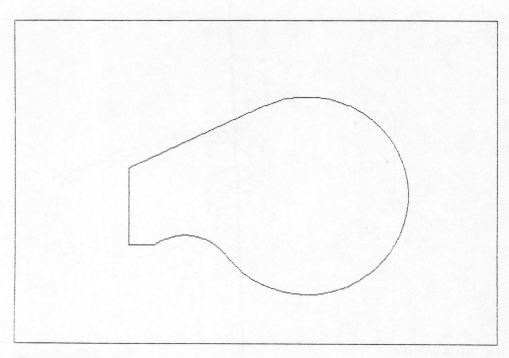

Fig. 9.19 Completed kurve display (XY plane)

Fig. 9.20 Kurve and tool-path simulation display (XY plane)

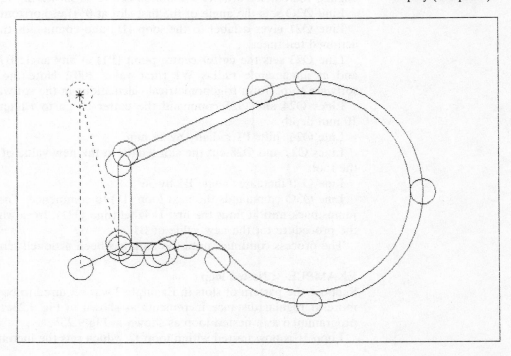

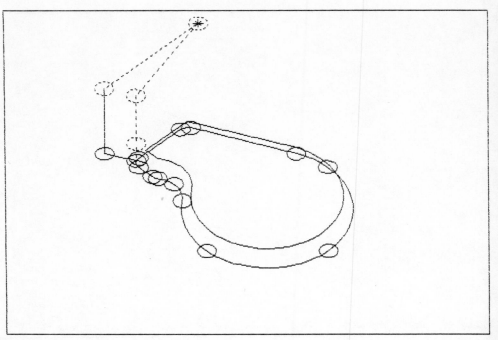

Fig. 9.21 Kurve and tool-path simulation display (XYZ plane)

EXAMPLE 2: **Repeat loop**

The following program extract uses a repeat loop to cut ten slots at equal angular increments around a common centre as shown in Fig 9.22.

Line Ø2Ø sets the angle of the first slot at 0° (i.e. horizontal slot).

Line Ø21 gives a label to the loop (I1) and commands that the loop be actioned ten times.

Line Ø23 sets the cutter centre point (P1) at any angle B1 (first value 0) and at pitch circle radius W1 (first value 100). Note the ability of the software to perform trigonometrical calculations in the software.

Lines Ø24 and Ø25 command the cutter to go to P1 and sink in to a 10 mm depth.

Line Ø26 shifts P1 radially by 25 mm.

Lines Ø27 and Ø28 cut the slot length to the new value of P1 and retract the tool.

Line Ø29 increases angle B1 by 36°.

Line Ø3Ø commands the next loop (I1) to commence. The program then jumps back until it finds the first I1 label (line Ø21), from whence it repeats the procedure for the new value of B1.

The process continues until the loop has been actioned ten times.

EXAMPLE 3: **Nested loop**

Suppose the pattern of slots in Example 2 was required to be repeated twice more at regular distance increments as shown in Fig 9.23a. This could be programmed as a nested loop as shown in Fig 9.23b.

Loop I1 is now nested within loop I2, which sets the increments at 500 by

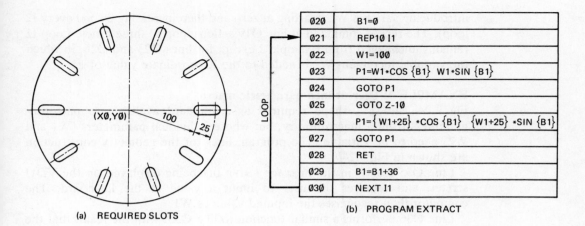

(a) REQUIRED SLOTS

(b) PROGRAM EXTRACT

020	B1=0
021	REP10 I1
022	W1=100
023	P1=W1*COS {B1} W1*SIN {B1}
024	GOTO P1
025	GOTO Z-10
026	P1={W1+25} *COS {B1} {W1+25} *SIN {B1}
027	GOTO P1
028	RET
029	B1=B1+36
030	NEXT I1

Fig. 9.22 Slot-drilling repeat loop

Fig. 9.23 Slot patterns nested loop

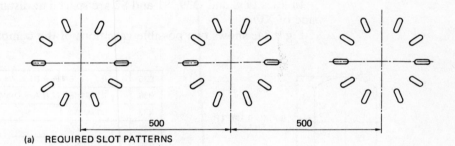

(a) REQUIRED SLOT PATTERNS

018	W2=0
019	REP3 I2
020	B1=0
021	REP10 I1
022	W1=100
023	P1=W2+W1*COS {B1} W1*SIN {B1}
024	GOTO P1
025	GOTO Z-10
026	P1=W2+ {W1+25} *COS {B1} {W1+25} * SIN {B1}
027	GOTO P1
028	RET
029	B1=B1+36
030	NEXT I1
031	W2=W2+500
032	NEXT I2

(b) NESTED LOOP PROGRAM EXTRACT

195

introducing variable W2 (starting at zero and then increasing by 500 every I2 loop). The repeat command at line Ø19 actions loop I2 three times. Loop I1 remains unchanged from Example 2 except for lines Ø23 and Ø26, in which the variable increment W2 is added to the X coordinate value of P1.

EXAMPLE 4: User-defined parametric macro

Fig 9.24*a* shows a shape required as a standard available to part programmers from a macro library, but whose individual parameters (W1 and W2) need to be variable. The program lines for the geometry construction are shown in Fig 9.24*b*.

Line Ø35 results in the message ENTER DIA being displayed on the VDU screen, and requires the user to input a value at the keyboard. The computer then recognises the inputed value as W1.

Line Ø36 performs a similar function to line Ø35, with the result that the computer recognises the across-flats dimension as W2. To avoid a nonsense result, the upper limit of W2 is set at the diameter size (W1), by adding TW1 (i.e. top value of W2 = W1) at the end of the line.

Line Ø37 describes circle C1 by setting its centre at X = 0, Y = 0 and radius value at half of W1.

In lines Ø38 and Ø39, S1 and S2 are spaced at distances half of W2 either side of XØ.

Fig 9.24*c* shows two possible variations of the completed component.

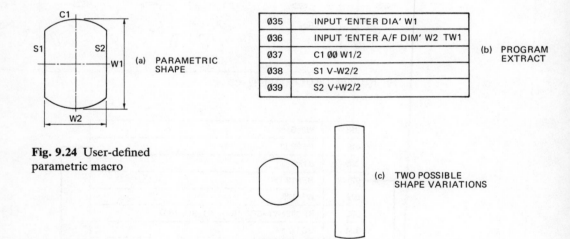

Ø35	INPUT 'ENTER DIA' W1
Ø36	INPUT 'ENTER A/F DIM' W2 TW1
Ø37	C1 ØØ W1/2
Ø38	S1 V-W2/2
Ø39	S2 V+W2/2

(a) PARAMETRIC SHAPE

(b) PROGRAM EXTRACT

(c) TWO POSSIBLE SHAPE VARIATIONS

Fig. 9.24 User-defined parametric macro

EXAMPLE 5: Turning program

Fig 9.25*a* shows a component which is required to be turned on a CNC lathe. Figs 9.25*b-f* show progressive VDU displays of the corresponding geometry and tool-cutting simulations throughout the creation of the part program.

Fig. 9.25*a* Required shaft for CNC lathe turning

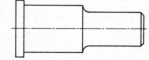

Fig 9.25b shows the display of the cutting profile kurve and the un-machined material profile. These are created via the geometric procedures outlined in the previous examples.

Fig 9.25c shows the tool-path simulation for the facing operation. The tool display is obtained from a macro library contained within the CAPP turning

Fig. 9.25b Profile kurve and raw material display

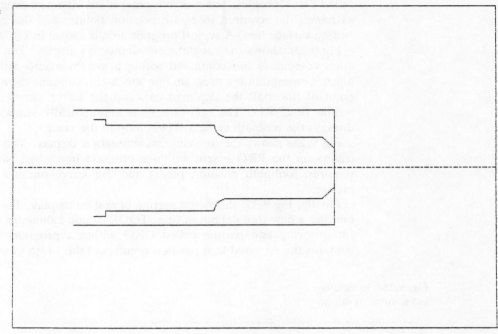

Fig. 9.25c Facing operation simulation display

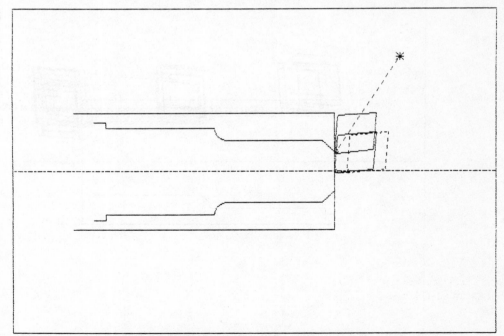

software. The macro is entered into the part program by quoting a tool definition (e.g. TOOL 1) and specifying the ISO tool shape code, the size, and the orientation of the tool. Fig 9.26*a* shows a range of ISO tool shapes contained within the macro library. Fig 9.26*b* shows the options with tool orientation. Fig 9.26*c* shows a typical tool definition program line.

The facing operation simulation is obtained via another system macro called PRO (profile). The macro is entered into the part program by quoting its name, the required tool-path position points, and the geometry of the cutting surface line. A typical program line is shown in Fig 9.26*d*.

Fig 9.25*d* shows the roughing-cut simulation display. The roughing operation commands are contained within a system macro called ROU. This name is entered into a program line which also contains the required starting point of the tool, the depth of cut, and the kurve number of the cutting profile (e.g. K1). The software then automatically scans the kurve and displays the toolpath using a repeat loop in the macro.

Fig 9.25*e* shows the finishing-cut simulation display. This is obtained by calling up the PRO macro within a program line which also contains the required tool-path position points and the kurve number of the cutting profile.

Finally, Fig 9.25*f* shows the parting operation display. This is obtained by quoting a new tool definition (e.g. TOOL 2) and calling up a system macro for grooving and parting called GRO within a program line which also contains the required tool position points and the width of parting tool.

Fig. 9.25*d* Roughing-cut simulation display

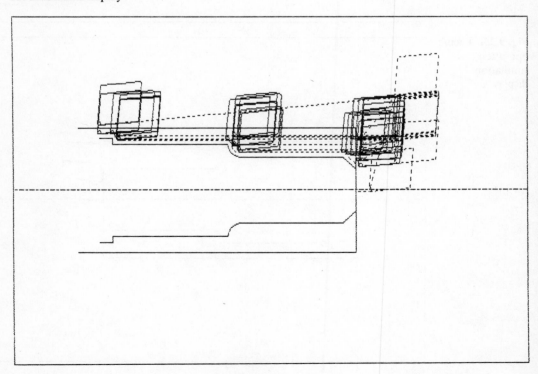

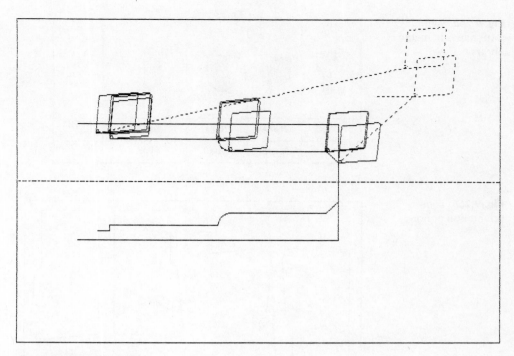

Fig. 9.25e Finishing-cut
simulation display

Fig. 9.25f Parting
operation simulation
display

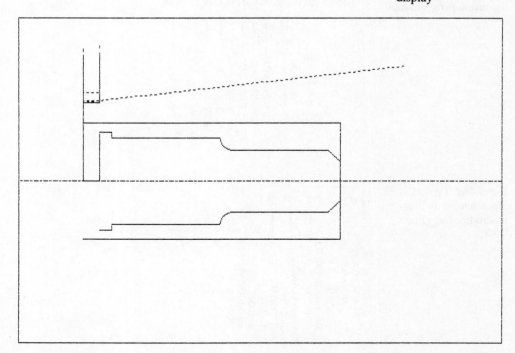

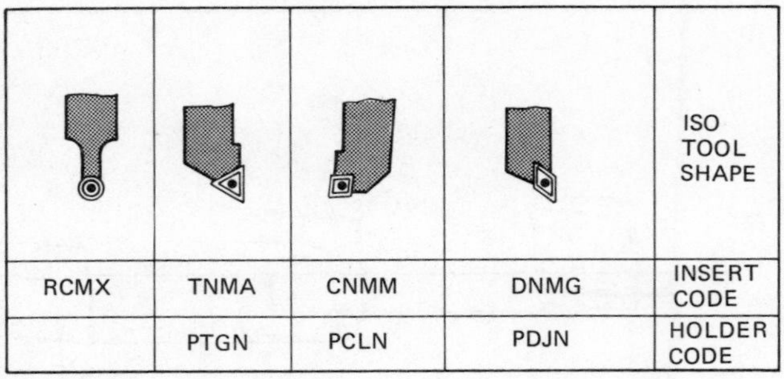

Fig. 9.26a Some ISO tool shapes in macro library

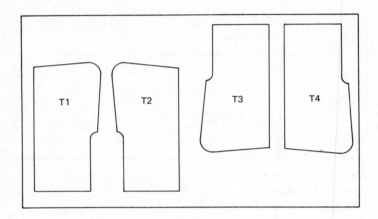

				ISO TOOL SHAPE
RCMX	TNMA	CNMM	DNMG	INSERT CODE
	PTGN	PCLN	PDJN	HOLDER CODE

Fig. 9.26b Tool-orientation options

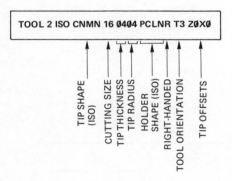

T1   T2   T3   T4

Fig. 9.26c Typical tool definition program line

TOOL 2 ISO CNMN 16 Ø4Ø4 PCLNR T3 ZØXØ

- TIP SHAPE (ISO)
- CUTTING SIZE
- TIP THICKNESS
- TIP RADIUS
- HOLDER SHAPE (ISO)
- RIGHT-HANDED
- TOOL ORIENTATION
- TIP OFFSETS

Fig. 9.26d Typical machining sequence macro program line

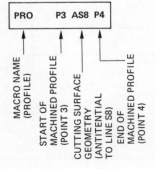

PRO   P3 AS8 P4

- MACRO NAME (PROFILE)
- START OF MACHINED PROFILE (POINT 3)
- CUTTING SURFACE GEOMETRY (ANTITENTIAL TO LINE S8)
- END OF MACHINED PROFILE (POINT 4)

EXAMPLE 6: **Nesting**

Nesting (not to be confused with the term "nested loop") is a cost optimisation procedure in which patterns of components are so arranged as to create the minimum possible material wastage from a rectangular sheet. Nesting is extensively used in milling, flame-cutting, and laser-cutting applications. Some systems allow component displays to be repeated and dynamically manipulated on the VDU screen to create the ideal nested pattern.

The following example is an extract from a simple nesting part program. Fig 9.27a shows the required finished component of which eight are to be cut from rectangular strip. Figs 9.27b and c show the stages of display. The relevant geometry program lines and interpretations are shown in Fig 9.28.

Fig. 9.27 Progressive displays in nesting part program

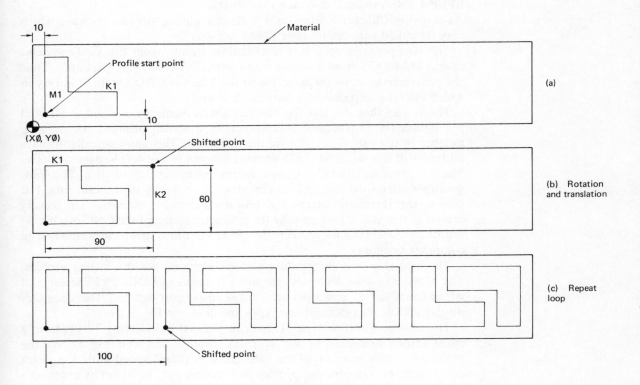

Fig. 9.28 Nesting part program: some relevant program lines (some intermediate lines omitted)

PROGRAM LINE	INTERPRETATION
SET M1	SET LABEL FOR SHAPE
W1=10	
REP4 I1	REPEAT LOOP, FOUR PROCEDURES
GOTO XW1 Y10	MOVE CUTTER TO START POINT OF PROFILE
ROT M1 Z180	ROTATE SHAPE M1 THROUGH 180° ABOUT Z AXIS
TRA M1 X {W1 + 90} Y60	TRANSLATE ROTATED KURVE TO NEW POSITION
COPY K1 K2 M1	COPY SHAPE M1 TO CREATE NEW ROTATED AND TRANSLATED PROFILE K2 FROM K1
W1=W1+100	SHIFT PROFILE K1 START POINT ALONG BY 100mm
NEXT I1	JUMP BACK FOR NEXT REPEAT LOOP

9.5 The Direct CADCAM Link—a Case Study

The CADCAM link is a logical extension of the CAPP principles previously outlined. It enables the part-programmer to define the component geometry automatically via direct access to the CAD drawing library files and thus avoids repeating the geometric construction.

To outline the principles of the CADCAM link, we will now record the major steps in manufacturing an oil pump cam ring designed by Hobourn-Eaton with the aid of the MAE CADCAM system. (This project has previously been discussed in Chapters 4 and 6.)

STEP 1 *Access CAD Software* (Maedos)
As stated in Chapter 4, Maedos is a 2D draughting software package which may be linked with appropriate CAM software.

The part-programmer, at a workstation remote from the CAD system, selects MAEDOS from a screen menu of available software packages. Thus the programmer gains ready access to the Maedos CAD database library in which the oil pump drawings have been stored.

The system then displays the Maedos screen menu, from which is selected the option RCAL (recall). In response to a screen prompt, the drawing number of the cam is entered via the keyboard. This automatically displays all layers of the required CAD drawing (shown in Fig 4.26*b*, page 67). The Maedos package contains eleven layers (numbered 0 to 10). The programmer selects the layer which contains the geometry of the cam ring. For clarity, the remaining layers and unwanted drawing elements are usually erased at this stage, leaving only the geometry required for CNC machining (all of the original data remains on the CAD drawing which is retained in computer memory).

The next step is to define the geometry elements for the cutting profiles. The Maedos system defines its geometry in terms of LINE TYPES; some of which (numbers 51 upwards) are alloted to be user-defined. The geometry display and its user-defined line types are shown in Fig. 9.29.

The cam profile (line type 51) may be defined by selecting TYPE from a small screen menu below the graphics display, and entering 51 via the keyboard. Each element of the cam curve is then located with a joystick cursor control. On complex profiles this process may be aided by entering a command which displays all construction points (e.g. arc centres) and tracing the CAD defined geometry onto another layer using a snapping-on graphics mode. With both layers displayed, the emerging traced profile appears in a different colour to the original and thus verifies that each element has been traced.

Line type 52 defines the slot profiles in the same manner as for the cam profile. TYPE is selected, 52 entered, and the circle centres and contours of each slot are located.

Similarly, line type 53 defines the centres and diameter of the four circular holes, with each hole being located during the definition procedure.

The defined geometry is then entered into the CAD library under a new drawing number.

Fig. 9.29 Geometry display and line types

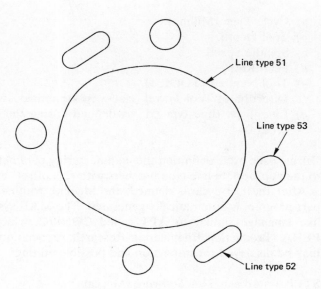

Line type 51

Line type 53

Line type 52

STEP 2 *Access CADCAM Link Software* (Maelink)
Maelink is a software package which provides a direct link between the Maedos CAD package and the MAE GNC part-programming package (Maecam).

MAELINK is selected from the screen menu in the same manner as Maedos and manufacturing parameters are attached to the CAD geometry via screen prompts and corresponding keyboard inputs.

Information entered at this stage includes:

a) Machine Type (defines CNC machine tool for the purposes of post-processing).
b) Part Number.
c) Tool Change Position.
d) Tool Parameters. These may be chosen from a tool library display. The required tool data for this component is

    TOOL 1 MØ2Ø (20 mm diameter end mill)
    TOOL 2 MØ6   (6 mm diameter end mill)
    TOOL 3 DØ8   (8 mm diameter drill)

The geometry defined during the Maedos tracing procedure is then recalled to the screen by entering the drawing number, and the specific parameters for each manufacturing cycle are defined in turn. For example, the following information would be entered when defining the cam profile parameters:

a) Cycle Type (Milling).
b) Tool Depth.
c) Spindle Speed.
d) Feed Rate.
e) Tool Number (TOOL 1).
f) Direction of Tool Travel (clockwise or anticlockwise).
g) Line Type (line type 51, as defined during the Maedos tracing procedure).

During each cycle definition the manufacturing parameters are thus matched to the appropriate line type numbers with tool offsets automatically created.

After the last cycle is defined, the Maelink routine is complete and the part program is automatically generated. The MAE system uses an English-like language similar to APT called CONPIC, which was developed by PERA (Production Engineering Research Association). The part program may be displayed for inspection and possible editing.

STEP 3   *Access GNC Software* (Maecam)
Once selected from the screen menu, the Maecam software converts the part program generated at the Maelink stage, into graphical commands. The machined profiles will automatically be displayed on the screen if correct data has been entered during the previous routines. Tool-path simulations may also be displayed for each manufacturing cycle. The part program may thus be checked graphically and edited if necessary until satisfactory manufacturing cycles are achieved.

Fig 9.30 shows the tool-path simulation displays for the oil pump cam ring geometry. The geometry and simulations may also be analysed via 3D display by selecting another package called Maesim. This provides visualisation options along two extra planes (XZ and YZ) and isometric views.

Fig. 9.30 Toolpath display of cam ring geometry

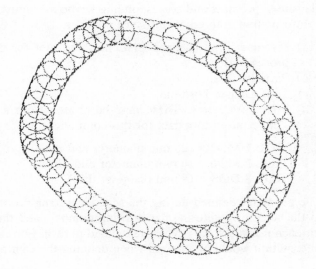

STEP 4 *Access Post-processor Generator* (Maegen)

As previously stated, post-processors are software packages which convert CAPP part program statements into G-code and M-code statements of the correct format to suit specific models of CNC machine. Maegen is a post-processing package which is selected after toolpath simulations and program editing has been finalized. Maegen contains a library of post-processors "tailor-made" by MAE for particular machines used by their customers. These post-processors may be updated and the library enlarged as company needs and machine tool systems alter.

At the time of publication, the Hobourn-Eaton Maegen package contains two post-processors which control their two types of CNC milling machines (a Bridgeport Series 1 and a Matchmaker CNC 750).

Once Maegen is selected, a simple keyboard command code is all that is required to select the CNC machine and to generate the appropriate G-code and M-code program format. The final data may then be displayed on the VDU screen, transferred to a paper-tape punching machine, or downloaded directly to the CNC machine using DNC. The DNC link is a simple serial cable between computer and CNC machine using RS-232 connections at each end (Fig 9.31).

Fig 9.32 shows the oil pump cam ring being machined on the Matchmaker 750 miller. The completed component is shown in Fig 9.33. Fig 9.34 summarises the CADCAM link steps in block diagram form.

Fig. 9.31 DNC serial cable link using RS-232 connections

Fig. 9.32 Cam ring
being machined on
CNC miller

Fig. 9.33 Completed
pump components
including cam ring,
rotor and pins

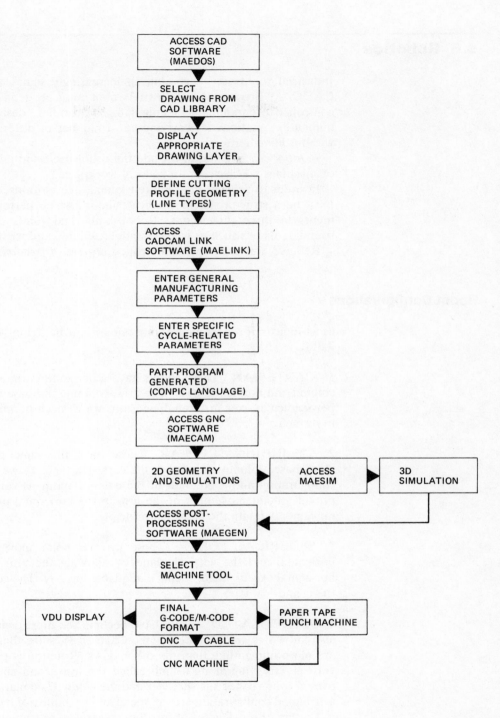

Fig. 9.34 Steps in CADCAM link

ACCESS CAD
SOFTWARE
(MAEDOS)

SELECT
DRAWING FROM
CAD LIBRARY

DISPLAY
APPROPRIATE
DRAWING LAYER

DEFINE CUTTING
PROFILE GEOMETRY
(LINE TYPES)

ACCESS
CADCAM LINK
SOFTWARE (MAELINK)

ENTER GENERAL
MANUFACTURING
PARAMETERS

ENTER SPECIFIC
CYCLE-RELATED
PARAMETERS

PART-PROGRAM
GENERATED
(CONPIC LANGUAGE)

ACCESS GNC
SOFTWARE
(MAECAM)

2D GEOMETRY
AND SIMULATIONS → ACCESS MAESIM → 3D SIMULATION

ACCESS POST-
PROCESSING
SOFTWARE (MAEGEN)

SELECT
MACHINE TOOL

VDU DISPLAY ← FINAL
G-CODE/M-CODE
FORMAT → PAPER TAPE PUNCH MACHINE

DNC   CABLE

CNC MACHINE

9.6 Robotics

Industrial robots are becoming an increasingly significant element of the CADCAM process. An industrial robot may be defined as a computer-controlled programmable manipulator or handler, designed to reproduce human-like motions for carrying out a number of different industrial tasks without human attendance.

A *robot cell* is taken to include the robot itself and any other equipment or machines which make up its local workplace.

In order to achieve the required human-like motions, an industrial robot must be a structure of mechanical "limbs" which perform multiple movements in three dimensions. Robot limbs and joints are given obvious-sounding names such as waist, shoulder, elbow, and wrist.

Relative limb movements are called *degrees of freedom*.

Robot Configurations

Most industrial robots incorporate one of four basic limb configurations (Fig 9.35).

1 CARTESIAN These robots have a horizontal arm affixed to a vertical column and horizontal base. The arm, column, and base thus form mutually perpendicular axes in three dimensions which each permit only straight-line movement.

2 CYLINDRICAL POLAR These have the same perpendicular axes along base, column and arm as the cartesian type. However, the cylindrical configuration allows rotation of the column about its vertical axis and thus provides polar movement of the arm in the horizontal plane only. Vertical movements retain the cartesian principle.

3 SPHERICAL POLAR These provide polar movement in both the horizontal and the vertical plane by allowing the arm to rotate about a horizontal axis as well as being extendable linearly. The column rotates as in the cylindrical type.

4 ARTICULATED These have become the most common type and are also known as *anthropometric* (see Chapter 8), since their limb movements are more human-like than the other types. Rotation is provided about one vertical axis lying along a limb called the *waist*, and about two horizontal axes at joints called the *shoulder* and the *elbow*. The main advantages of the articulated configuration are the speed and versatility of movement achieved.

The first three degrees of freedom, regardless of configuration, are usually supplemented by a further three applied to an additional compound limb called the *wrist* (Fig 9.36). Handling robots require grippers attached to the wrist. Gripper movements require degrees of freedom in addition to the six described.

Fig. 9.35 Basic robot limb configurations and degrees of freedom

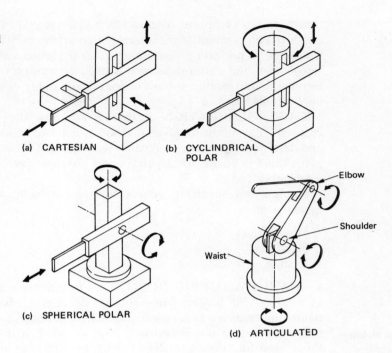

(a) CARTESIAN

(b) CYCLINDRICAL POLAR

(c) SPHERICAL POLAR

(d) ARTICULATED

Elbow

Shoulder

Waist

Fig. 9.36 Robot wrist movements

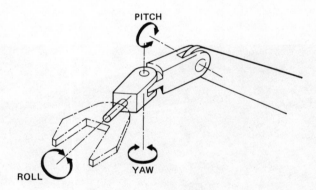

PITCH

ROLL

YAW

Robot Technology and Application

As in the case of the computer itself, robotics development has occurred in a number of progressive phases, called generations.

FIRST-GENERATION ROBOTS were introduced as an aid to production techniques in the early 1960s, and remain the most common type. They have no intelligence and are designed to action a programmed sequence of operations, irrespective of any change in local environment.

SECOND-GENERATION ROBOTS have some intelligence, which enables them to sense changes in local environment, learn from a program, and modify their actions accordingly. These robots are often equipped with touch sensors or optical sensors which can detect such things as presence, quantity and position of manufactured components. The robot will then be instructed to perform a variable program sequence, depending on feedback signals from the sensor detection. Second-generation robots exist at present in only limited numbers, but are continually being developed for industrial applications.

THIRD-GENERATION ROBOTS are now the subject of intensive research. The aim is to develop robots which can make intelligent decisions and determine optimum production techniques. The future role of this robot generation is likely to depend upon parallel developments in artificial intelligence (AI).

Applications involving robots may be broadly classified under the headings of

Manufacture
Handling
Testing.

Fig. 9.37a Spot welding robots [*Ford Motor Company*]

1 MANUFACTURING ROBOTS are commonly employed in such tasks as welding (Fig 9.37a); flame cutting; drilling; mechanical assembly (e.g. tightening threaded fastenings) (Fig 9.37b); fettling; and cleaning processes (such as blasting and deburring). Also included in this category would be those used for coating processes (such as paint dipping and spraying) (Fig 9.37c).

Fig. 9.37b Engine flywheel assembly by robot [*Ford Motor Company*]

Fig. 9.37c Robot spraying apparatus under computer control [*Ford Motor Company*]

Fig. 9.37d Robot handling during the final machining of camshaft bearing caps [*Ford Motor Company*]

2   HANDLING ROBOTS are service machines in production processes (Fig 9.37*d*). Typical applications include: pick-and-place tasks; machine tool loading; palletising (i.e. the loading of components onto pallets); packaging; and dispensing processes such as liquid pouring.

3   TESTING ROBOTS have an increasingly significant role in automatic test and inspection procedures, particularly for remote tests in hazardous conditions (e.g. toxic chemical, radioactive, and high impact).

Industrial robots comprise four basic elements:

1   The CONTROLLER
2   The MECHANICAL STRUCTURE
3   The POWER UNIT
4   The TOOLING

These elements may be incorporated into one machine or, alternatively, may be remotely located.

Typical controller systems include: microprocessors, pneumatic logic, or hydraulic logic. Control may be either open loop or closed loop. Open loop control supplies no feedback during operation, and employs limit switches for positioning. Closed loop systems supply feedback signals during operation until the destination has been reached. The mechanical structure comprises the base and the moveable limbs of the robot. The power unit may be electric, pneumatic or hydraulic. Hydraulic control requires an additional hydraulic power pack. The type of tooling depends on the task of the robot. Handling robots incorporate grippers or suckers, whereas manufacturing robots could include such tools as cutters, electrodes, flame torches, spray nozzles or assembly devices such as sockets.

Robot Programming Techniques

Several techniques have been developed for the programming of robots, the most common of which include:

1 WALK-THROUGH This is perhaps the most obvious technique. The operator manually moves the tool of the robot through the required actions of the production sequence. The robot thus "learns" from the operator by retaining the data for each physical movement in its computer memory. Typical applications include paint-spraying and spot-welding.

2 LEAD-THROUGH This is similar to method 1, in that the robot is taught its program via an actual sequence of movements. However, the lead-through method allows the operator to move the robot via a control-box, using keyboard, joystick, or digitiser commands.

3 REMOTE COMPUTER LINK This method has the most relevance to the CADCAM process. Robot programs may be downloaded from a remote computer workstation via a cable link similar to the DNC principle of CNC machine networks. The programming procedures of this method are also similar to those of CNC. Sets of operation commands are entered into the computer using languages and software packages which are very much akin to those discussed for computer-aided part-programming. Typical languages include such names as AML and AUTOPASS, and are commonly based on compilers such as Pascal. Also, highly sophisticated "object level" software is available, and will be discussed in the next case study. 2D and 3D graphical techniques allow robot actions to be simulated on a VDU screen whilst a further link to a CAD database may provide such facilities as solid modelling for clash detections. Programming robots by remote computer link thus provides the required flexibility for analysis of optimum robot installations and production methods at the design, development, and planning stages.

9.7 A Case Study in Robot Simulation Software

This case study is included by kind permission of BYG Systems Ltd, who market the GRASP software package on which this case study is based. GRASP is a CAD system which uses computer graphics to simulate industrial robot installations. GRASP (an acronym for Graphical Robot Applications Simulation Package) was originally developed by Nottingham University with funding from the Science and Engineering Research Council. Using GRASP, the feasibility of a potential robot or FMS (Flexible Manufacturing System) cell may be evaluated very early in the design process. GRASP is fully integrated and incorporates its own 3D modeller, programming, and simulation modules in a single package. It is compatible for a range of 32-bit computers and requires a minimum of 300 Kbytes user memory.

Kinematic Robot Modeller   The 3D solid modeller allows users to build and add their own robot models to the system. The positions and types of robot joint are first defined, together with other information such as the joint constraints and maximum velocities. The "flesh" of the robot is then modelled using primitive solid shapes, such as cuboids, regular and irregular prisms, cylinders and closed polyhedra. Typical robot models constructed by this method, and available from a GRASP library, are shown in Fig 9.38.

The modelling system may also be used to construct the rest of the workplace. Thus it is possible to build up a fully representative 3D model of the proposed robot cell displayed on the VDU screen. This model may then be evaluated and amended as required. Typical robot workplaces are shown in Fig 9.39.

Fig. 9.38 Robot models from the GRASP library

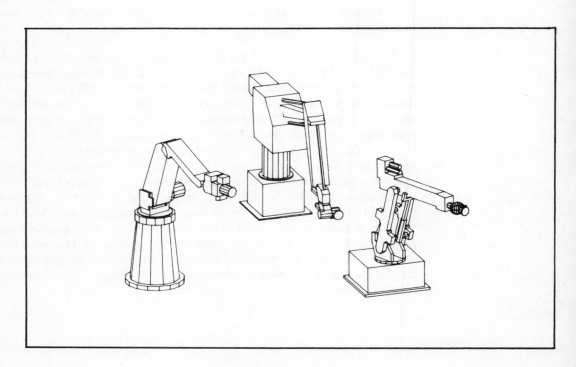

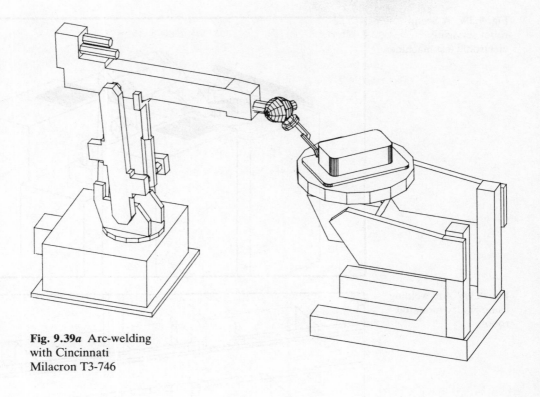

Fig. 9.39*a* Arc-welding
with Cincinnati
Milacron T3-746

Fig. 9.39*b* A robot
assembly cell

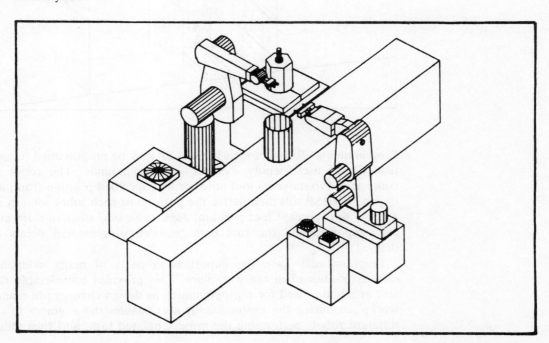

Fig. 9.39c A Scemi robot servicing electronic test machines

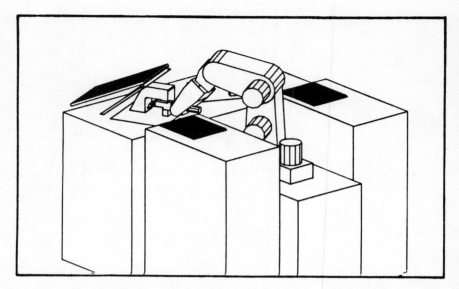

Fig. 9.39d Arc welding using gantry-mounted robots

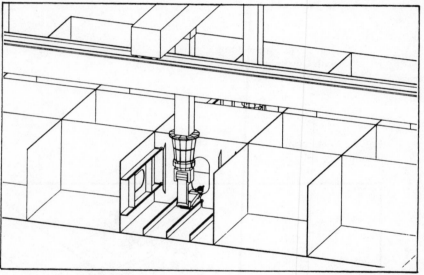

Programming   Robot models in GRASP may be programmed using sophisticated, yet user-friendly, "object-level" commands. The robot may be commanded to move its tool onto, or to a specified position from, a named object. GRASP will then derive the position of each robot joint in order to achieve the specified tool position. *Joint constraint violations* are automatically reported and the tool path between programmed points may be defined.

Programs may have the important property of being independent of objects positioned in the workplace. This provides considerable flexibility and avoids the need for reprogramming as design changes are made to the workplace during the evaluation. It also enables the engineer to compare different robots performing the same simulated task, and thus reduces the

Fig. 9.40 Examples of alternative configurations

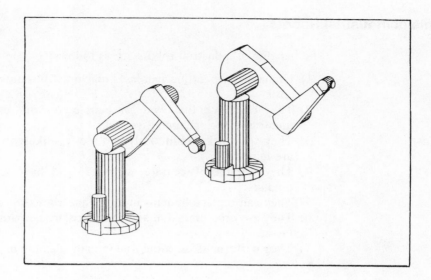

chances of making expensive mistakes, such as selecting too sophisticated a robot where a simpler one would suffice. In the opposite sense, it can also ensure that a selected robot is easily capable of performing the required task and thus avoids unnecessarily expensive engineering efforts to commission the cell.

Simulation GRASP incorporates an *event processor* which allows it to simulate the actions of objects and equipment other than robots, and combine these actions with those of the robot. This allows the user the synchronise motions between any number of robots and peripheral equipment such as conveyors or indexing tables.

Collision detection may also be performed, either visually, or automatically by the system. GRASP incorporates a collision detection facility which can be used either statically, i.e. at a particular instant in time, or dynamically. The dynamic collision detector may be used to check for clashes over a specified time period of a pre-defined robot program. At each stage in the simulation, alternatives may be tried and amendments made.

Many types of robot have a structure which allows them to reach a point in a number of ways by adopting different configurations. The GRASP simulation system gives flexibility and full control over these types of robot (Fig 9.40).

Another important function of the simulation process is the calculation of cycle times. GRASP can perform such calculations quickly and to a high degree of accuracy which accounts for the acceleration rates of the individual joints.

Off-line Production Programming In addition to design and planning, GRASP may also be used as a production tool for off-line robot programming. The data for the program is automatically created within the system during the simulation. This can be suitably post-processed for different controllers.

Benefits of Industrial Robots

The benefits of industrial robots are as follows:

1) Unmanned operation increases machine utilisation and reduces labour costs.
2) They eliminate the need for people to work unsociable hours and undertake boring, repetitive tasks.
3) They can work continuously and are less likely to make mistakes than are humans.
4) They are more accurate, stronger, and have a greater reach than humans.
5) They can replace humans in many hazardous working conditions.
6) They are programmable and can therefore perform a number of varied tasks.
7) They perform an essential role in many flexible manufacturing systems.

9.8 The Flexible Manufacturing System (FMS)

FMS is a computer-controlled approach to batch production which brings together all aspects of CAM into a single system. The underlying principle of this approach is to provide enough flexibility to produce components which may be introduced to the system on a completely random basis.

The Need for FMS

Traditional production systems are inevitably inefficient because of their inability to adapt to varying products, components, and batch sizes on an economic time basis.

Two common traditional approaches (compared in Fig 9.41) are

1 PRODUCT LAYOUT, in which machines are arranged in production lines, each of which are totally dedicated to a single product. This approach can only pay dividends in the mass production of very specialised products which are likely to require little design modification. A new product will require a completely new production line, whilst simple design modifications can cause extensive changes in machinery and layout. The inflexibility of the system also results in

a) Inability to transfer components from one line to the another. Thus, fluctuations in orders will produce queues during periods of high demand, and idle machines at low demand.

b) The essential role of each machine in the progressive series of operations along its line. Thus, machine breakdowns not only leave a whole line inoperative, but, due to (*a*), mean that the manufacture of a complete product is halted.

Fig. 9.41 Traditional production systems

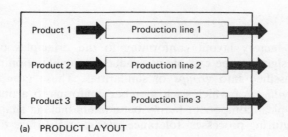

Product 1 → Production line 1 →

Product 2 → Production line 2 →

Product 3 → Production line 3 →

(a) PRODUCT LAYOUT

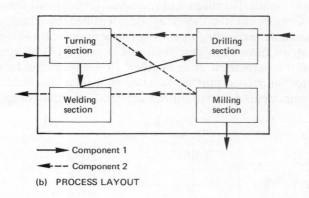

→ Component 1

←--- Component 2

(b) PROCESS LAYOUT

2 PROCESS LAYOUT, in which machines are classified and arranged in sections according to their function. Thus each component is sent to a different section for the various stages of its manufacture, e.g. drilling, turning, milling, welding. Complex route planning is often required to maximise machine utilisation and minimise queueing. The chief inefficiency of this approach results from the time-wasting during the excessive transportation and handling of work. The inflexibility of the system disallows local process variation due to the inability of a section to "turn its hand to other tasks".

A summary of traditional production systems must conclude that the particular nature of their inflexibility will result in excessive time-wasting, erratic and inefficient utilisation of machines, and unreliable estimation of completion times. Another aspect of inflexibility is the specialist knowledge required of the skilled and semi-skilled humans operating the machines. Traditional systems do not encourage the development of manufacturing skills which may easily be applied to varying types of product, machine, and process. It is also logical (particularly in view of modern market trends which reflect rapid changes in technology) that a more flexible approach to batch production should reduce these inefficiencies.

Group Technology

A factory layout conforming to the principles of Group Technology is designed to be capable of producing any variation of components which are classified into *groups* of similarities. These groups are called *component families*, of which each member conforms to a number of set parameters. Typical component family parameters include shape, size, material, manufacturing processes, tolerance bands, and surface finish. For example, component shape at the most primitive level is commonly grouped into *prismatic* (non-circular) families and *rotational* (cylindrical) families.

Component families may be identified by classifying each component parameter according to a *hierarchical numerical coding system*. (Such coding systems have been described in Chapter 7.) Each component may thus be given a parametric code number. Codes may then be analysed and grouped into naturally-occurring families of similar hierarchical number sequence. Components are then further analysed according to specific production data,

Fig. 9.42a Plan view of typical FMS [*KTM Ltd.*]

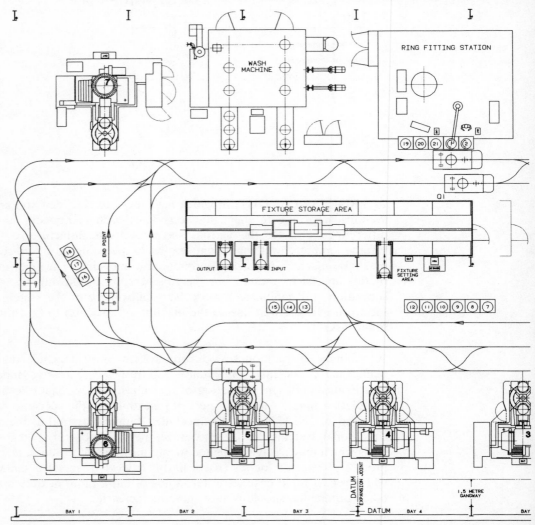

and the essential information concerning size and frequency of previous batches. Using this data, it is then possible to design a factory layout containing the types and optimum number of machines required to accommodate the component combinations within each family.

The main problem in implementing Group Technology has been the difficulty in accurately identifying component families and batch requirements. Traditional group technology layouts are commonly divided into machine groups, which are each dedicated to an allotted component family. Incorrect component families can render such a system inoperative, whilst the most minute inaccuracies in batch requirement predictions will cause inconsistent machine usage. Breakthroughs in CAM technology have solved many of the problems associated with traditional systems and have enabled engineers to develop the principles of group technology into systems which are flexible enough to produce components on a random entry basis.

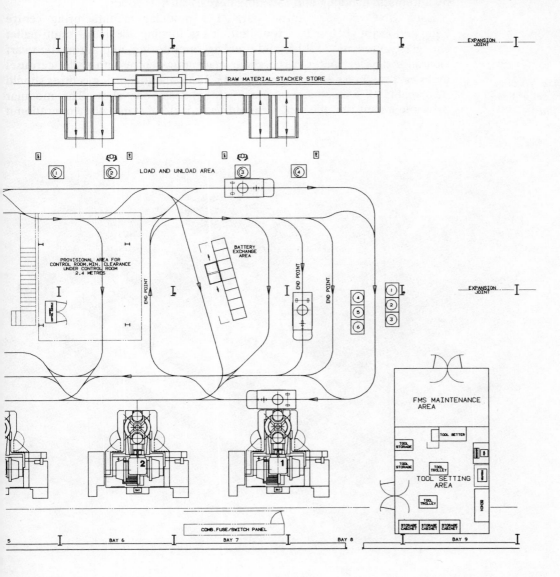

FMS Technology

Fig 9.42 shows a typical FMS layout. All flexible systems vary but should include the following elements:

a) Computer-controlled Manufacturing Equipment.
b) Host-computer DNC Link.
c) Appropriate Software.
d) Automatic Loading and Transportation Devices.
e) Automatic Storage and Retrieval Devices.

Manufacturing Equipment All manufacturing equipment is computer-controlled and contains a high degree of automation. CNC machines perform the main bulk of the machining operations and are directly supported by automatic handling and assembly devices such as robots.

Each CNC machine forms part of a modular manufacturing centre equipped with automatic tool and work-loading devices; multi-pallet changers; automatic tool life and breakage monitoring; and automatic swarf clearance devices. A typical modular machining centre with pallet carousel and swarf clearance is shown in Fig 9.43. FMS manufacturing centres should be capable of unmanned operation on at least one shift. The modular principle means that the centre should be capable of stand-alone operation if

Fig. 9.42b Wooden scale model of FMS [*KTM Ltd.*]

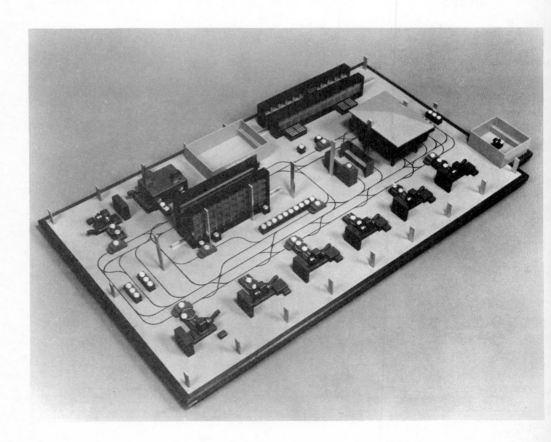

Fig. 9.43 Typical FMS machining centre with pallet carousel and swarf clearance equipment [*Deckel AG*]

necessary, whilst allowing a complete linked FMS to be built up by continually adding more manufacturing cells over an extended time period.

Some FMS layouts contain composite units known as *Flexible Manufacturing Cells* (FMCs). These comprise a small number of machine tools connected via a transport system or a handling robot.

DNC Link All manufacturing centres in the true FMS are connected by cable to a host computer which provides a DNC link. The task of the DNC network is to download part programs to different CNC machines in flexible fashion, as soon as the machines become available. Part programs and components may be instantly re-routed to alternative machines if breakdowns occur. The host computer can also provide various degrees of control, communication and backup support to the local intelligence of automatic equipment throughout the FMS.

Software An FMS can only be as efficient and versatile as its controlling software. The route to full flexibility lies in the ability of the software to effectively coordinate the actions of all the various sophisticated systems which make up the FMS.

More specifically, the software must be capable of

a) Analysing and managing statistical data, such as component family identification.

223

b) Identification and flexible downloading of part programs.
c) Devising flexible route plans.
d) Calculating throughput times.
e) Coordinating the selection of machines with the handling and transport of materials and tools.
f) Monitoring tool performance.
g) Organising the storage system.

Such software will inevitably be extremely complex. Reliable systems have thus taken decades to be developed and perfected. High outlay cost is another obvious consequence. Thus an important attribute of FMS software packages is the provision for easy updates and modular additions so that facilities may be continually developed.

Loading and Transporting Devices   The FMS cannot be successful unless the same principles of automation and computerised coordination applied to manufacture are equally applied to transportation. Equipment used includes:

a) MULTI-TOOL MAGAZINES, which convey a vast choice of tools to their loading position on the manufacturing centre. These magazines commonly contain 60–100 tools attached to an endless linkage, stretching around the perimeter of the centre (Fig 9.44).
b) PICK-AND-PLACE ROBOTS, to load and unload work and tools at the manufacturing centres. In FMS processes other than metal machining, robots may also be used for manufacturing, assembly, and inspection tasks.

Fig. 9.44*a* Machining centre with multi-tool magazine with endless linkage [*N.C. Engineering Ltd.*]

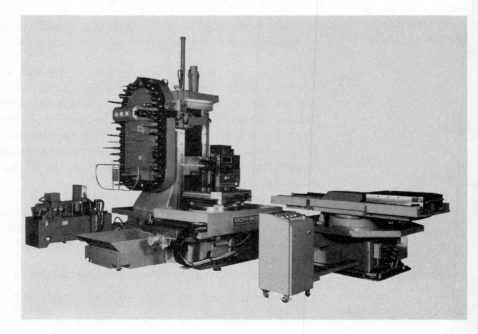

c) AUTOMATIC PALLET CHANGERS (APCs), which continually feed components on mounting pallets, through the CNC machine between operations. Common types of APC include rotating tables, as in the pallet carousel of Fig 9.44, and endless linkages, as shown in Fig 9.45.

Fig. 9.44*b* Machining centre with multi-tool magazine on rotary disc [*N.C. Engineering Ltd.*]

Fig. 9.45 Machining centre with automatic pallet changer with endless linkage [*N.C. Engineering Ltd.*]

d) CONVEYOR BELTS AND GANTRY CRANES, for transporting components between different manufacturing centres.

e) AUTOMATICALLY GUIDED VEHICLES (AGVs). An AGV is a wheel-mounted carriage which may be programmed to travel along a predetermined path between two specified locations. The AGV is thus principally used as a more versatile alternative to conveyors and cranes for transporting materials, components, and tools between manufacturing centres. The flexibility of the AGV lies in its ability to be easily reprogrammed to travel along alternative routes. A typical AGV is shown in Fig 9.46.

Most AGVs are guided "off-board" by inductive wires which are either concealed underground or adhered to the factory floor surface in the form of metallic strip. Kinetic power is usually provided by on-board electric batteries. Route programming is commonly achieved via on-board local intelligence. Many AGVs also incorporate sensors which can communicate information regarding location, cargo, and collision, and various handling devices such as integral conveyors and telescopic forks.

Flexible as they are, the majority of AGV's are constrained to the routes of the inductive wires and thus cannot truly be described as free-ranging. However, more sophisticated versions are now being developed. Most of these are based on the principle of software-programmable vehicle routes, which are thus very easily changed and are infinitely variable. Popular guidance systems utilize laser signals, ultrasonics and navigation via gyroscopic detection.

Fig. 9.46 AGV approaching machining centre [*Deckel AG*]

Fig. 9.47 ASR
warehouse equipment

f) FMS STORAGE AND RETRIEVAL DEVICES. Components are stored and retrieved using vehicles which are controlled in a similar manner to AGVs. These devices are programmed to identify, automatically store, and automatically retrieve cargo from a mapped matrix of storage racks. The working locality is known as an *Automatic Storage and Retrieval Warehouse* (ASR warehouse). Fig 9.47 shows typical ASR Warehouse equipment.

FMS in Industry

Although FMS has largely achieved its objectives in batch production, this has not been reflected in the number of systems installed to date. European companies have been particularly slow to respond, with the vast number of full FMS factory layouts concentrated in Japan and the USA. The main reason for the disappointing progress has been the high capital investment involved. However, with the recent significant developments in software and modular systems, the number of installations is expected to increase dramatically in the next few years, both in Europe and worldwide.

One of the most famous systems is Fanuc's Fuji factory, situated on a 100 000m^2 site near Lake Yamanaka, Japan. The plant has welding, machining, inspection and assembly stations in different areas of the shop floor, and is operated by 100 workers. Materials and parts are automatically stored and are transported on AGVs. 450 different work types may be processed in 30

227

machining centres. Since only one operator is needed for every five centres, and is assigned to them only during the daytime, the productivity per worker is about five times that of a conventional factory. A turnover of £400 000 per employee is claimed to have been achieved. The layout of Fanuc's Fuji factory is depicted in Fig 9.48. (Description and diagram are included by kind permission of the *IEE Journal*.)

Fig. 9.48 Layout of Fanuc's Fuji factory

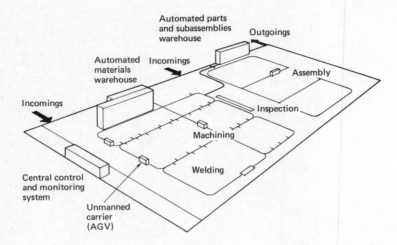

One of the first authentic FMS layouts in the UK was SCAMP (600 Group Computer Aided Manufacturing Project) which was installed at Colchester Lathes in 1983. The SCAMP FMS combines nine machining operations with eight robots and an automatic conveyor. It is unusual among FMS installations in being designed to produce rotational parts—shafts, discs, and gears. (The majority of existing FMSs produce prismatic parts, which may be loaded into machine tools without robot intervention.) Batches of 25–100 parts are capable of completion within 3 days as compared with a need for 50 handlings over a period of 8 weeks in conventional manufacture. Six load/unload stations release coded workpiece pallets to the first available machining centre via the conveyor, on instructions from the supervisory computer. At the stations, robots remove components from the pallets, insert them into chucks, reverse them for machining on both sides, and then return them to the pallet. The whole system is controlled by two Systime Series 500E computers. Software is purpose-developed for the application and written mainly in Fortran, running under the RSX11M operating system. Fig 9.49 shows the SCAMP layout. (Description and figure are shown with kind permission of the *IEE Journal*.)

A more recent UK FMS is the impressive JCB Transmissions factory at Wrexham. JCB estimate that full automation will boost their production of earth-mover gearboxes by 30%, to 40 units per day, and that the £6.75 million investment will have paid for itself within three years. The JCB FMS consists basically of a flexible machining system for producing high-value, often low-volume prismatic parts, namely the gearbox casings. This is supported by an ASR warehouse and a network of AGVs. On arrival at the factory, the casings are weighed and checked for size, and the information

Fig. 9.49 SCAMP
layout [*Colchester Lathe
Company*]

sent to the computer, which instructs one of the three medium-sized AGVs
to take the pallet into the store. The ASR warehouse consists of three aisles,
each with 10-metre-high stacks, served by two automatic cranes (one each
for raw materials and assembly-bound finished components). Three in-
duction-loop AGVs transport materials and components between the ASR
warehouse and the seven machining centres, each of which hold an 80-tool
magazine and robot tool-changing facility. A further three AGVs are used
for general distribution work, whilst another carries the machined prismatic
parts to washing and measuring machines, and to unloading stations for
transportation to the assembly lines. Five smaller AGVs move progressively
between five manned assembly stations, where they stop for pre-pro-
grammed eight-minute time intervals. Fig 9.50 shows the component route
through the factory. (Diagram and description are included by kind permission of JCB and the *Sunday Times*.)

Fig. 9.50 Component route through the JCB FMS factory

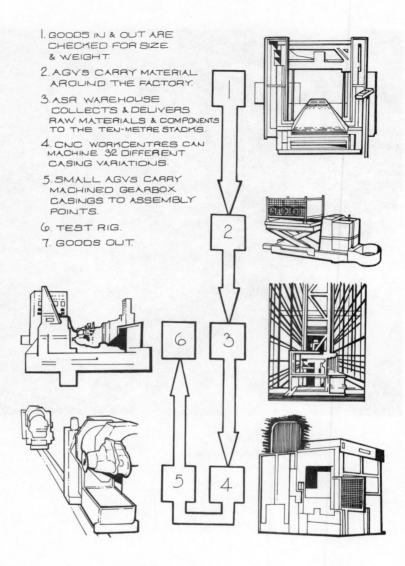

1. GOODS IN & OUT ARE CHECKED FOR SIZE & WEIGHT.
2. AGVS CARRY MATERIAL AROUND THE FACTORY.
3. ASR WAREHOUSE COLLECTS & DELIVERS RAW MATERIALS & COMPONENTS TO THE TEN-METRE STACKS.
4. CNC WORKCENTRES CAN MACHINE 32 DIFFERENT CASING VARIATIONS.
5. SMALL AGVS CARRY MACHINED GEARBOX CASINGS TO ASSEMBLY POINTS.
6. TEST RIG.
7. GOODS OUT.

Advantages of FMS

FMS has the following advantages over traditional batch production systems:

1) Unmanned operation shifts increase machine utilization, reduce labour costs, and eliminate the need for people to work unsociable hours.
2) Flexibility accommodates a wide range of components and batch sizes.
3) Improved estimation of throughput times.
4) Increased output.
5) Random component production and coordinated DNC link eliminates work in progress, queueing, and machine under-utilization.
6) Machine breakdowns can be more readily accommodated.
7) Stock levels may be reduced.

The Complete Cadcam Process — A Case Study

10

10.1 Introduction

This chapter interrelates some of the previous discussions into the case study of a complete CADCAM process. It is included by kind permission of the Ford Motor Company Ltd, who have provided all the information on which the chapter is based.

Background

The Ford Motor Company is one of the world's major manufacturers of motor cars and trucks. It is Ford's use of CADCAM in the design and manufacture of cars which will be discussed here.

Ford's European product development activities are based in two major engineering centres. These are at Dunton in the UK (3000 employees) and at Cologne in Germany (2000 employees).

The automotive industry was one of the leaders in the development of interactive computer graphics in the 1960s. Initial efforts were focussed on a problem unique to the industry, i.e. the design of sheet metal surfaces which are defined by a clay model.

A system known as the PDGS (Product Design Graphics System) was developed by Ford's parent company in the USA, to overcome the drawbacks of 2D paper drawings in capturing the complex structure of a modern 3D car body panel. The first pilot system ran from a stand-alone minicomputer but, with decreasing hardware costs, the workstation capacity increased tenfold in five years. The first European PDGS was installed in 1978, and subsequent developments have vastly increased the capabilities of the system. In 1980, Prime computers were used to link workstations for the purpose of sharing a central store of graphics model data. At Dunton, modern PDGS workstations share a Prime 2250 minicomputer, linked in a local ring network to a Prime 750 mainframe computer, which acts as a centralised database.

The Ford International Computer Network

One of the keys to the success of the Ford CADCAM installations is the vast communications network that links them together. A leased-line link to America enables designers and engineers from the UK and Germany to share the resources of the parent company at Dearborn, USA. The link provides access to over ten mainframe and mini-computers.

For example, an engineer in Dunton, having designed a component, may send the design to colleagues at Cologne, Germany, in minutes via computer communication over the network. Designs and ideas may also be shared between the European centres, the USA, and affiliate companies in other parts of the world. The inter-computer communication effectively gets all Ford engineers and designers "working around the same desk".

The computer systems within this network fall into three general categories:

1) Computer-aided Design and Analysis (55% of overall capacity).
2) Computer-aided Development and Testing (30% of overall capacity).
3) Calculation and Data-Processing Aids (15% of overall capacity).

The Ford CADCAM Process

The network described brings greater speed and accuracy in turning a design concept into a mass-produced motor car. The two primary activities in this CADCAM process involve the design, manufacture, development, and testing of:

a) Car body components
b) Mechanical components

The body of a car is made from sheet metal and the techniques used for its design and manufacture are quite different to those used for the other components of the car. In this chapter we will follow the development of a body part (a door panel) and a mechanical component (a crankshaft) from concept to the final product. The process followed is broadly similar for the design and production of all parts.

10.2 Design to Manufacture: Car Body

Styling   The aesthetics of a new car begins with designers producing countless ink renderings, all of which conform to the original design image brief in the product specification. The purpose of the initial sketches is to capture the theme of shape and style. At present they are done mainly by hand, although CAD solid modelling and holography will have an increasing role to play. Typical such designer's sketches are shown in Figs 10.1 and 10.2.

Management then examine the sketches and select the most suitable for the market requirements of the specification.

Package and Pre-program Once the theme of the new car has been selected, design engineers develop the package. Within the theme, engineers have to fit people, luggage space, and major components such as the engine, transmission, and exhaust system. CAD enables the design engineer to analyse and evaluate many different packages and to find the best solution.

The first step in the package development involves deciding on the HARDPOINTS. These are the critical dimensions such as overall length, wheelbase, and roof-height. Package engineers use ergonomic software such as that described in Chapter 8 to manipulate manikin "man-model" screen displays within the hardpoints, and thus to determine the most successful package for passenger and luggage space (Fig 10.3). The system may be used to examine a wealth of ergonomic considerations, such as the driver's angle of vision through front and rear windscreens, as shown in Fig 10.4. In Fig 10.5, the package engineer is using an end view to check on projected headroom. Passengers are shown from the rear, with dotted lines indicating the headroom.

Pre-program engineers ensure that the new design may be feasibly engineered and manufactured. A colour CAD workstation is used to check on the efficient assembly of major components. Collision detections, such as the exhaust interfering with the underbody, may be undertaken at this stage.

Clay Model Working from the selected ink renderings, several full-size models are hand-crafted in industrial clay to assess and refine the visual impact of the design. Just one of these is finally selected, and this is pursued and perfected during the later stages of the package development. Interior features and external panels are all clay modelled to accurately resemble the finished parts. Highly skilled modellers use a variety of templates and carving tools to create the required forms (Fig 10.6). Because of the symmetry of the car, only one side of the body needs to be modelled, and thus only one front door is created.

Scan-Mill The next stage in the process is to transform the clay model into an equivalent mathematical model in the computer. Information is retrieved from the clay model using scan-mill columns, which are installed in both the UK and Germany. A scanning probe is moved over the modelled half of the clay with no more pressure than a record needle. The probe is a touch-sensitive device which closes a circuit on light contact with the surface beneath it. At each point of contact, the machine automatically records the position in space by measuring the three ordinates from a base datum point. Thus the scanner records the body shape in 3D by measuring thousands of discrete points on the clay surface. The scan data is then transferred to a mini-computer, which is linked to the scan-mill machine. The scanner can record 3D coordinates at the rate of 4 points/second, and can be controlled to register more points over a critical area (Fig 10.7).

Once the information is in the computer, it may be displayed on a CAD workstation VDU screen and manipulated for possible re-styling. Also, the best features of several designs may be combined (Fig 10.8). The scanning head of the scan-mill may then be changed for a milling head which, under computer control, mills back the manipulated data into the clay, and mills out the second half of the model.

After management have approved the complete 3D shape, the new car goes into the "program" phase, where the urgency is to develop the design into the finished product.

Surface Layout   Once the scan data from the clay model is in the computer memory, surface layout designers use the system to develop smooth, flowing surfaces consistent with one another. Any minor irregularities in the data (small bumps or dips in the clay) must be smoothed-out to maintain the artistic flow of the sheet metal. These irregularities are not always visible to the naked eye, but are easily detected by the CAD system. PGDS mathematically refines lines and surfaces to remove imperfections.

Fig 10.9 shows the magnified detail of the car door panel. This reveals the uneven data from the hand-finished clay and the refinement of the data into the smooth geometry of the door exterior.

Structure Engineering   The refined mathematical model is transmitted over the Prime network, for the engineering of the structure panels and components.

The European Body Engineering Group has the largest application of PGDS at Ford (60% of about eighty workstations), and is split between Britain (closures and trim) and Germany (car framework). Close communications and coordination enables thousands of drawings to be transferred between these locations. Engineers develop layouts and components as their local workstations, and transfer designs over the local network to the central database for storage and security. The linkage of the central databases at each site allows quick access to the designs in the other country.

The attractive surface geometry of the door exterior is used to design the interior door panel, which provides the structural strength for the whole door, and a framework for the interior features such as the lock and door hinges (Fig 10.10).

Finite Element Modelling   Using the component geometry, structural engineers build a finite element mesh mathematical model of the panel (Fig 10.11), to ensure that the design is optimised. The model is used to determine the points of high and low stress, and display the maximum distortion in the panel. Fig 10.12 shows the simulated distortion of the top right-hand corner (exaggerated 500 times for clarity), revealing the need for more refinement.

Similar analysis is undertaken elsewhere in the structure the car. Fig 10.13 shows a torsion simulation throughout the body shell.

Crash Modelling   Finite element analysis is also used to model the effects of a crash, thus helping to reduce the number of actual crash tests required. It is the inner structural panel which provides most of the resistance to intrusion through the door. The crash model is thus used to stimulate the behaviour of the panel under the action of a very large force.

Dynamic Modelling The analysis of the door panel dynamics provides a further application of finite element techniques. The natural frequency of the panel may be quickly determined. If this falls within the range of the engine revs/minute, resonance will occur, creating unsatisfactory vibrations during motion. By making minor design modifications on the CADCAM system, the panel may be stiffened to bring the natural frequency beyond the range of the engine.

The CADCAM system also calculates the movement of each door component and displays the travel dynamically. Fig 10.14 shows displays of the hinge mechanism, which must move with the swing of the door and be more than adequate to support it. Further dynamic displays are shown in Fig 10.15, which simulates the movement of the door limited by the check arm, and in Fig 10.16 which analyses the window winder rotation and the corresponding window glass movement.

Prototype Although finite element analysis simulation greatly reduces the amount of testing required, the computer model must always be finally cross-checked with results from a real test on a prototype component.

Prototype panels are pressed from "soft tools" which have a life of only about one hundred pressings. They are made from a relatively soft metal and are therefore easily and cheaply manufactured. Once a part-program has defined the required tools and cutting paths, the soft tools are made on a CNC machine tool and are then used to form the prototype door panel under action of special presses.

Testing The prototype is then fitted to a test rig that will emulate the vehicle system around the door. The computer-controlled rig is programmed by a test engineer to inflict the loads and stresses that will exist in the new vehicle. Fig 10.17 shows the door handle rig test, in which the handle is subjected to a continuous reciprocating load from a computer-controlled pneumatic arm. Such rigs are advantageous over a real car-and-driver at this stage. They provide continuity of test and identical test conditions for the comparison of different prototype designs. The behaviour of the prototype is also measured via the computer and these results are correlated with the results predicted by the finite element model.

Stamping Engineering and Tooling Body panels are formed from a sheet steel blank with a series of press dies which stamp-out more features during each successive press operation (Fig 10.18). A die consists of two halves (upper and lower), each carrying a pressing face which forms the shape of the panel, and a structure connecting the die face to the press (Fig 10.19).

Once the panel design and prototype have been verified, the component geometry held in the computer becomes the basic data for the manufacture of the press dies. Design of the die face and the die structure proceed in parallel.

The panel display is tipped to the optimum position for press operation, given such constraints as the depth of draw (i.e. the distance that the blank must move before it contacts the die face). CAD is particularly useful in helping to visualise, and hence determine, the tip angle (Fig 10.20).

The next stage is the design of the *binder*. This is a ring of steel which is used to clamp the blank in the die and control the flow of metal as the panel is formed. The amount of flow is critical. Excessive constraint will cause the panel to tear, whilst too much flow will cause buckling. Once the panel is stamped, the binder is scrapped. This necessitates minimizing the binder material to save waste and cost.

The structure of the die consists of essential features incorporating many standard components which are contained in a computer library inside the database. The engineer enters the parameters of the new design, and the CADCAM system uses appropriate standard components to complete the design of the die (Fig 10.21).

Tool Room A set of tool drawings is produced for the tool room via a high speed plotter. Pattern-makers use the tool drawing to make a polystyrene pattern which is shipped to the foundry for the purpose of producing a sandmould (Fig 10.22). Molten steel is then poured into the mould, melting the polystyrene and leaving a rough casting of the die.

Part Programming While the die structure is being designed, process engineers make the tooling aids. These are the computer models from which pressing faces are copy-milled into the die steel castings. Computer-Aided Part Programming (CAPP) and Graphical Numerical Control (GNC) techniques are used to simulate the movement of the milling cutter as it carves out the shape of the door (Fig 10.23). The cutter paths generate a CNC part program which is used to control the movements of the milling tool. The Ford Integrated Numerical Control (FINC) module of the PDGS is used to create the part program.

Cubing Model and Pressing Face Manufacture The part program data is transmitted via DNC cable link to a CNC milling machine which manufactures the cubing model. This is the manufactured model which acts as the final check against the original component geometry (Fig 10.24). Once the cubing model is verified, the door pressing face is copy-milled into the hard tool steel of the die (Fig 10.25). A five-axis milling machine enables the milling of the pressing faces to be undertaken directly from the CADCAM system, and reduces the need for hand-finishing (Fig 10.26a).

Panel Forming and Final Assembly After testing for flawless stamped panels, the die sets are taken to the plants and fitted to large press tools, which form the body panels under high pressure. The panels are then assembled to make up the complete body shell, using the latest robot technology. Once completed, robotics is used to coat and paint the body shell (see Chapter 9). Fig 10.26b shows the robot plant and production flow for a typical Ford car body construction. Fig 10.26c shows part of the body frame assembly line.

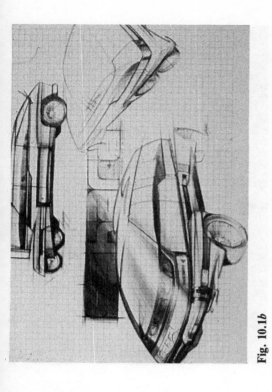

Fig. 10.1*b*

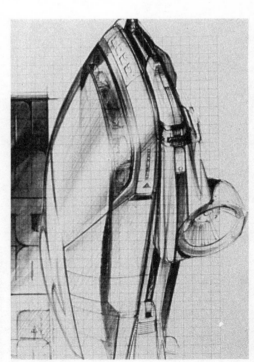

Fig. 10.2*b*

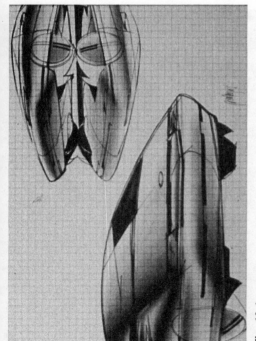

Fig. 10.1*a*

Fig. 10.2*a*

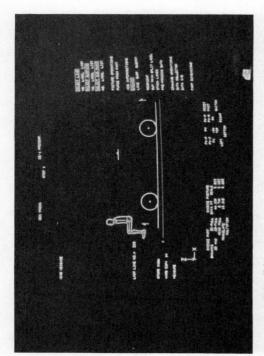

Fig. 10.3a Package engineers manipulating manikins on screen

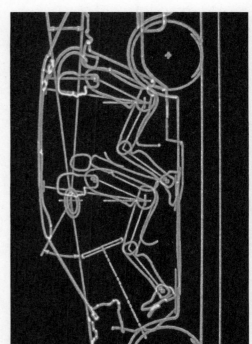

Fig. 10.3b Manikin inserted

Fig. 10.3c

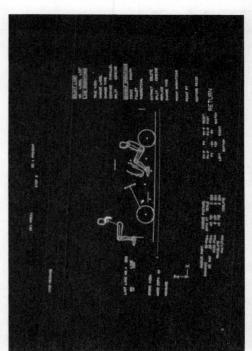

Fig. 10.3d Seated

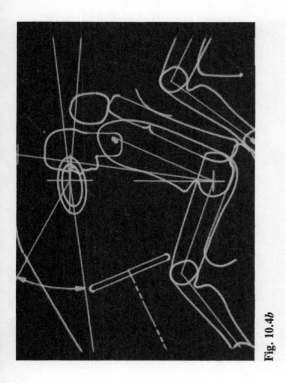

Fig. 10.4a Analysis of
driver's angle of vision

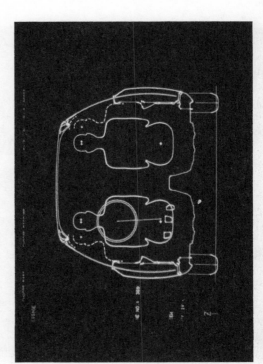

Fig. 10.4b

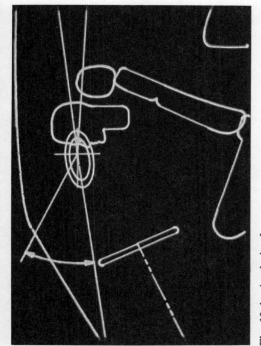

Fig. 10.5a

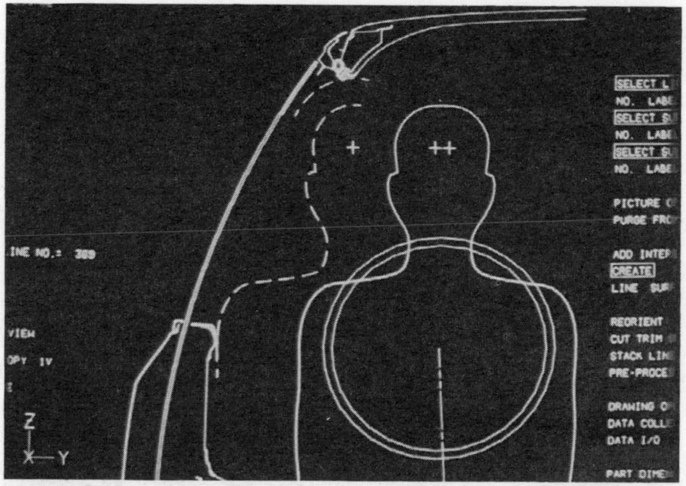

Fig. 10.5b

Fig. 10.6b

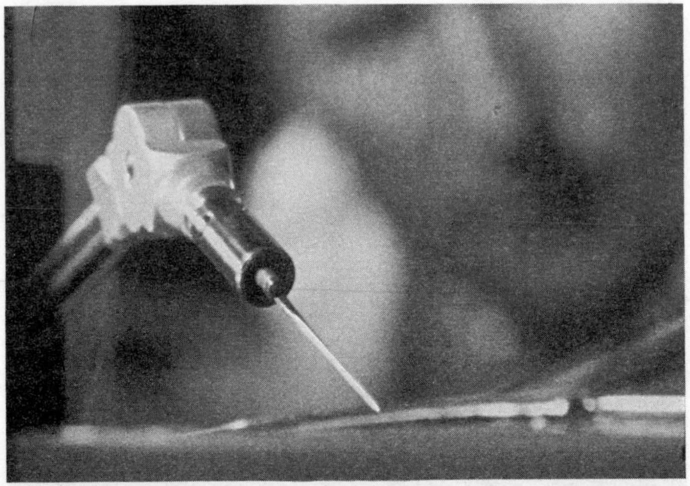

Fig. 10.7 Scanning probe

Fig. 10.6a

Fig. 10.6c

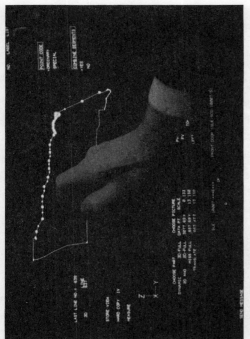

Fig. 10.9a Refinement of scan data on small part of door panel

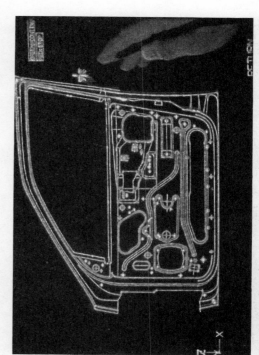

Fig. 10.10a Interior door panel

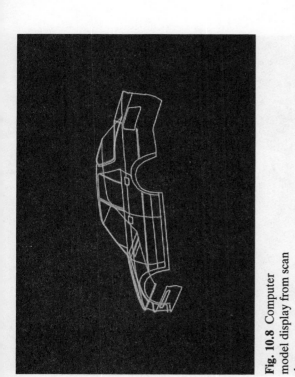

Fig. 10.8 Computer model display from scan data

Fig. 10.9b Door panel exterior: smoothed mathematical curves

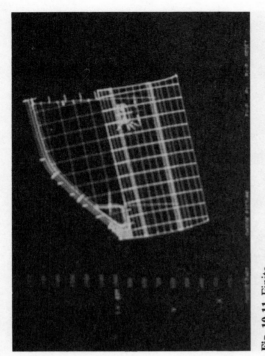

Fig. 10.10b Close-up of interior door panel

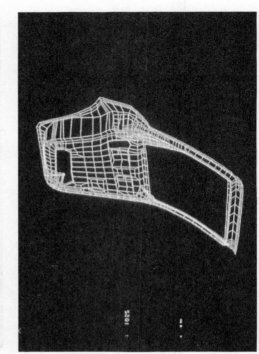

Fig. 10.11 Finite element mesh of panel

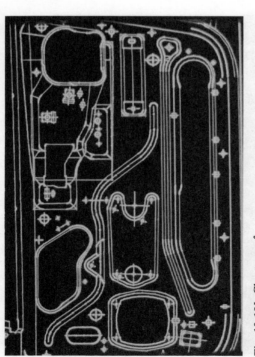

Fig. 10.12a Distortion simulation of panel corner

Fig. 10.12b Distortion simulation of panel corner

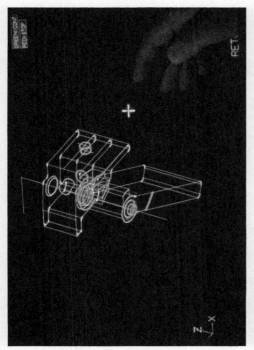

Fig. 10.13 Torsion simulation on body shell

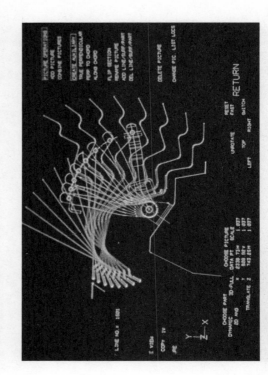

Fig. 10.14 Dynamic display of door hinge

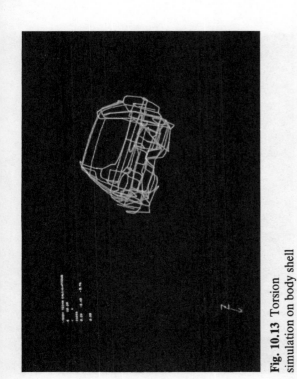

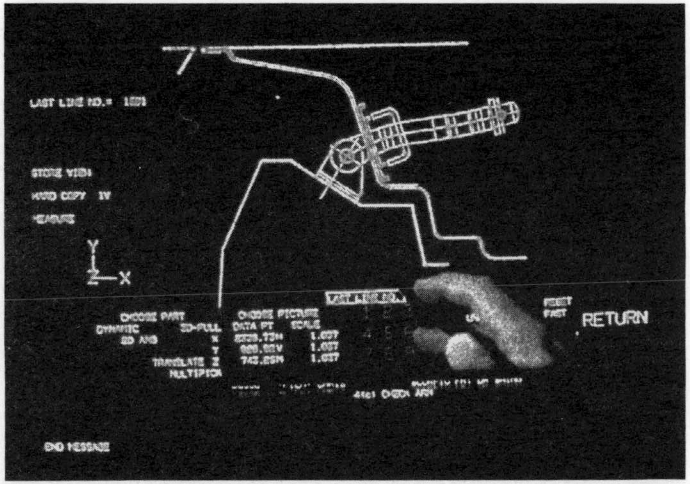

Fig. 10.15a Door check arm

Fig. 10.15b Simulated movement of door with check arm

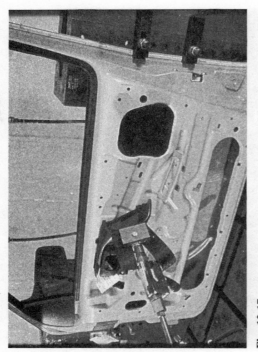

Fig. 10.17
Reciprocating load test on door handle

Fig. 10.19a Upper and lower die halves

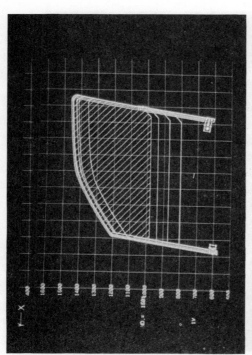

Fig. 10.16 Window-glass movement

Fig. 10.18 Panel pressing

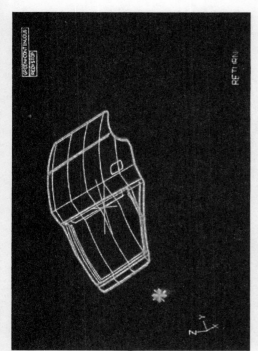

Fig. 10.20 Panel display tipped to optimum press position

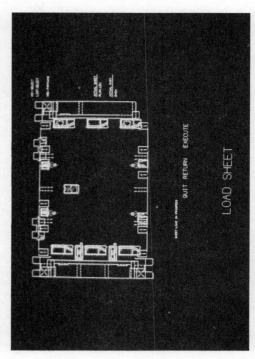

Fig. 10.21b Standard components displayed on die design

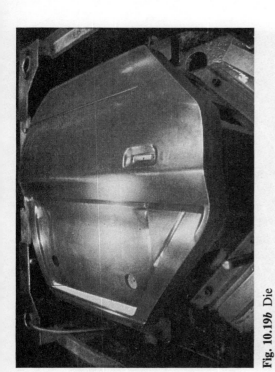

Fig. 10.19b Die pressing face

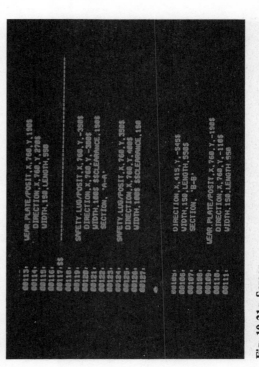

Fig. 10.21a Screen display of standards list

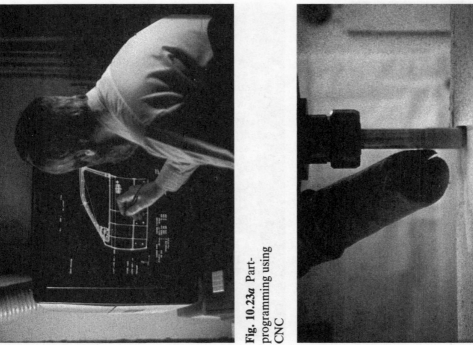

Fig. 10.23a Part-programming using CNC

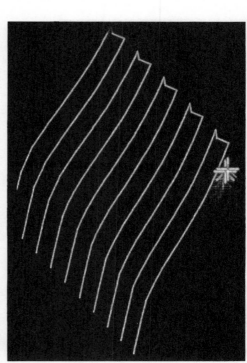

Fig. 10.24a CNC milling of cubing model from part program

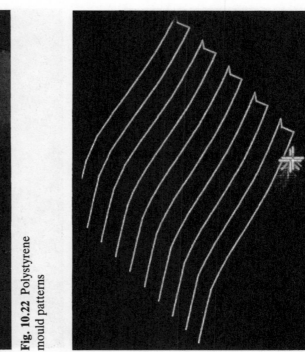

Fig. 10.22 Polystyrene mould patterns

Fig. 10.23b Simulated milling cutter paths on part of door panel

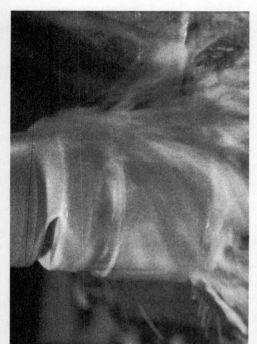

Fig. 10.25 Copy milling of die pressing face

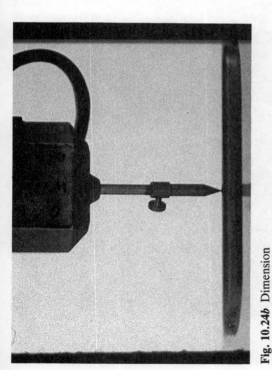

Fig. 10.24b Dimension checking of finished cubing model

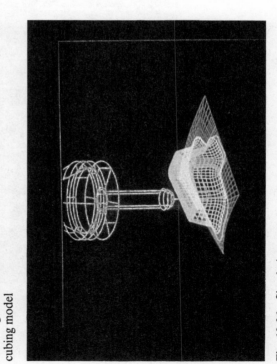

Fig. 10.26a Simulation of five-axis CNC milling operation

Fig. 10.26*b*

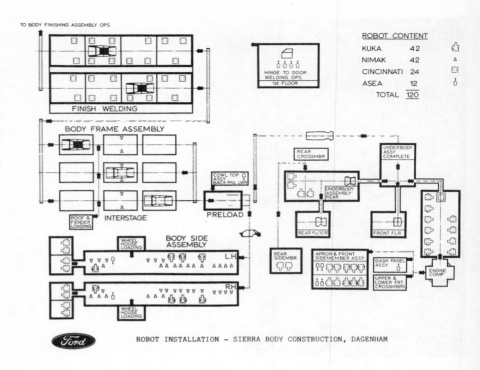

ROBOT INSTALLATION – SIERRA BODY CONSTRUCTION, DAGENHAM

Fig. 10.26*c*

10.3 Design to Manufacture: Engine

The new car engine is designed in parallel with the body.

Specification   The design specification originates from management directives for criteria that must be met by the new engine. Management defines both the weight of the car that the engine is to propel and the performance required. It also sets objectives for fuel economy and reliability. With a wealth of experience to draw from, engineers then interpret the management directives to form the specification that meets the criteria. Power and torque requirements are calculated, and dimensions controlled, to conform to the previously-defined hardpoints and packaging requirements (Fig 10.27).

Component Parameters and Dynamic Modelling   From the capacity requirements, various bore and stroke options are investigated, and the basic shape of the new engine begins to emerge.

Fig 10.28 shows VDU displays of the crankshaft taking shape. Its size is determined largely by the stresses that will exist under the most adverse conditions.

Using a menu tablet system on ComputerVision workstations, the designers generate the geometric model around which everyone will work. The powerful 3D modelling system ensures that any changes in the design are immediately reflected in all views (Fig 10.29).

Having determined the throw of the piston and the size of the crankshaft and its bearings, the basic parameters of the con-rod are defined. The length of the con-rod is determined from the geometric studies of the piston travel relative to the crankshaft and the cylinder bore. CADCAM helps the engineers to examine the dynamic relationship between the con-rod and the crankshaft, and so to progress to the design of the engine block. Fig 10.30 shows a dynamic display for investigating the projected movement of the con-rod.

Fig 10.31 shows how 3D colour displays may be used to examine the location of the pistons and the crankshaft in relation to the engine block and cylinder head. Dynamic analysis of the complete assembly (including collision detection) may also be undertaken at this stage.

Finite Element Analysis and Strength/Material Optimisation   Once the component parameters have been defined, the detailed design commences. The engine components must be made of the smallest amount of material which is sufficient for their function. This not only keeps the cost and weight to a minimum, but also reduces inertia in the engine and thus improves its efficiency.

As in the body design, the CADCAM system enables a finite element mesh to be made of each component. The mesh can be analysed to detect steep stress gradients and, if necessary, the component can be quickly redesigned to obtain a more even, and thus a more economical, stress distribution.

The completion of the analysis effectively concludes the details of the design shape.

Process Engineering Using the defined geometry, process engineers determine the stages of manufacture for each engine component. Fig 10.32 shows a screen display process sheet for the crankshaft. The required size of crankshaft casting is calculated and tool-path simulation techniques are then used to aid the engineers in determining the steps required to machine the rough casting into the finished crankshaft.

Factory Layout CADCAM is also used to determine the layout of the production equipment. Fig 10.33 shows a display of a robot being positioned on a transfer line. Fig 10.34 shows how this is extended to the design of the complete manufacturing plant.

Component handling layout is also designed on the CADCAM system, as shown in the pick-and-place robot VDU simulation (Fig 10.35), and the display of a component handling basket design (Fig 10.36).

Manufacture As in the case of body manufacture, the computer-generated engine component models are transmitted from the development offices, to the plants, for tool design. The FINC module of PGDS is used to create the part program, which controls the CNC and robotic machine tools.

In an automatic production line, each computer-controlled machine has a specific machining task for transforming the "rough" cast and forged items into high precision finished components. Fig 10.37 shows a computer-controlled robot deburring the oilways of the crankshaft.

Computer terminals on the shop floor ensure that supervisors have constant visual reference to the current state of the manufacturing operation (Fig 10.38). In the event of a breakdown, the maintenance engineer uses the CADCAM system to quickly obtain screen display reference drawings for the faulty machine (Fig 10.39).

Assembly Once finished, the crankshaft is placed in the new block. The complete engine assembly is undertaken on a computer-controlled transfer line. Computer-controlled techniques are also employed for rigorous inspection procedures on each component prior to assembly (Fig 10.40).

Before the finished con-rods are fitted into the engines, they are sorted into batches of corresponding masses during a computer-controlled weighing process. This finely accurate process ensures that each engine is fitted with a set of con-rods which are practically the same weight, thus keeping the engine in balance. To reduce manufacturing costs, a fairly wide tolerance band is allowed in the con-rods machining operations. Then, using selective assembly techniques, a microcomputer matches the con-rods which are of similar shape.

Some stages of the engine assembly are shown in Fig 10.41 (see also the examples of Ford robot-aided manufacture in Chapter 9).

The Finished Product After the engine is fully assembled and tested, the powertrain is completed with the additional driveline components, and the whole assembly is then "married" with the trimmed bodyshell.

Ford have become heavily involved in CADCAM for the purpose of creating a superior product and the latest Ford cars clearly reflect the commitment to quality that has been made possible by extensive investment in computer technology.

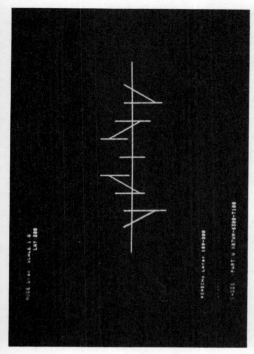

Fig. 10.27 Formulation
of engine specification

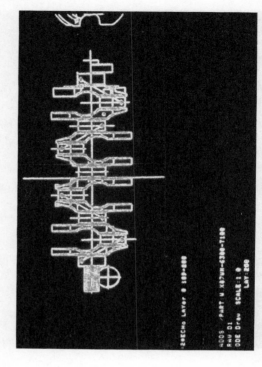

Fig. 10.28a

Fig. 10.28b

Fig. 10.28c

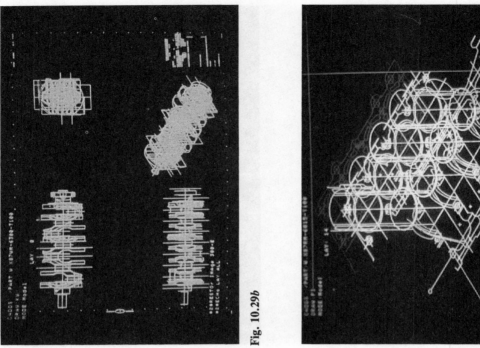

Fig. 10.29a 3D modelling of crankshaft

Fig. 10.29b

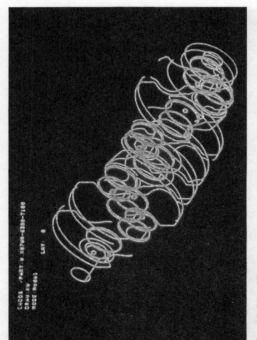

Fig. 10.30 Dynamic display of con-rod movement

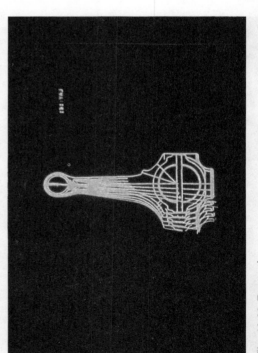

Fig. 10.31 Dynamic analysis of pistons and crankshaft in engine

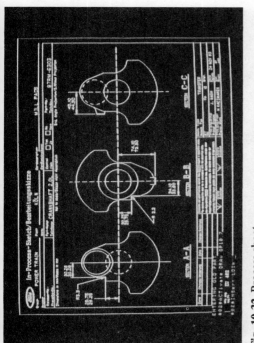

Fig. 10.32 Process sheet display for crankshaft

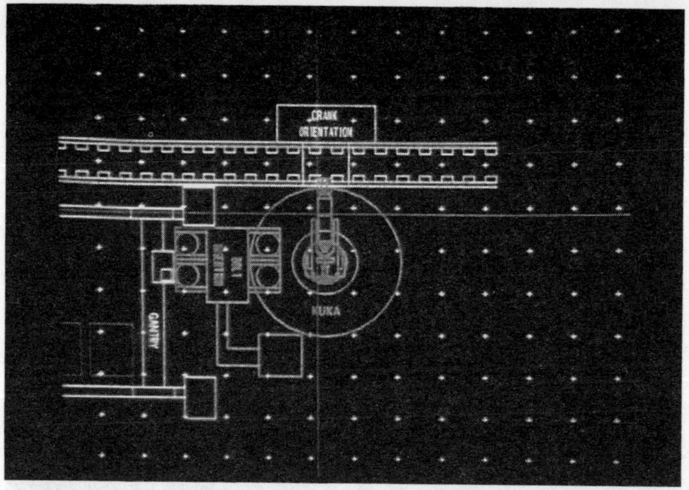

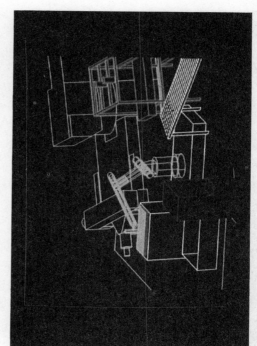

Fig. 10.33

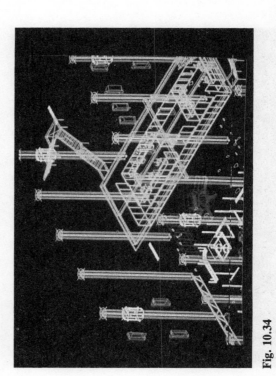

Fig. 10.34

Fig. 10.35 Robot pick-and-place simulation

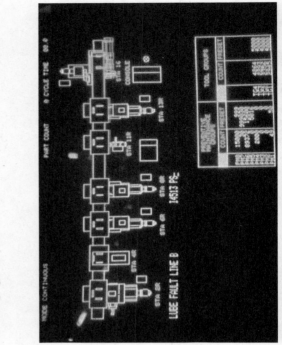

Fig. 10.37 Robot deburring operation

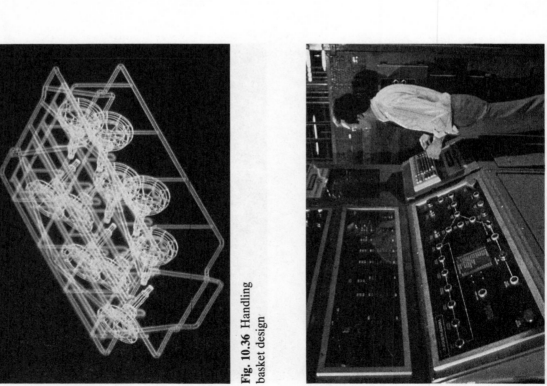

Fig. 10.39 Display of faulty machine

Fig. 10.36 Handling basket design

Fig. 10.38 Factory computer terminal

Fig. 10.41a Measuring the height of combustion chamber inserts relative to the cylinder head face by computer-controlled machines. Adjustment for tool wear is automatic.

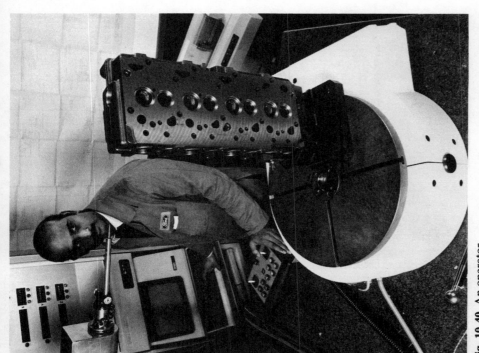

Fig. 10.40 An operator checks engine cylinder head measurements using a computer-controlled three-axis coordinate machine

Fig. 10.41*b* Spark plugs, selected from two types, are inserted and tightened automatically

Fig. 10.41*c* Final stages of engine assembly

The Conversion to CADCAM

The three important stages in the conversion to CADCAM are

1 FEASIBILITY
2 SPECIFICATION
3 COMPARISON and EVALUATION.

It is a common practice for companies considering a conversion to CADCAM, to appoint a *Project Group*, which will investigate these aspects and report to management.

11.1 Feasibility

Despite the advantages and applications of CADCAM, there can be little doubt that the installation of a CADCAM system constitutes a major commitment for any company, both in terms of cost and changes to its organisational structure. In attempting to justify the installation of a system, the project team should pay particular attention to the financial and social considerations involved.

1 FINANCIAL CONSIDERATIONS
The following factors could improve the financial position of the company:

a) Superior Product.
b) Cheaper Product.
c) Shorter Delivery Times.
d) Quicker Sales Quotations.
e) Faster Drawing and Production Rates.
f) Lower Production Costs.
g) Lower Labour Costs.
h) Lower Development Costs.

The arguments, presented thus, may seem impressive, with points *a*, *b*, *c*, and *d* enhancing the company's reputation, and points *e*, *f*, *g*, and *h* cutting costs. However, these can only be predictions, and must be set against the following negative factors:

a) Possible High Purchase Cost of the System.

Although becoming less of a problem with advances in technology, purchase costs for the larger systems can be extremely discouraging if benefits cannot be immediately realized. Full advantage should be made of government grants which may be available from the Department of Trade and Industry (DTI). Local authority grants are also sometimes available.

b) Installation Costs.

These could include: set-up; building structural alterations (materials and labour); purchase of new furniture; cable installations; security systems; and sometimes less-obvious considerations, such as new lighting and air-conditioning systems, and conversion to anti-static carpeting (some carpet materials have an adverse effect on the computer operation).

c) Maintenance and Support Costs.

These can be substantial, particularly with turnkey systems. To avoid long delays in breakdowns, it is a common practice to enter into a quick-service support contract with the supplier. These may be between 10 and 15% of the purchase price, annually.

d) Cost of Training.

Suppliers often provide some training covered by the purchase price. However, this may be for a limited number of personnel and hours. If the company is to train its own personnel, this must, of course, be considered under the cost of lost production during the training period.

2 SOCIAL CONSIDERATIONS

It is not only management who are confronted with the immediate effects of a conversion to CADCAM. The following factors could improve the working environment of the company employees:

a) Many repetitive, boring tasks could be replaced with work involving more job satisfaction.

b) Automation may result in less unsociable hours being worked.

c) Possibility of a shorter working week.

d) Financial benefits of CADCAM could result in improved wage prospects.

These possible advantages to the employees should be set against the following negative possibilities:

a) Redundancy.

This is obviously the principal fear of any employee involved with the change to new technologies. The fear is perhaps less justified in CAD disciplines than those of CAM. Although increased drawing production rates are an important feature of CAD, the overriding philosophy is one of superior drawings and designs. CAM activities, whilst all being concerned with the superior product, are also associated with automation. Logically this leads to fewer personnel. However, if the superior product generates more orders, the resulting improved finances may be used to the employee's advantage.

b) Inability or Reluctance to Learn New Skills.

This could be more relevant to older employees who are set in their ways.

Many people who are happy and able in their existing work have an inbuilt fear of computers, which could inhibit transference of their skills to CADCAM.

c) Passing of Old Skills.

This is closely associated with the previous consideration. Some employees may feel resentment that particular skills in which they may have excelled (such as the ability to produce beautiful hand-printing, or turn fine surfaces) are irrelevant to CADCAM.

d) Health Hazards.

Working with computers can create mental stress and physical fatigue. For example, VDU screens can cause headaches when viewed all day. It is even claimed they have caused some expectant mother operators to experience defective births.

UNION CONSULTATION A wise company converting to CADCAM will take note of the foregoing social implications and will attempt to avoid damaging conflicts between management and employees. In many cases this will require diplomatic consultation with the relevant trades unions.

British unions, while sceptical about the intentions of some employers, tend to have a realistic attitude to CADCAM. For example, the manufacturing union, TASS, believes that the new technologies may be used in the positive senses already discussed, i.e. to create better working conditions and higher living standards for its members.

However, TASS strongly condemns companies who to seek to make high profits by shedding labour when automation is introduced. They thus make a case for their members to have some control, through collective bargaining, over the introduction of new technology.

The optimistic viewpoint is that the financial benefits of CADCAM may be used to help achieve early retirement schemes and a shorter working week.

11.2 Specification

A successful outcome to the CADCAM installation project cannot be ensured until the specific requirements of the company have been identified and clearly stated in a *specification*.

The specification is made up of a number of *objectives*, which need to be achieved. Typical objectives include:

"The system is to be obtained as a complete hardware/software package from one supplier under a turnkey arrangement."

"The system should be capable of producing A0 plottings".

"The system should have facilities for at least 16 drawing layers."

"The system should be capable of expanding to incorporate a solid-modelling facility at a later date."

"The system should be able to transfer drawing data from the CAD package to a CNC lathe-turning part-programming package."

An effective specification check-list is shown on page 260.

HARDWARE REQUIREMENTS

TURNKEY?	✓
NO. OF WORKSTATIONS (INITIAL)?	6
NO. OF WORKSTATIONS (FINAL)?	12
NETWORKED?	✓
REMOTE WORKSTATIONS?	2
SIZE OF PLOTTER?	A0
TYPE OF PLOTTER?	VERTICAL
COLOUR VDU?	X
NO. OF PRINTERS?	6
MINI-PLOT SCREEN DUMP?	✓

2D MANIPULATION AND EDITING REQUIREMENTS

ZOOM (SCALE)?	✓
ZOOM (DRAWING EXTENTS)?	X
ZOOM (WINDOW)?	✓
ZOOM (PREVIOUS)?	✓
PAN?	✓
GRID (ORIGIN CHANGE)?	✓
NO. OF LAYERS?	12
ROTATE (ELEMENT)?	✓
ROTATE (REGULAR WINDOW)?	✓
ROTATE (IRREGULAR WINDOW)?	X
GRID (ROTATE)?	X
TRANSLATE (ELEMENT)?	✓
TRANSLATE (REGULAR WINDOW)?	✓
TRANSLATE (IRREGULAR WINDOW)?	✓
MIRROR (ELEMENT)?	✓
MIRROR (REGULAR WINDOW)?	✓
MIRROR (IRREGULAR WINDOW)?	✓
ERASE (ELEMENT)?	✓
ERASE (REGULAR WINDOW)?	✓
ERASE (IRREGULAR WINDOW)?	✓
TRIM (ELEMENT END)?	✓
TRIM (ELEMENT INTERSECTION)?	✓
TRIM (INSIDE ELEMENT)?	X
SNAP (REGULAR INTERVALS)?	✓
SNAP (ELEMENT END)?	✓
SNAP (ELEMENT INTERSECTIONS)?	✓

2D GEOMETRY CONSTRUCTIONAL REQUIREMENTS

ABSOLUTE COORDINATES?	✓
INCREMENTAL COORDINATES?	✓
LINE (CARTESIAN)?	✓
LINE (POLAR)?	✓
CIRCLE?	✓
ARC (3 POINTS)?	✓
ARC (CENTRE, START, ANGLE)?	✓
ARC (CENTRE, START, END)?	X
ARC (START, END, RADIUS)?	X
FILLET (LINES)?	✓
FILLET (RADIUS)?	✓
FILLET (ARC/LINE)?	✓
CHAMFER (45°)?	✓
CHAMFER (ANY ANGLE)?	X
HATCH (BETWEEN SPECIFIED ELEMENTS)?	✓
HATCH (INSIDE REGULAR WINDOW)?	✓
HATCH (INSIDE IRREGULAR WINDOW)?	X
HATCH (ANY ANGLE)?	X
HATCH (OPTIONAL PATTERNS)?	X
SPLINE?	X
STANDARD COMPONENT MACROS?	✓
MACROS (INDEPENDENT X/Y SCALE)?	✓
PARAMETRIC MACROS?	✓

2D ANOTATION REQUIREMENTS

SOLID LINETYPE?	✓
HIDDNE LINETYPE?	✓
CENTRE LINETYPE?	✓
CUSTOMIZED LINETYPE?	✓
TEXT SLANT?	X
TEXT ROTATION?	X
CUSTOMIZED FONTS?	X
TEXT HEIGHT?	X
VERTICAL/HORIZONTAL DIMENSION?	X
RADIUS DIMENSION?	✓
DIAMETER DIMENSION?	✓
ANGLE DIMENSION?	✓
LIMITS DIMENSION?	✓
±DIMENSION?	✓
DIMENSION LEADER?	X
GEOMETRIC TOL.?	✓
MACHINING SYMBOLS?	✓

ANALYSIS SOFTWARE REQUIREMENTS

VOLUME/MASS?	✓
CENTROID?	X
2ND MOMENT OF AREA?	X
BEARING LOADS?	X
FEA (PLANE STRESS)?	✓
FEA (AXISYMMETRIC)?	✓
FEA (SOLID)?	X
FEA (VIBRATIONAL LOADING)?	✓
FEA (HEAT TRANSFER)?	X
ERGONOMICS?	X

3D GEOMETRY REQUIREMENTS

WIREFRAME?	X
SURFACE?	X
SOLID?	✓
3D MASS PROPERTIES?	✓
CLASH DETECTION?	✓
SURFACE SHADING?	X

CAM SOFTWARE REQUIREMENTS

CAPP?	✓
GNC (TURNING)?	✓
GNC (MILLING)?	✓
MACRO LIBRARY?	✓
TOOL LIBRARY?	✓
PARAMETRICS?	✓
DNC?	X

ORGANISATIONAL SOFTWARE REQUIREMENTS

DBMS?	✓
CAPP?	✓
CAPM?	✓
PERT?	X
WORD PROCESSOR?	X
CAMP/CAM?	✓
CAD/CAPM?	X
CAPM/BUSINESS?	X

LINKAGE SOFTWARE REQUIREMENTS

CADCAM?	✓
FEA/CAD?	✓
2D/3D?	✓
CAD/CAPM?	✓
IGES?	X

Typical Company CADCAM checklist

11.3 Comparison and Evaluation

The next formidable decision to be made is *which* system will most aptly conform to the specification devised. To assist the project team in this task, some important sources of information and advice exist. Indeed, these may also be utilised during the feasibility and specification stages. Common sources include:

a) CONSULTANTS. A large number of consultancy services have emerged in response to the increasing demand for advice on CADCAM systems. If a consultancy is to make a valuable contribution to the installation project, it is essential that they have sound experience in the type of technology involved and the industry of their client. Some consultants base their advice purely on their experience as salesmen. Also, some companies offering consultancy services may have interests in the CADCAM industry, and may even be vendors. The project team should therefore endeavour to determine previous experience and possible vested interests before drawing up a short-list of consultants.

Many private consultants are based at universities and polytechnics and, in some cases, the educational establishments themselves act as the consultant. Services may also be obtained for research associations, such as PERA (Production Engineering Research Association) and from government research establishments such as the NEL (National Engineering Laboratory). The fees charged by the majority of consultancies may seem prohibitive (often ranging between £100 and £500 per man day). However, the cost of reliable outside advice should be set against that of making expensive mistakes.

b) BENCHMARK TESTS. A benchmark is a customised program which may be used as a standard to test and evaluate the performance of different CADCAM systems. For example, a company project team evaluating CAD systems could use a typical selection of its existing drawings as the benchmark specification. These could then be re-drawn by a number of possible system suppliers, and the productivity improvements compared.

c) SYSTEM USER LISTS AND ASSOCIATIONS. These are useful sources of information from fellow companies who have had practical experience of a system under consideration. User lists are commonly available from the system suppliers.

d) TECHNICAL MAGAZINES, some of which publish regular comparison lists of available systems. Comparisons of consultancy companies are also sometimes published.

e) PROFESSIONAL INSTITUTIONS, which may be a reliable source of free advice, and may publish their own magazine.

f) AWARENESS PROGRAMMES, by organisations such as the DTI. In the UK, the most important of these has been the DTI's Advanced Manufacturing Technology (AMT) Awareness Programme, conducted in partnership with the Institution of Mechanical Engineers. The term AMT has formerly been applied to aspects of FMS, but has now been described by the IMechE as including CADCAM, CAPM, FMS, and robotics. The latter definition appears to be the same as that of CAE. However, AMT may currently be considered as much as a philosophy of learning as a list of disciplines. The AMT programme includes seminars, training work-shops, consultancy services, visits to selected demonstration firms, technology briefs, and information packs. AMT is likely to be an important factor in the further expansion of the CADCAM process.

11.4 Case Study in CADCAM System Installation

Hobourn-Eaton is a Rochester-based pump-manufacturer employing around 500 people (Fig 11.1). Examples of this company's design and production work have been discussed in previous chapters and are a direct result of their successful CADCAM installation project in 1984. This case study thus serves as a useful conclusion to our discussions.

A 30-member engineering team is responsible for the product design and testing of new pumps. These are lubricating-oil and power-steering types, which are sold mainly to the motor industry. The department has a small machine shop, which includes two CNC milling machines (see Chapter 9) for making prototypes in batches ranging from one to fifty.

Spurred by the DTI's CADCAM awareness seminars, and the availability of grants, the department began plans for the introduction of CADCAM. A small project team was formed. The team took six to nine months to investigate feasibility, devise a specification, compare available systems, visit suppliers, and finally select a system.

The most important objectives in their specification were

a) The system should be "affordable", so that, for example, if it were replaced in five years, little would have been lost in terms of awareness, training, and experience.

b) The department's lead times (from conceptual design to the start of full-scale production) should be reduced, thus necessitating an integrated CADCAM system, rather than just CAD.

c) Because two major customers (Ford and BL) both use ComputerVision CAD equipment for their mechanical design, it was imperative that the system be compatible under IGES (Initial Graphics Exchange Specification) to allow accessing of drawings and other data between the firms (IGES is discussed in Chapter 3).

d) It should be possible to automatically transfer data from the CADCAM system, such as product parts lists, to the company's commercial systems (for example, a production control package running on an IBM System 36).

e) The system should be capable of accepting in-house programs written in Microsoft Basic; for example, a program for the design of oil pump rotors. (The team discovered that many systems did not have this extremely useful facility. However, the reader will find program examples using such as facility on a versatile CAD package called Autocad, in Chapter 3.)

Fig. 11.1 Hobourn-Eaton's factory at Rochester

To meet the "affordability" criterion, the evaluation narrowed to a contest between a single-user ComputerVision system or a low-cost multi-user configuration. The team decided to opt for the largest number of terminals possible and to maximise their usage. It was concluded that medium-sized systems offered the worst compromise, and often were not compatible with ComputerVision set-ups.

The project team finally chose Micro-Aided Engineering's Integrated Engineering System, a networked, microcomputer-based package. The system comprised two Altos 586 processors with 512 Kbytes of main memory and 60 Mbytes of disc storage for a common master file, and four VDU colour terminals with keyboards and joysticks. Three terminals were installed in the engineering office (Fig 11.2), connected to a fourth used for CNC programming in the machine shop (p.205). A Benson A0 plotter produces hard-copy drawings on paper or film.

An important feature of the system is the modular manner in which a complete integrated system may be built up from a few essential software packages purchased at the initial installation. Fig 11.3 shows the modules available in the Micro-Aided Engineering product development layout. A number of the CAD, CAM, and CADCAM link modules were originally supplied with the system. (These are discussed in Chapters 4, 6 and 9.)

Fig. 11.2 Engineering
office terminals

It soon became obvious that the careful preparation had resulted in the
correct choice of system. Immediate benefits included:

a) Cutting lead times, and calculation errors, through the integrated
CADCAM facility—a major objective of the specification.

b) Faster production of prototypes—particularly through the system's
standard symbols and parametrics facilities—for new designs of rotor and
vane pumps (Fig 11.4).

c) Time savings in the machine shop. For example, a previous production
time of 3½ hours on one type of component was reduced to only 20
minutes.

The success of the system did bring one unforeseen problem. The design
and manufacturing for prototypes was now faster than the validation and
testing of prototypes. A finite element analysis model was thus added to
assist towards a "right-first-time" philosophy and eliminate the development
bottleneck. (See Chapter 6, case study 3.)

Hobourn-Eaton's engineering team are now creating software for linking
the system to IBM's production module on the company's database. They
are also heavily involved in an IGES communication link to their customer's
ComputerVision equipment. This will further reduce start-to-finish times.
Future plans include a production linkage for designing jigs and fixtures, and
the installation of the supplier's Maepec planning and estimating module.

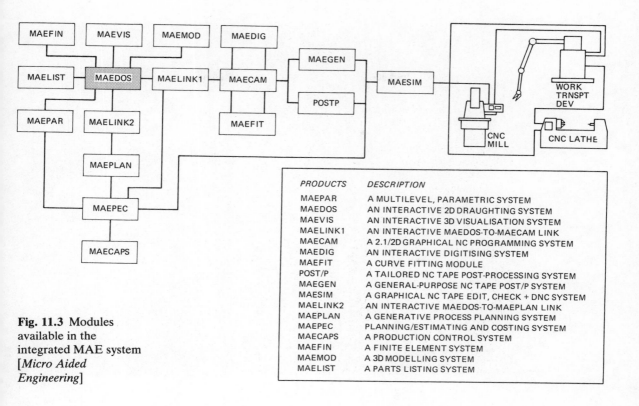

Fig. 11.3 Modules available in the integrated MAE system [*Micro Aided Engineering*]

PRODUCTS	DESCRIPTION
MAEPAR	A MULTILEVEL, PARAMETRIC SYSTEM
MAEDOS	AN INTERACTIVE 2D DRAUGHTING SYSTEM
MAEVIS	AN INTERACTIVE 3D VISUALISATION SYSTEM
MAELINK1	AN INTERACTIVE MAEDOS-TO-MAECAM LINK
MAECAM	A 2.1/2D GRAPHICAL NC PROGRAMMING SYSTEM
MAEDIG	AN INTERACTIVE DIGITISING SYSTEM
MAEFIT	A CURVE FITTING MODULE
POST/P	A TAILORED NC TAPE POST-PROCESSING SYSTEM
MAEGEN	A GENERAL-PURPOSE NC TAPE POST/P SYSTEM
MAESIM	A GRAPHICAL NC TAPE EDIT, CHECK + DNC SYSTEM
MAELINK2	AN INTERACTIVE MAEDOS-TO-MAEPLAN LINK
MAEPLAN	A GENERATIVE PROCESS PLANNING SYSTEM
MAEPEC	PLANNING/ESTIMATING AND COSTING SYSTEM
MAECAPS	A PRODUCTION CONTROL SYSTEM
MAEFIN	A FINITE ELEMENT SYSTEM
MAEMOD	A 3D MODELLING SYSTEM
MAELIST	A PARTS LISTING SYSTEM

Fig. 11.4 Examples of parametric standards at Hobourn-Eaton

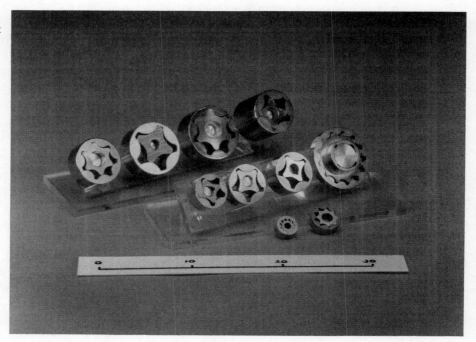

Index

Fortran 35,39,170
FMS (Flexible Manufacturing Systems) 3,218–30
Function box 14,21

G-code 183
Gantt chart 148
GKS (Graphics Kernel System) 42
GNC (Graphical Numerical Control) 188
Graphics manager 14
Grid (2D draughting) 57,58
Group technology 220,221

Hierarchical classification 123,152,156,171,220
Hard copy 21
Hardware (CAD) 7
Hatching (automatic) 56
Holography 96
Host computer 5,180,188
Hue 13

Icon 38
IGES (International Graphics Exchange Specification) 42–43,262,264
Incremental mode 54,184
Integrated organisation 140
Intersection (Boolean) 82,88,89
Interpreters 35
ISO (International Standards Organisation) 41,178

Joystick 18

Keyboard (CAD) 8,20
Kilobyte (Kbyte) 7
Kitting list 158
Kurve 192

LAN (Local Area Network) 25
Layering 28,40,60–63
Light-pen 11,18
Linear interpolation 184
Lisp 52

M-code 183
Machining simulation 88,89,193,194,197,198,199,205,247
Machine code 35
Machine control unit (MCU) 177
Macro
    applied to CAD draughting standards 63–65
    applied to CAD software subroutines 40
    applied to CNC part-programming 187
    applied to keyboard commands 21